Physical

Electronics

Wadsworth Engineering Science Series

T. L. Martin, Jr., Editor

Physical

Electronics

Robert L. Ramey

Associate Professor
Department of Electrical Engineering
University of Virginia

Wadsworth Publishing Company

Belmont, California

L.C. Cat. Card No.: 61–15843
Printed in the United States of America

First printing: September 1961
Second printing: September 1962

Preface

The realm of physical electronics is continually expanding, with the result that the successful engineer or physicist working in this field must be aware of all phases of the subject.

Physical electronics embraces far more than the straightforward design of signal amplifiers and associated circuitry and control devices. New methods and new devices can only be based upon the proven theories and experimental findings of physics and engineering. The demand for new electronic devices to accomplish operations of a nature unparalleled in the past has sent the designer searching into all fields of physical research. Extensive recourse to journals, periodicals, and treatises marks every step of modern electronic research and development.

The engineering and physics graduate must be better prepared today than at any time in the past to read and understand the literature in all fields of the physical sciences. It is the purpose of this book to introduce the reader to the foundations of physical electronics.

The book will fit easily into third- and fourth-year courses. The particular background and needs of the class can determine the approach used to accomplish the aims of the course and also to maintain the degree of interest required to spark students toward excellence.

The first five chapters form the physical basis of the rest of the text. The reader is encouraged to cover this material in the sequence in which it is presented as the remaining chapters will often refer to it. (The reader may, however, wish to omit Section 3.7 which deals with the fundamental concepts of quantum mechanics.) The problems have been selected, wherever possible, to emphasize additional phases of physical electronics.

I wish to express my deep appreciation to Dean Lawrence R. Quarles of the School of Engineering of the University of Virginia for his encouragement and cooperation in the writing of this book and to Dean Thomas L. Martin, Jr., of the College of Engineering of the University of Arizona who read the manuscript and made many helpful suggestions and criticisms. I am also indebted to Professor James F. Gibbons of the Stanford University Electronics Laboratories and to Professor William H. Hartwig of the University of Texas for their valuable suggestions.

Finally, I wish to acknowledge the large amount of encouragement and help received from my family, especially my wife, who typed the manuscript.

Robert L. Ramey
Charlottesville, Virginia

Contents

APPENDIX I   **341**

APPENDIX II   **342**

INDEX   **347**

Physical

Electronics

CHAPTER I

Historical background

Physical electronics is the study of the behavior of electric charge carriers that move under the influence of applied electric and magnetic fields. The design of electronic devices originates from the consequences of the physical behavior of electrons and ions. The specific configurations of electronic devices change as the state of the art advances; however, the underlying physical laws and phenomena remain.

Physical electronics deals with the application of the basic laws of physics to the study of the role played by electric charge carriers in the operation of a specific device. Historically, this is in contrast to the subject of electron circuitry, which deals with the terminal characteristics of such devices and their behavior in conjunction with other external electric circuitry. The sharp distinction between these two fields is continually disappearing as electronic devices that include their own circuitry make their appearance.

1.1 Background

The foundations of physical electronics were probably laid by Clerk Maxwell in 1857 in his kinetic theory of gases. These foundations remained incomplete until 1926, when Erwin Schrödinger and Werner Heisenberg brought together the theories of Max Planck, Albert Einstein, Niels Bohr, and Louis de Broglie in the powerful tool of quantum mechanics. In 1864 Maxwell presented the electromagnetic theory which represented the mathematical explanation of Michael Faraday's experimental investigations. The

I

theory, as expressed by Maxwell's equations, applies to all electrical phenomena. In 1887 Heinrich Hertz experimentally produced the electromagnetic radiation predicted by Maxwell and demonstrated that the electromagnetic waves could be reflected, refracted, and focused. With this distinguished beginning, the dawn of the era of "radio" was ushered in.

In 1899 Guglielmo Marconi established communications across the English Channel via wireless telegraphy. Radio eventually gave birth to radar and television, but in its early days there was little need for a knowledge of physical electronics. The electron had been known for only ten years when Marconi demonstrated the practical applications of electromagnetic radiation.

Probably the experimental beginnings of physical electronics occurred in 1752, when William Watson in London studied the passage of "electricity" through air at low pressures. Later, in 1869 at Bonn, three associates, Heinrich Geissler, Julius Plücker, and J. W. Hittorf investigated the relation between air pressure and the electrical conductivity of air. They referred to their discharge tube as an "aurora tube," because beautiful, colored lights similar to the northern lights were obtained within the tube for various degrees of vacuum. Plücker noted that the position of the light could be affected by a magnetic field. At lower pressures the three men observed that all visible light in the discharge ceased and only the glass walls of the tube fluoresced, and Hittorf noted that, when direct current was used, a shadow of the electrode used as the anode was cast upon the fluorescent walls of the tube. In 1876, in Berlin, Eugene Goldstein gave the name "canal" or "cathode ray" to the yet unknown medium that seemed to move from cathode to anode in a straight line.

In London in 1879, William Crookes experimented with a type of aurora tube in his home laboratory. A sketch of Crookes' tube is shown in Fig. 1.1. The anode was made in the shape of a Maltese cross. Crookes evacuated the tube to a low pressure and then applied a high voltage between the anode and the cathode. The inner end wall of the tube fluoresced with a pale blue-green light, with the exception of a distinct shadow cast by the anode. Hence, whatever these cathode rays were, they distinctly moved in straight lines from their source at the cathode to the anode. Crookes hinted at a particle theory and constructed a tube that contained a paddle wheel which was free to rotate and mounted so that its upper blades lay in the direct path from cathode to anode (Fig. 1.2). When voltage was applied, the paddle wheel rotated—which indicated a cathode-ray movement from cathode to anode.

Crookes' major observations were made in 1879 and in 1883. Elsewhere in 1883, other very important discoveries were being made that would soon give birth to modern electronics. Thomas Edison[1] at his Menlo Park, New Jersey, laboratory was investigating one of the numerous problems that plagued the development of his electric lamp. The inner surface of the glass bulb quickly darkened with use, which indicated that material from the

white-hot filament was somehow condensed upon the relatively cool surface
of the glass bulb. These bulbs were exhausted to a high vacuum, in contrast
to present-day bulbs which operate at pressures on the order of one mm Hg
and are filled with inert gases. Edison used a high vacuum to lower the
oxygen content of the bulb to protect the delicate filament, and thus prolong

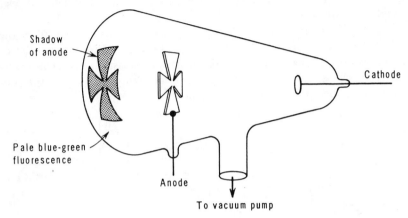

Fig. 1.1. A Crookes' Tube.

its life. His use of high vacuums made possible the following observation of a
very important phenomenon.

In an effort to determine what caused the darkening of the bulbs, Edison
sealed into a lamp a small metal plate, insulated electrically from the filament
structure. A galvanometer connected between this plate and the positive

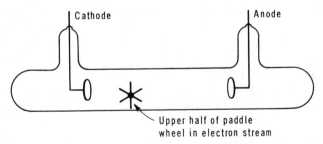

Fig. 1.2. Crookes' Tube with paddle wheel.

filament lead resulted in a current flow. Edison reported upon his observations, and then dropped the matter, turning his attention to the numerous
technical problems involving the incandescent lamp. The phenomenon
he observed is commonly referred to as the *Edison effect*, although at the same
time in Germany, Elster and Geitel were making a more thorough investigation of the same phenomenon.

During 1884 and 1885, Preece[2] studied the Edison effect in England and made the first analysis of the volt-ampere characteristics of what was soon to be recognized as a *diode tube*. He noted the effects of interelectrode spacing and filament temperature. At the same time Hittorf[3] and Goldstein[4] were also studying the volt-ampere characteristics of vacuum diode tubes that had cathodes constructed of various materials and were operated over a range of temperatures.

About 1894 in England, J. A. Fleming[5] attempted to derive from the work of Crookes, Edison, and others an explanation of the mechanism of the conduction of electricity through air at low pressures. Little headway was made because there existed no plausible mechanism to explain the conduction of an electric current in a vacuum.

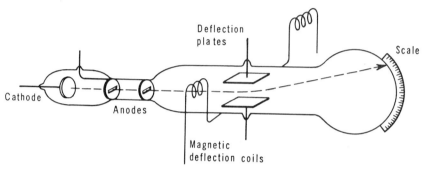

Fig. 1.3. Thomson's Tube for measuring e/m.

In 1897 Professor J. J. Thomson[6] brought the principles of electromagnetism and electrostatics to bear upon the problem and postulated the existence of the electron. Thomson was not able to determine specifically the mass or the charge of the electron, but he was able to determine their ratio. A sketch of his apparatus is shown in Fig. 1.3. Thus, Thomson was the first man to work in the field of physical electronics, for he applied the laws of Newtonian dynamics to the electron to determine its behavior or ballistics in the presence of the applied electric and magnetic fields.

1.2 The valve

The preparatory work was finished. Hertz had demonstrated the existence of electromagnetic radiation; Thomson had postulated the electron and had applied Newtonian dynamics to the computation of the electron trajectory, thus establishing the science of physical electronics; Marconi had introduced radio; and Edison had stumbled upon a unilateral vacuum-tube device. In 1905 Fleming was now ready to re-enter the field, quite successfully this time, with the suggestion that the unilateral properties of the Edison tube with a plate included be used as a detector for wireless telegraphy. Fleming referred to this first electronic device as a "valve," a name that still persists in England today.

The Fleming valve was an immediate success, for up to this time all radio detectors in common use depended upon surface contact phenomena in one form or another. The two most common were the Branly *coherer* and the *crystal detector*. The Branly coherer assumed many forms, one essentially a glass tube partially filled with a powdered conductor such as carbon and fitted with a terminal plug in each end. Poor contact between particles gave rise to rectifying junctions which served as the detector. The crystal detector was very similar to those used today as microwave detectors. Modern refinements have gone into the production of the crystal and the "catwhisker" used to form a rectifying contact with the crystal surface. No longer does one adjust the catwhisker to establish a sensitive junction with the crystal. Instead, a sensitive contact is formed by the manufacturer and sealed in position by the entire unit's being potted in wax. The Fleming valve provided for a more reliable detector, especially for shipboard use where its independence with respect to motion and environment was extremely important.

In 1901, O. W. Richardson[7,8] developed in theory and experiment a complete explanation of the mechanism of electronic emission. Several years later A. Wehnelt[9] discovered and made a thorough investigation of the emission of electrons from filaments coated with oxides of the rare earths.

With this background, Lee De Forest[10] conceived the triode electron tube in 1905 and made the amplification of electrical signals possible by practical means. De Forest completed his development of the triode in 1912 while serving as a research engineer with the Federal Telegraph Company in a Palo Alto laboratory. Many other great advancements in electronics were to originate in the Palo Alto vicinity the following half-century. De Forest gave the name "audion" to his tube, which for many years remained as a trade name.

While De Forest was completing his work on the triode tube, C. D. Child[11] in 1911 and I. Langmuir[12] in 1913 made a comprehensive theoretical analysis of the vacuum diode. The result of this analysis was the well-known Child-Langmuir expression for the anode current as a function of the anode voltage for the diode.

$$i_b = K e_b^a \qquad (1.1)$$

The appearance of the triode in 1912 prompted Langmuir[13] to present one of the earliest analytical treatments of the device. The resultant expression

$$i_p = A(e_p + k e_g)^{3/2} \qquad (1.2)$$

gave the anode current as a function of the anode voltage and the grid voltage. It remained for H. J. Van der Bijl[14] in 1917 to recognize that the coefficient k

in Langmuir's equation (1.2) was actually the amplification constant of the tube.

In 1918, J. M. Miller of the National Bureau of Standards suggested a method for measuring the dynamic circuit characteristics of the triode with a theoretical explanation of their interpretation. In the same year, L. A. Hazeltine[15] made a thorough investigation of the parameters of the triode tube. He suggested the terminology "mutual conductance" to describe the plate current-grid potential tube characteristic. The direct measurement of the tube parameters was given considerable attention by S. Ballantine[16] in 1919.

The problems of interelectrode capacities and their effects upon circuit operation were solved in 1919 by H. W. Nichols[17] and J. M. Miller.[18] The *Miller effect*, which arises from the net input capacitance, threatened to limit the early amplifiers to frequencies below 4 megacycles. These early amplifiers required elaborate neutralizing circuits to achieve operation at the higher frequencies. It was W. Schottky[19] who, in 1919, suggested the addition of a "screen grid" to electrostatically screen the control grid from the anode and thus materially reduce the Miller effect and the need for elaborate neutralizing circuits. Tubes that utilized two grids for the mixing of signals or the reduction of space charge effects had been introduced around 1917. The true screen-grid tube was not developed until 1926 by Hull[20] and Williams.[21]

The pentode tube followed the tetrode very closely, and in short order multigrid tubes became exceedingly common. Special-purpose tubes seem to be the remaining frontier—for example, beam-switching and traveling-wave tubes are among the most recent developments.

1.3　The rise of mathematical design

The earliest attempts at true mathematical tube design began in 1919 with papers by M. Abraham,[22] R. W. King,[23] W. Schottky,[19] and M. von Laue.[24] The problem that confronted these men was the development of an expression for the amplification factor of a tube in terms of the interelectrode spacings and dimensions. Their methods of attack were essentially identical. Clerk Maxwell[25] had worked out in detail the electrostatic problem of partial shielding due to a wire grid. The problem was very similar to that of the triode, and a direct adaptation was made by the men named above.

Of all the preceding papers, that by R. W. King is of special interest because it considers unusual physical arrangements of the grid, cathode, and anode. King's paper dealt with cylindrical and plane-parallel electrode structures in their idealized constructional forms; however, it was applicable to low-mu tubes primarily. In 1924, F. B. Vodges, F. R. Elder,[26] and W. G. Dow[27] developed more refined expressions for the amplification factor that were applicable to medium-gain tubes. Finally, in 1929, Y. Kusunose[28] made a comprehensive analysis applicable to the practical tube structures preferred by manufacturing engineers.

The tremendous developments in the field of electron tubes are beyond the scope of this chapter. The interested reader would do well to select the specific electronic device of interest and trace its history from this point on.

1.4 Solid-state devices

Although very little was known about its physical operation, the crystal detector of the pre-vacuum-tube era was a solid-state device. Upon the introduction of the vacuum tube, the early crystal detector was dropped as commercial equipment. However, with the introduction of radar in the late thirties, the need for a detector capable of operating at very high frequencies brought the crystal back.

Early radar crystals were little better than those of pre-vacuum-tube days. The pressing war effort stimulated large-scale, government sponsorship of teams of scientists in universities such as the Massachusetts Institute of Technology, the University of Pennsylvania, and Purdue University, as well as in industrial laboratories such as those of Bell Telephone, Westinghouse, General Electric, and Sylvania. These groups engaged in both fundamental and applied research on the problem of semiconductor diodes.[29]

Following the war, research continued in semiconductor physics and in the late forties the solid-state research group at the Bell Telephone Laboratories demonstrated theoretically that signal amplification by means of semiconductors was physically possible. A *field effect amplifier* was envisioned by this group as consisting of a thin film of semiconductor material as one plate of a parallel-plate capacitor. The second plate was a normal conductor. An applied potential caused a surface charge to appear on the semiconducting film at the expense of the electrons and holes available for volume conductivity through the semiconductor, and thus controlled a conduction current through the semiconductor.

The possibilities of devising a real solid-state device which possessed the property of amplification encouraged research primarily aimed at attaining an understanding of electrical surface phenomena for semiconductors. A theory of surface states was proposed by J. Bardeen[30] in 1947. Experimental investigations of the surface states were made by Bardeen's co-workers at Bell Laboratories, principally W. H. Brattain[31] and W. Shockley.[32] It was the experimental investigation of the surface phenomena of semiconductors that led Bardeen and Brattain to the invention of the contact transistor[33,34] in 1948.

The point-contact transistor possessed relatively wide-band frequency response, and it was constructed in a manner quite similar to point-contact crystal diodes. Thus, the point-contact transistor was manufactured commercially for several years prior to the introduction of the junction transistor.

The junction transistor was developed by W. Shockley[35] in 1949; however, it did not appear on the market as a commercial product for several years. Currently, the junction transistor has replaced the point-contact transistor in all but a few very-high-frequency applications and low rise-time switching circuits. Special-purpose transistors such as the junction tetrode and "fieldistor"[37,38] were announced in 1952. In 1957 L. Esaki introduced the tunnel diode, which serves as a very-high-frequency oscillator and amplifier.

The short historical sketch given here and the accompanying references are intended to provide the serious reader with not only a history of electronics but also a set of guideposts for searching the literature when beginning a research project. The methods and solutions devised and employed by the researchers listed may often be used directly or upon modification to solve new problems arising in modern research.

REFERENCES

1. T. A. Edison, *Engineering*, p. 553, Dec. 12, 1884.

2. W. H. Preece, *Proc. Roy. Soc. (London)*, **38**, 219 (1885).

3. J. W. Hittorf, *Ann. Physik*, **21**, 119 (1884).

4. E. Goldstein, *Ann. Physik*, **24**, 79 (1885).

5. J. A. Fleming, *Phil. Mag.*, **42**, 52 (1896).

6. J. J. Thomson, *Phil. Mag.*, **44**, 293 (1897).

7. O. W. Richardson, *Comb. Phil. Proc.*, **11**, 286 (1901).

8. O. W. Richardson, *Emission of Electricity from Hot Bodies*, Longmans, Green & Co., New York, 1916.

9. A. Wehnelt, *Ann. Physik*, **14**, 425 (1904).

10. L. De Forest, U.S. Patent 879,532, filed Jan. 29, 1907.

11. C. D. Child, *Phys. Rev.*, **32**, 498 (1911).

12. I. Langmuir, *Phys. Rev.*, 2nd series, **2**, 450 (1913).

13. I. Langmuir, *Proc. I.R.E.*, **3**, 261 (1915).

14. H. G. Van der Bijl, *Phys. Rev.*, **12**, 171 (1918).

15. L. A. Hazeltine, *Proc. I.R.E.*, **6**, 63 (1918).

16. S. Ballantine, *Proc. I.R.E.*, **7**, 134 (1919).

17. H. W. Nichols, *Phys. Rev.*, **13**, 405 (1919).

18. J. M. Miller, National Bureau of Standards Bulletin 351.

19. W. Schottky, *Arch. Elektrotech.*, **8**, 299 (1919).

20. A. W. Hull, *Phys. Rev.*, **27**, 439 (1926).

21. A. W. Hull and N. H. Williams, *Phys. Rev.*, **27**, 433 (1926).

22. M. Abraham, *Arch. Elektrotech.*, **8**, 42 (1919).

23. R. W. King, *Phys. Rev.*, **15**, 256 (1920).

24. M. von Laue, *Ann. Physik*, **59**, 465 (1919).

25. J. C. Maxwell, *A Treatise on Electricity and Magnetism*, 3rd ed., Oxford University Press, Fair Lawn, N.J., 1904, Vol. I, p. 310.

26. F. B. Vodges and F. R. Elder, *Phys. Rev.*, **24**, 683 (1924).

27. W. G. Dow, *Engineering Electronics*, John Wiley & Sons, New York, 1937.

28. Y. Kusunose, *Proc. I.R.E.*, **17**, 1706 (1929).

29. H. C. Torrey and C. A. Whitmer, *Crystal Rectifiers*, McGraw-Hill Book Company, New York, 1948.

30. J. Bardeen, *Phys. Rev.*, **71**, 717–727 (1947).

31. W. H. Brattain and W. Shockley, *Phys. Rev.*, **72**, 345 (1947).

32. W. Shockley and G. L. Pearson, *Phys. Rev.*, **74**, 232–233 (1948).

33. J. Bardeen and W. H. Brattain, *Phys. Rev.*, **74**, 230 (1948).

34. J. Bardeen and W. H. Brattain, *Phys. Rev.*, **75**, 1208–1225 (1949).

35. W. Shockley, *Bell System Tech. J.*, **28**, 435 (1949).

36. R. L. Wallace, Jr., L. G. Schimpf, and E. Dickter, *Proc. I.R.E.*, **40**, 1395–1400 (1952).

37. W. Shockley, *Proc. I.R.E.*, **40**, 1365–1376 (1952).

38. O. M. Stuetzer, *Proc. I.R.E.*, **40**, 1377–1381 (1952).

CHAPTER 2

Kinetic gas theory

The subject of physical electronics is concerned with the kinetic as well as the electric aspects of matter. For instance, electron tubes can be divided into high-vacuum and gas tubes. The high-vacuum tube depends upon electron ballistics and, just as important, the pumping and measuring of the vacuum depend upon the kinetic theory of gases. Gas tubes are first pumped to a high vacuum and then filled with appropriate gases at some low pressure. Electrical conduction takes place by way of ionization of the gas, and again a knowledge of gas kinetics is necessary to describe properly the phenomena involved. Finally, many of the concepts of gas kinetics are applicable to solid-state theory. For these reasons the basic concepts of the kinetic theory of gases will be considered here.

2.1 Pressure measurement

In the mks system of units, gas pressure is measured in newtons per square meter, although it is common to express a pressure in millimeters of mercury (mm Hg) for vacuum work and in pounds per square inch for pressures above atmospheric.

Consider the basic vacuum gauge shown in Fig. 2.1, constructed by closing off one end of a small-bore glass tube, then thoroughly cleaning the tube, and finally carefully filling it with mercury and excluding all trapped gases. The tube is then inverted and the open end placed in a reservoir of mercury. For vacuum measurements the top of the reservoir is sealed to the tube, with a suitable tubulation provided for making connections to the vacuum system. The void above the column of mercury will contain Hg gas at the vapor pressure of Hg corresponding to the ambient temperature (vapor pressure will be discussed later).

The *specific gravity* of mercury is 13.55; hence, the density of mercury in the mks system is

density = sp. gr. $\times$ (mass of 1 m^3 of H$_2$O)

$$D = 13.55 \times 10^6 \quad g/m^3$$
$$= 13.55 \times 10^3 \quad kg/m^3$$

at standard conditions; i.e., 0°C or 273°K and 760 mm Hg (one atmosphere).

The weight of the column of mercury is

$$w = gALD \qquad (2.1)$$

where g is the acceleration of gravity and is equal to 9.88 m/sec^2, L is the height of the mercury column, and D is the density of Hg. The cross-sectional area is A. The pressure supporting the column is then

$$P = \frac{w}{A} = gLD \qquad (2.2)$$

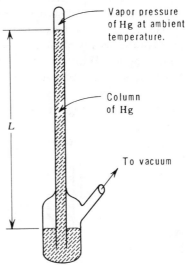

Fig. 2.1. A mercury vacuum manometer. The vapor pressure of Hg at 20°C (approximately room temperature) is 10^{-3} mm Hg.

It is important to note that the height of the column of Hg is independent of the tube area. In the mks system

$$P = 9.88 \times 13.55 \times 10^3 L$$
$$= 1.34 \times 10^5 L \quad newtons/m^2 \qquad (2.3)$$

where L is in meters. Atmospheric pressure has the average value of 760 mm Hg, and by Eq. (2.3) this is equal to 1.013×10^5 newtons/m^2. For pressure expressed in pounds per square inch, recall that one cubic foot of water weighs 62.4 pounds, thus

$$P = 13.55 \times \frac{62.4}{(12)^3} L$$

or $$P = 0.490L \quad lb/sq\ in. \qquad (2.4)$$

where L is expressed in inches.

Regardless of the system of units employed, the pressure is equal to a constant times the height of the mercury column. This has led to the common practice of expressing low pressures directly in terms of the height of the mercury column, usually in millimeters (mm Hg) or microns (μ) of mercury (Hg). One micron is one millionth of a meter of mercury, or 10^{-3} mm Hg;

thus, atmospheric pressure is 760 mm Hg. A typical high-vacuum electron tube operates at a pressure of about 10^{-6} mm Hg. The *bar* is another unit of pressure, equal to a force of one dyne per square centimeter.

The manometer described is an absolute gauge, because the measurement is made directly in terms of the height of the mercury column and indirectly in terms of the density of mercury and the acceleration of gravity. For pressures above one mm Hg, the manometer previously described is quite satisfactory; however, at lower pressures the change in the height of the column with pressure is difficult to ascertain. A variation of the basic manometer, known as the *McLeod gauge*, is used to overcome this problem. Its principle of

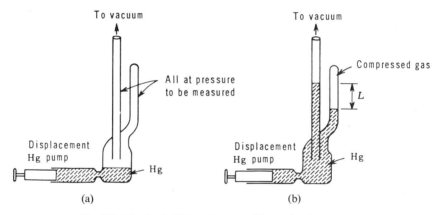

Fig. 2.2. The basic McLeod gauge: (a) venting to pressure to be measured, (b) compression stroke.

operation consists of venting a known volume to the region of low pressure to be measured, thus establishing the same pressure within the known volume. The gas within this volume is then compressed a predetermined amount by a factor of, say, 1000. The pressure of the gas is now measured by a manometer similar to that of Fig. 2.1. The actual pressure in the vacuum system is the pressure of the compressed gas divided by the volume compression ratio. In this manner absolute pressures as low as 10^{-5} mm Hg can be measured.

Figure 2.2 shows a typical McLeod gauge. In (a) the mercury level has been lowered, thereby venting the entire gauge to the pressure to be measured within the vacuum apparatus. After venting, the displacement pump is used to raise the mercury level. At the moment the mercury blocks the lower end of the tube connected to the vacuum, gas compression begins. The mercury rises in each tube as the pump pressure is increased. The level in the closed tube does not rise as far as the level in the tube leading to the vacuum because of the pressure developed in the compressed gas. The difference in mercury levels, L, is a measure of the pressure of the compressed gas. If it is assumed that the compression ratio is large, then the pressure on the open column can be neglected and L is the pressure of the compressed gas in mm Hg. The compression ratio is known; therefore, an application of the gas law

$$P_1V_1 = P_2V_2 \tag{2.5}$$

permits calculating the pressure within the vacuum system.

2.2 Fundamental gas laws

The molecules of a real gas exhibit a noticeable mutual attraction. This complicates the formulation of a simple kinetic theory of such gases. If an ideal gas is postulated wherein the molecules exhibit no mutual attraction, then a mathematical theory can be formulated to describe its behavior. At low pressures and at high temperatures the real gas exhibits only negligible mutual attraction among its constituent molecules and thereby approximates the behavior of an ideal gas. Because physical electronics is concerned primarily with low-pressure gas problems, this permits the kinetic theory of ideal gases to be accurately applied.

There are three basic laws which govern the behavior of an ideal gas:

1. BOYLE'S LAW: *If the temperature of a gas is held constant, its density is directly proportional to the absolute pressure.*
2. CHARLES' OR GAY-LUSSAC'S LAW: *If the pressure of a gas is held constant, its density is inversely proportional to the absolute temperature.*
3. AVOGADRO'S LAW: *At the same temperature and pressure, each gas possesses a density that is proportional to its molecular weight.*

A combination of the above three laws results in

$$\rho = \frac{1}{R}\frac{Pm'}{T} \tag{2.6}$$

where ρ is the density in kg/m³, P is the gas pressure in newtons/m², T is in °K (degrees Kelvin), and m' is the molecuar weight of the gas. The coefficient of proportionality is $1/R$. Density is equal to the reciprocal of the specific volume V_s, and therefore Eq. (2.6) may be written as

$$PV_s = \frac{1}{m'}RT \tag{2.7}$$

In actual calculations it is not convenient to deal with the dimensionless molecular weight, m', but rather to consider a mass of gas that is proportional to the molecular weight. When using the cgs system of units it is common practice to consider a quantity of gas whose mass is equal to as many grams as there are units in the element's molecular weight. Such a mass is called a *gram molecule* or *mole*. If the mks system of units is used in the calculations, then it is necessary to measure mass in kilograms. This makes it necessary to define a new term, the *kilogram molecule* or *kilomole*, corresponding to a mass of gas equal to as many kilograms as there are units in the element's molecular weight. For instance, a mass m_T of nitrogen gas, which is diatomic, has an atomic weight w' of 14.008 and a molecular weight m' of 28.016. The number of kilomoles in this sample of gas would be

$$M = \frac{m_T}{m'} \quad \text{kg molecules} \tag{2.8}$$

The total mass, m_T, is equal to the product of the density and the volume occupied by this mass of gas, or

$$m_T = \rho V = \frac{V}{V_s} = Mm' \tag{2.9}$$

Substituting Eq. (2.9) into Eq. (2.7) results in

$$PV = MRT \tag{2.10}$$

This is the *general gas equation*. The coefficient R is defined as the *universal gas constant*. In the mks system its value is 8.317×10^3 joules/(kilomole $\times$ °K).

Standard conditions for a gas are usually taken as 273°K (0°C) and 760 mm Hg. Under standard conditions one kilomole of any gas will ocupy a volume

$$V = \frac{MRT}{P} = \frac{1 \times 8.317 \times 10^3 \times 273}{1.013 \times 10^5}$$

$$= 22.4 \quad \text{m}^3/\text{kilomole}$$

If Eq. (2.10) is divided by the molecular weight m' and Eq. (2.9) is used to eliminate the volume V, then

$$PV_s = \frac{R}{m'} T$$

$$PV_s = rT \tag{2.11}$$

where r replaces R/m' and is the gas constant for the specific gas under consideration, in contrast to Eq. (2.10) which employs the universal gas constant and applies to any gas. Equation (2.11) is sometimes used in engineering work where it is desirable to use a specific volume, V_s, in the calculations.

Because R is a constant, then for M kilomoles of any gas the product

$$MR = \frac{PV}{T} = \text{constant}$$

Therefore, under different conditions of pressure, volume, and temperature,

$$\frac{P_1 V_1}{T_1} = \frac{P_2 V_2}{T_2} \tag{2.12}$$

The kilomole (or mole) is a mass of gas which is proportional to the mass of the individual molecules that compose it. Therefore, the kilomole (or mole) contains a definite number of molecules regardless of the kind of gas under consideration. This number is 6.023×10^{26} molecules per kilomole (or 6.023×10^{23} molecules per mole).

Because there are 6.023×10^{26} molecules per kilomole and because one kilomole occupies a volume of 22.4 m³ at standard conditions, the number of molecules, N, of any gas at standard conditions is

$$N = \frac{6.023 \times 10^{26}}{22.4} = 2.687 \times 10^{25} \quad \text{molecules/m}^3$$

This is known as *Loschmidt's number* and holds only for standard conditions corresponding to a pressure of 1.013×10^5 newtons/m² and a temperature of 273°K. Under any other conditions of pressure and temperature, referring to the gas equation (2.12), we may write

$$N = \frac{6.023 \times 10^{26}}{22.4} \left(\frac{P}{1.013 \times 10^5} \right) \left(\frac{273}{T} \right)$$

$$N = 7.29 \times 10^{22} \frac{P}{T} \quad \text{molecules/m}^3 \tag{2.13}$$

where P is in newtons/m² and T is in °K.

Solve for P and replace the constant by k so that

$$P = NkT \tag{2.14}$$

where k is $1/(7.29 \times 10^{22})$ or 1.38×10^{-23} wattseconds per degree Kelvin. This is *Boltzmann's constant*. In terms of pressure in mm Hg, Eq. (2.13) may be written

$$N = 2.687 \times 10^{25} \frac{P}{760} \frac{273}{T}$$

or

$$N = 9.70 \times 10^{24} \frac{P}{T} \tag{2.15}$$

2.3   Kinetic gas theory

The ideal gas laws are unique in their simplicity. For this reason, a simple theory was proposed by J. C. Maxwell, L. Boltzmann, and others during the latter part of the nineteenth century to explain these laws. It was noted experimentally that the specific thermal energy of a gas depends upon the temperature alone and not upon pressure or volume. The specific thermal energy of a gas is the thermal energy per unit mass of the gas. If one mole of a gas is considered, then the specific thermal energy is a function of the type of gas and its temperature. This means that any theory must deal with the free motion of the gas molecules and, therefore, must not include any boundary effects such as pressure and volume.

The kinetic theory visualizes the gas molecules as spheres which are free to move in straight-line motion until they collide with another molecule or with a boundary wall of the container. The kinetic energy of the molecules is taken to be proportional to the specific thermal energy. If the gas is monatomic, then all of the kinetic energy is translational. However, if the gas is diatomic, a fraction of the specific thermal energy will be represented by the rotational kinetic energy of these diatomic molecular "dumbbells."

Consider a unit volume, containing N molecules per unit volume at a given temperature, located adjacent to the surface B of Fig. 2.3. Let m be the average mass of each of the molecules. If the gas is to exert an equal pressure on all surfaces of its container, then the force exerted upon wall B must be equal in magnitude and opposite in direction to the force exerted upon the opposite wall, A.

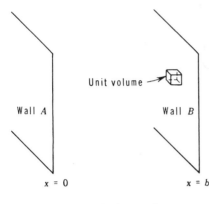

Fig. 2.3. The kinetic theory of pressure.

On the average, each gas molecule will possess x-, y,- and z-components of motion. In addition, under equilibrium pressure conditions, of those molecules having x-components of motion, one half must be traveling in the positive x-direction and the other half in the negative x-direction. The same thing is true for y- and z-directed molecules. Those molecules with $+v_x$ velocity components strike surface B; each one undergoes a change of momentum of $2mv_x$ upon striking and rebounding from the surface. Each molecule may possess a different velocity component, v_x; therefore, the instantaneous force exerted upon the wall will be equal to the product of the change in momentum for a given velocity v_x times the instantaneous number of wall collisions per second. The latter equals the instantaneous density of molecules, $\frac{1}{2}n_i$, which possess $+v_x$ velocity components, times v_x. The instantaneous pressure is then

$$p = (2mv_x)(\tfrac{1}{2}n_i v_x) \tag{2.16}$$

The mean pressure exerted upon the wall is

$$P = Nmv_{mx}^2 \tag{2.17}$$

where v_m is the root-mean-square velocity and v_{mx} is the x-component of this velocity. The velocity is given by the expression

$$v^2 = v_x^2 + v_y^2 + v_z^2$$

It follows from this that the rms velocity v_m is given by

$$v_m^2 = v_{mx}^2 + v_{my}^2 + v_{mz}^2 \tag{2.18}$$

There is no preferred component of velocity; therefore, all rms components are equal, or

$$v_{mx}^2 = v_{my}^2 = v_{mz}^2 \tag{2.19}$$

Substitute Eq. (2.19) into (2.18) and (2.17) and the equation for the mean pressure in terms of the rms velocity becomes

$$P = \frac{1}{3} N m v_m^2 \quad \text{newtons/m}^2 \tag{2.20}$$

If the expression for pressure from Eq. (2.20) is substituted into the gas law, Eq. (2.10), then the pressure is

$$P = \frac{MRT}{V} = \frac{1}{3} N m v_m^2$$

If the volume is constant, it is apparent from this equation that the temperature T and the rms velocity squared are the variables. Therefore, the kinetic energy is directly proportional to the gas temperature and Eq. (2.20) may be written as

$$P = \frac{2}{3}\left(\frac{1}{2} N m v_m^2\right) \tag{2.21}$$

The product Nm is the net mass of the gas per cubic meter and the term $(\frac{1}{2} N m v_m^2)$ is the kinetic energy of translational motion per cubic meter. If Eq. (2.21) is multiplied by the volume V, then

$$PV = \frac{2}{3}\left[\frac{1}{2}(NmV)v_m^2\right] \tag{2.22}$$

where NmV represents the mass of all the gas within the volume V. The bracketed term is now the total kinetic energy of the gas contained within V. Equation (2.22) could be written as

$$PV = VNkT = \frac{2}{3}\left[\frac{1}{2} N m V v_m^2\right]$$

by use of Eq. (2.14). Upon simplification

$$\frac{1}{2} m v_m^2 = \frac{3}{2} kT \tag{2.23}$$

Equation (2.23) applies to particles which obey the kinetic theory of gases. For example, at a room temperature of 300°K the kinetic energy of any molecule is

$$\frac{1}{2} m v_m^2 = \frac{3}{2} \times 1.38 \times 10^{-23} \times 300$$

$$= 6.2 \times 10^{-21} \quad \text{joules}$$

or

$$= \frac{6.2 \times 10^{-21}}{1.6 \times 10^{-19}} = 0.0387 \quad \text{electron volts}$$

where the *electron volt* (ev) is defined as the work done in moving an electron through a potential difference of one volt.

The rms velocity can now be determined if the mass of the molecule is known. There are several ways to determine the mass of a molecule. One method is based upon the known atomic weight w'. The mass of any molecule is equal to the product of the atomic weight multiplied by the ratio of the mass of the hydrogen atom to the mass of the electron; this product is multiplied by the mass of the electron. If the gas is diatomic, then the resultant product is multiplied by 2.

$$m = (2) \times w' \times 1837.13 \times 9.11 \times 10^{-31}$$
$$= (2)1.675 \times 10^{-27}w' \quad \text{kg} \tag{2.24}$$

The mass of an oxygen molecule, for instance, equals

$$m = 2 \times 16 \times 1.675 \times 10^{-27}$$
$$= 5.35 \times 10^{-26} \quad \text{kg}$$

It follows that, at room temperature, the rms velocity of oxygen molecules is

$$v_m = \sqrt{\frac{2 \times 6.2 \times 10^{-21}}{5.35 \times 10^{-26}}} = 482 \quad \text{m/sec}$$

Equation (2.22) can also be written as

$$PV = \frac{2}{3} W_{\text{total}} \tag{2.25}$$

The total energy of a mixture of gases, each of which closely approaches the behavior of an ideal gas and do not chemically react with one another, is simply the sum of the kinetic energies contributed by each gas, or

$$W_{\text{total}} = W_1 + W_2 + W_3 + \cdots W_n \tag{2.26}$$

Substitute Eq. (2.25) and set $V = V_1 = V_2 = V_3 = \cdots = V_n$. We obtain

$$\frac{3}{2} P_{\text{total}}V = \frac{3}{2}[P_1 + P_2 + P_3 + \cdots + P_n]V$$

or
$$P_{\text{total}} = P_1 + P_2 + P_3 + \cdots + P_n \tag{2.27}$$

The total pressure exerted by the mixture of nonreacting gases is the sum of the *partial pressures* that each gas would exert individually if it alone were to occupy a vessel of volume V. This is John Dalton's *law of partial pressures*.

When a liquid *evaporates* into a closed space, molecules fly off the liquid into the space and move about with random velocities, some re-entering (condensing) into the liquid state. Molecules evaporate into the vapor state faster than *condensation* occurs until an *equilibrium* is attained. At this point the rate of evaporation is balanced by the rate of condensation. The equilibrium pressure existing above the liquid is called the *vapor pressure*.

Figure 2.4 is a plot of the vapor pressures of liquids commonly used in high-vacuum research. The *boiling point* of any liquid is the *temperature* at which its *vapor pressure becomes equal to the external pressure* (760 mm Hg unless otherwise stated).

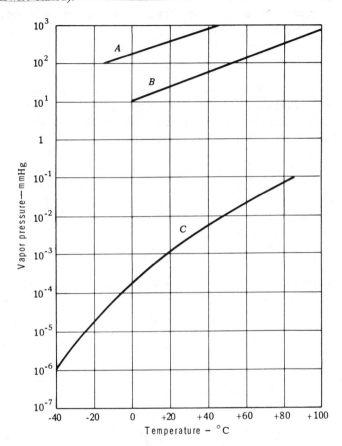

Fig. 2.4. The vapor pressure of (A) ether, (B) water, and (C) mercury as a function of temperature.

2.4   Statistical distribution of translational velocity

Theoretically, gas molecules may be found that have translational velocities that lie between zero and infinity. With submicroscopic particles it is common practice to speak of a *group* of particles instead of an individual particle. Further, because there is no way of measuring the velocity of the individual particle, it is more fitting to speak of the *probability* that a *group* of particles have velocities that lie between a velocity v_1 and another velocity v_2.

As an example, suppose there are ten molecules in a very small box. Their velocities are 240, 330, 380, 420, 430, 530, 590, 810, 950, and 1500 meters per second. The *probability* of finding a molecule that possesses a velocity in the range of 400 to 550 meters per second is, by definition, the number of molecules that possess a velocity in this range divided by the total number in the volume in question.

$$\Delta P = \frac{\Delta N}{N} \tag{2.28}$$

For the example, $\Delta P = 0.3$. Suppose that the velocity range were extended to cover velocities between 400 and 1000. Then $\Delta N = 6$ and $\Delta P = 0.6$. As a final example, compute the probability of finding a molecule that has a velocity between 100 and 2000 meters per second. Obviously the probability is 1.

In Eq. (2.28), N and ΔN are measured in molecules per cubic meter in the mks system. ΔN is the number of molecules per cubic meter that have velocities that lie within the range of v to $v + \Delta v$ meters per second. In general, the ratio $\Delta N/N$ is a function of velocity, which is easily seen in the example. For the range of 200 to 400 meters per second, the probability of finding a molecule is $\Delta P = 0.3$. However, for the range of 400 to 600 the probability is $\Delta P = 0.4$.

If the velocity range Δv is kept small, then ΔN is proportional to Δv and the factor of proportionality is, in general, a function of velocity, $f(v)$. Equation (2.28) may be written as

$$\Delta P = \frac{\Delta N}{N} = f(v)\,\Delta v \tag{2.29}$$

where $f(v)$ is the *probability density function* or, more specifically, in this case the *velocity density distribution function*. If Eq. (2.29) is summed over all possible velocities, then

$$\sum P = \frac{1}{N}\sum \Delta N = 1 = \sum f(v)\,\Delta v \tag{2.30}$$

$f(v)$ is a continuous distribution function so that the summation may be replaced by integration. That is,

$$\int_0^\infty f(v)\,dv = 1 \tag{2.31}$$

Equation (2.31) may be expanded into component form, which will introduce negative velocities and therefore require that the summation be between $-\infty$ and $+\infty$.

$$\int_{-\infty}^\infty \int_{-\infty}^\infty \int_{-\infty}^\infty f(v_x, v_y, v_z)\,dv_x\,dv_y\,dv_z = 1 \tag{2.32}$$

Equations (2.31) and (2.32) are said to be *normalized* inasmuch as the integration yields unity. Should $f(v)$ result upon integration in a numeric other than unity, then $f(v)$ must be normalized by dividing it by this numeric.

The mean or average of the variable v whose density is described by the probability function $f(v)$ is, by definition, the *average velocity*

$$v_a = \int_0^\infty vf(v)\, dv \qquad (2.33)$$

where it is assumed that $f(v)$ has been normalized. From Eq. (2.33) it follows that the average component of velocity in the x-direction is

$$v_{xa} = \int_{-\infty}^\infty \int_{-\infty}^\infty \int_{-\infty}^\infty v_x f(v_x, v_y, v_z)\, dv_x\, dv_y\, dv_z \qquad (2.34)$$

In a similar manner, the *root-mean-square velocity* is defined as

$$v_m = \left[\int_0^\infty v^2 f(v)\, dv \right]^{\frac{1}{2}} \qquad (2.35)$$

or, in the case of the x-component, the rms velocity would be

$$v_{xm} = \left[\int_{-\infty}^\infty \int_{-\infty}^\infty \int_{-\infty}^\infty v_x^2 f(v)\, dv_x\, dv_y\, dv_z \right]^{\frac{1}{2}} \qquad (2.36)$$

The form of the probability density function must be ascertained. To do this, consider two molecules and let $p(W_1)$ be the probability that the first molecule has an energy W_1. Let $p(W_2)$ be a similar probability density function for the second molecule. The sum of the two energies may be written as

$$W_1 + W_2 = (W_1 - \delta W) + (W_2 + \delta W) \qquad (2.37)$$

by simply adding and subtracting a small energy change δW. Let the probability density functions for these two new energy states $(W_1 - \delta W)$ and $(W_2 + \delta W)$ be $p(W_1 - \delta W)$ and $p(W_2 + \delta W)$ respectively. The number of energy exchanges such as described by Eq. (2.37) that could occur per unit volume of gas would be directly proportional to the probabilities of the occurrence of molecules possessing energies W_1 and W_2. In a state of equilibrium, Eq. (2.37) must describe a balanced process; that is, there must be an equal number of energy exchanges from $(W_1 - \delta W)$ and $(W_2 + \delta W)$ to W_1 and W_2. These exchanges would be directly proportional to the probabilities of the occurrence of molecules possessing energies $(W_1 - \delta W)$ and $(W_2 + \delta W)$. This may be expressed as

$$p(W_1)p(W_2) = p(W_1 - \delta W)p(W_2 + \delta W) \qquad (2.38)$$

An examination of Eq. (2.38) reveals that there is only one simple mathematical expression for the probability density function that will satisfy the equation. It is

$$p(W) = A\epsilon^{-\beta W} \qquad (2.39)$$

Kinetic gas theory

This can be verified by substitution:

$$A_1\epsilon^{-\beta W_1}A_2\epsilon^{-\beta W_2} = A_1\epsilon^{-\beta W_1+\beta\delta W}A_2\epsilon^{-\beta W_2-\beta\delta W}$$

If two other energies W_3 and W_4 are considered, the result is the same. Therefore, β is a universal coefficient.

The form of the probability density function $f(v)$ is now known and the coefficient A may be ascertained by normalizing the function. Substitute into Eq. (2.32)

$$\int_{-\infty}^{\infty}\int_{-\infty}^{\infty}\int_{-\infty}^{\infty} A\epsilon^{-\beta W}\,dv_x\,dv_y\,dv_z = 1$$

But $W = \frac{1}{2}m(v_x^2 + v_y^2 + v_z^2)$ for any one particle; therefore

$$A\int_{-\infty}^{\infty}\int_{-\infty}^{\infty}\int_{-\infty}^{\infty} \epsilon^{-(1/2)m\beta(v_x^2+v_y^2+v_z^2)}\,dv_x\,dv_y\,dv_z = 1 \qquad (2.40)$$

To integrate this equation set

$$x = \tfrac{1}{2}m\beta v_x^2, \qquad y = \tfrac{1}{2}m\beta v_y^2, \qquad z = \tfrac{1}{2}m\beta v_z^2 \qquad (2.41)$$

Then

$$dv_x = \frac{1}{2}\left(\frac{m\beta}{2}\right)^{-1/2} x^{-1/2}\,dx$$

$$dv_y = \frac{1}{2}\left(\frac{m\beta}{2}\right)^{-1/2} y^{-1/2}\,dy \qquad (2.42)$$

$$dv_z = \frac{1}{2}\left(\frac{m\beta}{2}\right)^{-1/2} z^{-1/2}\,dz$$

Substitute Eqs. (2.41) and (2.42) into (2.40) and obtain

$$A(2m\beta)^{-3/2}8\int_0^{\infty}\int_0^{\infty}\int_0^{\infty} \epsilon^{-x}x^{-1/2}\epsilon^{-y}y^{-1/2}\epsilon^{-z}z^{-1/2}\,dx\,dy\,dz = 1 \qquad (2.43)$$

Each part of this integral is independent of the other variables and is of the form

$$\int_0^{\infty}\epsilon^{-x}x^{n-1}\,dx = \Gamma(n) \qquad (2.44)$$

where $\Gamma(n)$ is the gamma function. In this case $n = \frac{1}{2}$. With reference to tables of $\Gamma(n)$,* we find that $\Gamma(\frac{1}{2}) = \sqrt{\pi}$. Equation (2.43) becomes

$$A\left(\frac{m\beta}{2\pi}\right)^{-3/2} = 1$$

The velocity density distribution function $f(v)$ will be normalized if

$$A = \left(\frac{m\beta}{2\pi}\right)^{3/2} \qquad (2.45)$$

---

* *Mathematical Tables from Handbook of Chemistry and Physics*, Chemical Rubber Publishing Co., Cleveland, Ohio.

The function is therefore

$$f(v_x, v_y, v_z) = \left(\frac{m\beta}{2\pi}\right)^{3/2} \epsilon^{-(1/2)m\beta(v_x^2 + v_y^2 + v_z^2)} \tag{2.46}$$

2.5 The Boltzmann factor

Once the velocity density distribution function (Eq. (2.46)) is known, the total average energy of the system may be found. The kinetic energy of any given molecule is $\frac{1}{2}mv^2$; therefore, if both sides of Eq. (2.35) are multiplied by $\frac{1}{2}mN$, where N is the number of molecules per cubic meter, an expression for the continuous summation of the individual kinetic energies of all of the molecules is obtained.

$$W = \frac{1}{2}Nmv_m^2 = N\int_0^\infty \frac{1}{2}mv^2 f(v)\, dv \tag{2.47}$$

Substitute the expression for the velocity distribution function into this integral for $f(v)$ and expand the variable into Cartesian coordinate form:

$$W = \frac{1}{2}Nmv_m^2$$
$$= \int_{-\infty}^\infty \int_{-\infty}^\infty \int_{-\infty}^\infty \frac{1}{2}m\left(\frac{m\beta}{2\pi}\right)^{3/2}(v_x^2 + v_y^2 + v_z^2)\epsilon^{-(1/2)m\beta(v_x^2 + v_y^2 + v_z^2)}dv_x\, dv_y\, dv_z \tag{2.48}$$

If the indicated integration is carried out in a straightforward manner using tables of the definite integrals, the result is

$$W = \frac{3N}{2\beta} \quad \text{joules/m}^3 \tag{2.49}$$

By means of Eqs. (2.14) and (2.17) we may write for pressure:

$$P = NkT = \frac{2}{3}\left(N\frac{1}{2}mv_m^2\right) = \frac{2}{3}W \tag{2.50}$$

where all the terms have been defined previously. By Eq. (2.49) this equation becomes

$$NkT = \frac{2}{3}\left(\frac{3}{2}\frac{N}{\beta}\right)$$

Therefore, the coefficient β is a funtion of the absolute temperature

$$\beta = \frac{1}{kT} \tag{2.51}$$

and the density distribution function is completely known. The term $\epsilon^{-W/kT}$ is known as the *Boltzmann factor*, which is extremely useful and occurs repeatedly in theoretical work.

2.6   The Maxwellian velocity distribution

The velocity density distribution function (Eq. (2.46)) may now be written as

$$f(v_x, v_y, v_z) = \left(\frac{m}{2\pi kT}\right)^{3/2} \epsilon^{-(1/2)m(v_x^2+v_y^2+v_z^2)/kT} \tag{2.52}$$

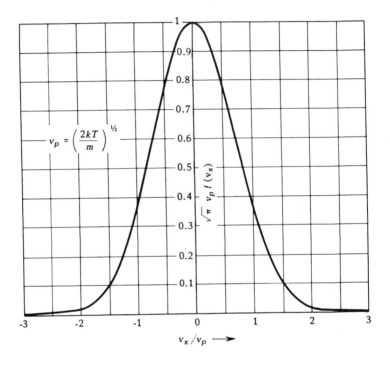

Fig. 2.5. A plot of the normalized Maxwell-Boltzmann distribution function for one degree of freedom. This is the familiar "bell-curve."

This distribution function is often called the *Maxwell-Boltzmann distribution function*. For one degree of freedom, Eq. (2.52) reduces to

$$f(v_x) = \left(\frac{m}{2\pi kT}\right)^{1/2} \epsilon^{-(1/2)mv_x^2/kT}$$

A plot of this function is shown in Fig. 2.5. From this function it is possible to compute the probability ΔP that a molecule will have a velocity between v and $v + \Delta v$, according to Eq. (2.29).

$$\Delta P = f(v)\,\Delta v = \left(\frac{m}{2\pi kT}\right)^{3/2} \epsilon^{-(1/2)m(v_x^2+v_y^2+v_z^2)/kT}\,\Delta v_x\,\Delta v_y\,\Delta v_z$$

The velocity components

$$v_x^2 + v_y^2 + v_z^2 = v^2$$

describe a sphere in velocity space (or momentum space, i.e., $1/m[p_x^2 + p_y^2 + p_z^2]$) of volume $\frac{4}{3}\pi v^3$. $\Delta v_x \, \Delta v_y \, \Delta v_z$ represents a volume element in this space, which corresponds to $4\pi v^2 \, \Delta v$ in size. Therefore, the probability of finding a molecule with a velocity between v and $v + \Delta v$ is

$$\Delta P = 4\pi \left(\frac{m}{2\pi kT}\right)^{3/2} v^2 \epsilon^{-(1/2)mv^2/kT} \, \Delta v \qquad (2.53)$$

Equation (2.53) is known as the *Maxwell velocity distribution* because it yields the probability of finding a molecule that possesses a velocity between v and $v + \Delta v$. This distribution is of fundamental importance in engineering physics. It is convenient to place it in a more compact form by setting

$$x^2 = \frac{\frac{1}{2}mv^2}{kT} = \frac{v^2}{2kT/m} \qquad (2.54)$$

$$x^2 = \frac{v^2}{v_p^2} \qquad (2.55)$$

where $\sqrt{2kT/m}$ is denoted by v_p, called the *most probable velocity*; i.e., the velocity most apt to be found experimentally. That v_p is the most probable velocity will be shown directly. Write y for $(\Delta P/\Delta x)$ and Eq. (2.53) may be written as

$$y = \frac{4}{\sqrt{\pi}} x^2 \epsilon^{-x^2} \qquad (2.56)$$

This Maxwellian velocity distribution is plotted in Fig. 2.6. The ordinate axis y is the dependent variable. This is the probability that a molecule will have a velocity ratio x. The axis of the abscissa is the independent variable or velocity ratio, x. Consider two velocities v_1 and v_2; these define the velocity ratios x_1 and x_2. The area under the Maxwellian distribution curve, defined by the velocity limits v_1 and v_2, divided by the total area of the curve gives the fraction of molecules having velocity ratios lying between x_1 and x_2. As an example, the fraction of molecules having velocity ratios v/v_p between 0.6 and 0.8 is equal to the summation of the small-area rectangles lying within the area defined by these limits and the curve. Each area represents 1 per cent of the total area. In this example, 13.6 per cent of the total molecules will lie within the specified velocity ratio range.

This distribution curve holds for all temperatures; the only difference is that the most probable velocity increases with the square root of the absolute temperature. To show this and to prove that the most probable velocity is equal to $\sqrt{2kT/m}$, refer to the distribution curve and its mathematical equation ((2.53) or (2.56)). Use the form of Eq. (2.56), and the most probable

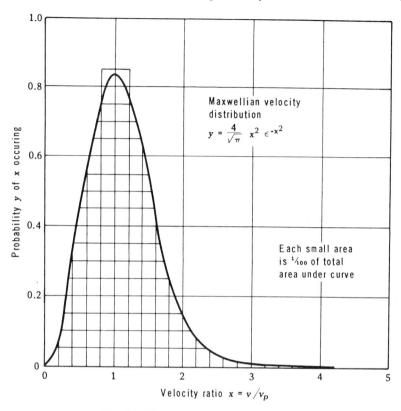

Fig. 2.6. The Maxwellian velocity distribution.

velocity, v_p is found by taking the derivative of the probability y with respect to velocity ratio x and equating to zero.

$$\frac{\partial y}{\partial x} = 0, \qquad x^2 = 1$$

but $x^2 = \frac{1}{2}mv^2/kT$. For this case v is the most probable velocity v_p; therefore,

$$x^2 = \frac{\frac{1}{2}mv_p^2}{kT}, \qquad v_p = \sqrt{\frac{2kT}{m}} \tag{2.57}$$

This expression for the most probable velocity is easily evaluated in terms of T and the molecular weight m' (see Eq. (2.24)).

$$v_p = \sqrt{\frac{2k}{1.675 \times 10^{-27}}} \sqrt{\frac{T}{m'}}$$

$$= 129 \sqrt{\frac{T}{m'}} \quad \text{m/sec} \tag{2.58}$$

The average velocity ratio may be determined from the Maxwellian distribution curve

$$x_a = \frac{v_a}{v_p} \tag{2.59}$$

where v_a is the average velocity. In a similar manner the root-mean-square velocity ratio may be found.

$$x_m = \frac{v_m}{v_p} \tag{2.60}$$

where v_m is the rms velocity. The relationship among these three velocities is

$$v_a = \frac{2}{\sqrt{\pi}} v_p = 1.124 v_p \tag{2.61}$$

and

$$v_m = \sqrt{\frac{3}{2}} v_p = 1.224 v_p \tag{2.62}$$

Also,

$$v_m = \sqrt{\frac{3\pi}{8}} v_a = 1.085 v_a \tag{2.63}$$

The rms velocity is used in total energy calculations. For instance, the total kinetic energy of the gas molecules in one cubic meter of gas would be

$$W_{\text{total}} = \frac{1}{2} N m v_m^2 \quad \text{joules} \tag{2.64}$$

N is the number of molecules per cubic meter.

The average velocity is used in computations such as the determination of the average number of molecules that will cross a plane of area S in a given direction per unit time. The result, which is developed in the following example, is

$$N_r = \frac{1}{4} N S v_a \quad \text{molecules/sec} \tag{2.65}$$

The derivation of each of these velocities proceeds directly from an application of Eq. (2.52) and the appropriate choice of Eq. (2.33) or (2.35). As an example of Maxwell-Boltzmann statistics, let us consider the proof of Eq. (2.65).

Consider a gas-filled region that is in thermodynamic equilibrium. Further, let the pressure be constant throughout the region (i.e., no mass flow due to a pressure differential). Choose a reference plane of area S square meters located either on a wall or well within the volume so that a very long and uninterrupted column of gas molecules extends normal to the surface. Those molecules that possess a velocity lying within the range between v and $v + dv$ and which are vt meters or less from this surface will strike or cross the reference surface. Here, in order to simplify the calculations, we consider only motion normal to the surface (see Fig. 2.7). The proportion of molecules to be found in this velocity range is given by dN/N, where N is the molecular density. Refer to Eq. (2.29) and write

$$\frac{dN}{N} = f(v)\, dv \quad \text{or} \quad dN = N f(v)\, dv$$

This is the number of molecules contained in the volume vtS corresponding to the velocity range v to $v + dv$. Let t be one second; then the incremental number of molecules that cross the reference surface in one second is

$$dN_r = NSvf(v)\, dv$$

Integrate over all possible velocities to obtain the total number of molecules per second that cross the reference surface:

$$N_r = NS \int_0^\infty vf(v)\, dv$$

Because we specified both thermal and pressure equilibrium conditions, the velocity distribution function $f(v)$ is of the Maxwell-Boltzmann type. Refer to Eq. (2.52), but note that, because we are considering only one degree of freedom, the function reduces to

$$f(v) = \left(\frac{m}{2\pi kT}\right)^{1/2} \epsilon^{-(1/2)mv^2/kT}$$

Substitute and integrate; the result yields

$$N_r = \frac{1}{2\sqrt{\pi}} NS \sqrt{\frac{2kT}{m}}$$

$$= \frac{1}{4} NS \frac{2v_p}{\sqrt{\pi}}$$

$$= \frac{1}{4} NS v_a$$

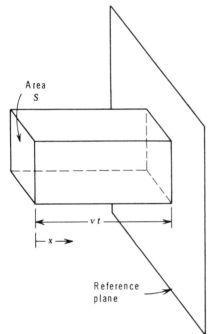

Area S

vt

x →

Reference plane

Fig. 2.7. The volume Svt contains dN molecules all having a velocity between v and $v + dv$.

2.7 Mean free path

A direct consequence of the kinetic theory of gas is the concept of a mean molecular path length between elastic collisions of the gas molecules. Imagine for the moment that all of the gas molecules are at rest. Now let one other molecule of the same gas or some other gas be shot into the gas. This incident molecule travels along the centerline of an imaginary cylinder whose diameter is equal to the sum of the diameter d_1 of the incident molecule plus the diameter d_2 of the ambient gas molecules which we have imagined to be at rest (see Fig. 2.8).

If any ambient gas molecule lies with its center on or within this imaginary cylinder, then a collision results. If the cylinder is one meter long and there are N molecules per cubic meter, then the number of collisions per path length L is

$$n_c = \frac{\pi(d_1 + d_2)^2}{4} LN \quad (2.66)$$

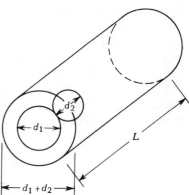

Fig. 2.8. Condition for elastic collision between gas molecules of diameter d_1 and d_2.

n_c is often called the *collision probability*. The average or mean path between molecular collisions is

$$\lambda = \frac{L}{n_c} = \frac{4}{\pi(d_1 + d_2)^2 N} \quad (2.67)$$

If only one gas is involved, then $d_1 = d_2$. The above expression is valid only if the ambient gas molecules are stationary relative to the incident molecules. If the average molecular velocity is v_a, then the number of collisions per second is

$$\zeta = n_c v_a = \frac{\pi}{4}(d_1 + d_2)^2 N v_a \quad (2.68)$$

The factor ζ is called the *collision frequency*. A detailed analysis indicates that, because the ambient gas is not at rest, some of the molecules are moving into the imaginary volume to be hit while still others are moving out to escape. The net result is that there is a greater probability that the molecules will move in and be hit, introducing the factor $\sqrt{2}$ into Eq. (2.68):

$$\zeta = \sqrt{2}\frac{\pi}{4}(d_1 + d_2)^2 N v_a \quad \text{collisions/sec} \quad (2.69)$$

for a real gas. From Eq. (2.69) the mean *collision time* is

$$\tau = \frac{1}{\zeta} \quad \text{sec} \quad (2.70)$$

and the mean free path, mfp, in a real gas is

$$\lambda = \frac{v_a}{\zeta} = \frac{4}{\sqrt{2}\,\pi(d_1 + d_2)^2 N} \quad (2.71)$$

Because the pressure is related to the number of molecules per cubic meter by Eq. (2.14), Eq. (2.71) may be written

$$\lambda = \frac{4kT}{\sqrt{2}\,\pi(d_1 + d_2)^2 P}$$ (2.72)

This equation for the molecular mfp holds true under constant temperature conditions and thereby expresses the inverse proportionality between molecular mfp and pressure. For small changes in temperature the equation is still valid; however, the effective molecular diameters vary inversely with temperature. It can be shown experimentally and theoretically that the more energetic molecules may approach more closely without experiencing an elastic collision. Sutherland's formula yields an expression for the effective molecular diameter as a function of the temperature which fits experimental results fairly closely.

$$d^2 = d_\infty^2\left(1 + \frac{T'}{T}\right)$$ (2.73)

where d_∞ is called the *core diameter* of the molecule, by Sutherland, and T' is a reference temperature which varies for each gas. Table 2.1 gives the

Table 2.1

Mean free paths and effective collision diameters
0°C, 1 mm Hg

Gas	λ Microns	d Angstrom units[†]	d_∞* Angstrom units	T'*
H_2	136	2.4	2.4	72
He	210	2.2	1.9	80
N_2	63	3.5	3.2	111
O_2	72	3.3	3.0	127
Ne	115	2.4	..	56
A	76	3.2	2.9	170
H_2O	85	3.6	..	550

* J. H. Jeans, *The Dynamical Theory of Gases*, 4th ed., Cambridge University Press, London, 1925.
† 1 Angstrom unit equals 10^{-10} meters.

mean free path λ, the effective molecular diameter, and Sutherland's constants for the standard conditions of 1 mm Hg and 0°C. It should be noted that the values vary depending upon the method of measurement and other conditions; however, although the error may be as high as 30 per cent, this will have little effect upon most calculations because boundary effects and other problems make exact calculations infeasible in many experiments and applications. The order of magnitude is of primary importance. The material for this table has been derived from many sources, principally those listed in the reference at the end of this chapter.

2.8 The distribution of free paths

As a reference point in a gas, take the position of a molecular collision and let I molecules start out from this reference point. Let the number of molecules that as yet have not experienced a collision after leaving the reference point be y.

The collision frequency is ζ collisions per second, and the average velocity of the molecules is v_a. The number of collisions experienced by a single molecule in going a unit distance is

$$n_c = \frac{\zeta}{v_a} = \frac{1}{\lambda} \quad \text{collisions/m}$$

where λ is the mean free path. The number of collisions which occur in an incremental distance is

$$\frac{\zeta}{v_a} dx \quad \text{collisions}$$

The number of collisions experienced in an increment of distance dx must equal the fractional decrease in the number of molecules that as yet have not experienced a collision; therefore,

$$-\left(\frac{dy}{y}\right) = \frac{\zeta}{v_a} dx \quad \text{collisions}$$

Solve for y:

$$y = A\epsilon^{-(\zeta/v_a)x}$$

The boundary conditions are that when x is 0, then y is I; therefore, $A = I$ and

$$y = I^{-(\zeta/v_a)x} \tag{2.74}$$

where y is the number of molecules that have not yet experienced a collision. Equation (2.74) may also be written in terms of the mfp.

$$y = I\epsilon^{-x/\lambda} \tag{2.75}$$

Let the fraction of molecules that have not yet experienced a collision be

$$f_x = \frac{y}{I} = \epsilon^{-x/\lambda} \tag{2.76}$$

Figure 2.9 is a plot of Eq. (2.76). Notice that after a distance of one mfp, only 36.8 per cent of the molecules have not experienced a collision. The average distance traveled by a molecule would be

$$L_{\text{avg}} = \int_0^\infty \epsilon^{-x/\lambda} \, dx = \lambda$$

which is the mean free path, as we would expect.

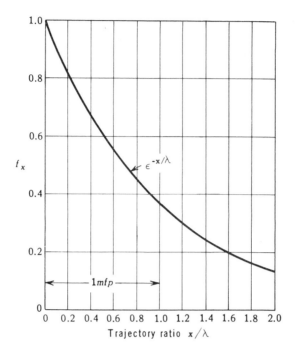

Fig. 2.9. The fraction, f_x, of molecules traversing a distance ratio x/λ without experiencing a collision.

2.9 Free molecule conductivity

When molecules originally at a temperature T_i strike a hot surface at temperature T_s $(T_s > T_i)$, complete interchange of energy does not occur at the first collision. Quite often many collisions are required for this to occur. To describe this effect, Knudsen introduced a constant, known as the *accommodation coefficient*, α, which represents the fractional extent to which those molecules that fall on the surface and are reflected or re-emitted from it have their mean energy adjusted or accommodated toward what it would be if the returning molecules were issuing as a stream out of a mass of gas at the temperature of the surface. Let the reflected or re-emitted molecules have a temperature T_r. Then

$$\alpha = \frac{T_r - T_i}{T_s - T_i} \tag{2.77}$$

2.10 Diffusion

Gas diffusion is the phenomenon by which the constituent gases of a mixture distribute themselves uniformly throughout the volume of the containing vessel. This permits each gas to exert its partial pressure uniformly over the entire surface of the container. Diffusion is not necessarily associated with the mass flow of gas but occurs readily in a system under conditions of constant pressure and temperature. For instance, vacuum pumping at very low pressures approaches a diffusion process, because pressure differentials are almost nonexistent.

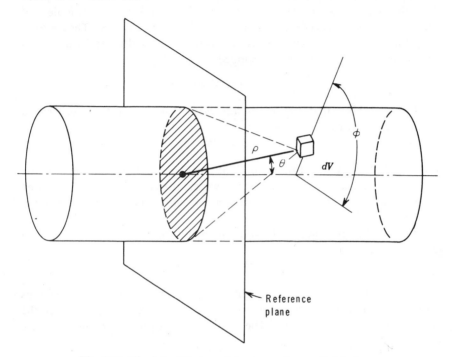

Fig. 2.10. The interdiffusion of two gases in a cylindrical tube.

Basically, any local concentration of one type of gas molecule in a mixture (at constant pressure and temperature) will diffuse away from a region of high concentration gradient. In the same way, ions or electrons that are unevenly distributed throughout a region in an electron tube or semiconductor will diffuse in a manner that eliminates any concentration gradient. In conductors, the electron gas concept of the free conduction electrons permits the application of diffusion theory to the motion of these electrons. This subject of electron diffusion is of importance and will be discussed in detail in Chap. 4.

To develop the concept of diffusion mathematically, consider a cylindrical container of infinite length, as shown in Fig. 2.10. Let there be no temperature or pressure gradients throughout the entire volume, but suppose that two gases, 1 and 2, fill the volume and that concentration gradients of each of these gases do exist. Specifically, there may be initially more molecules of type 1 gas on the right of the reference plane than on the left. The condition of uniform pressure then requires a greater concentration of type 2 gas on the left of the reference plane than on the right-hand side.

The number of molecules of type 1 gas that start out on *new free paths* from the incremental volume element dV is equal to the number of molecules that have just experienced a collision within this volume element. The collision frequency, ζ per cubic meter as given by Eq. (2.69), multiplied by dV yields the number of new free paths developed within dV, or

$$\zeta_1 \, dV \quad \text{collisions/sec}$$

The probability that a molecule traverses a distance ρ without suffering a collision is given by

$$P = \epsilon^{-\rho/\lambda_1} \tag{2.78}$$

(see Sec. 2.8). λ_1 is the mean free path of type 1 gas molecules in the mixture. λ_1 will be a function of the mixture; however, the error involved in treating λ_1 as a constant is small if λ_1 is approximately equal to λ_2 of type 2 gas molecules in the mixture.

The number of molecules leaving the incremental volume that proceed a distance ρ is

$$\zeta_1 \epsilon^{-\rho/\lambda_1} \, dV \quad \text{molecules/sec}$$

These molecules travel in straight paths and spread out in all directions from the volume dV. A certain number of these molecules pass through the area A of the reference plane. The area A subtends a solid angle Ω, where

$$\Omega = \frac{A \cos \theta}{\rho^2} \tag{2.79}$$

The integral of the solid angle over any surface which completely encloses the volume element is 4π. Therefore, the fraction of molecules that pass through the area A is $\Omega/4\pi$. This may be written as

$$\frac{\Omega}{4\pi} = \frac{A}{4\pi\rho^2} \cos \theta \tag{2.80}$$

The rate at which type 1 molecules cross area A, from right to left, is

$$\frac{\zeta_1 A n_1(\rho)}{4\pi\rho^2} \epsilon^{-\rho/\lambda_1} \cos \theta \, dV \quad \text{molecules/sec}$$

where $n_1(\rho)$ is the concentration of type 1 molecules throughout the volume to the right of the reference plane.

Before we proceed further, an explicit expression for the concentration distribution is required to replace the implicit expression $n(\rho)$. A typical and not unrealistic distribution is one that is linear along the cylinder.

$$n(z) = n_0 + \alpha z$$

or, in terms of ρ:

$$n(\rho) = n_0 + \alpha\rho \cos\theta \qquad (2.81)$$

Express the incremental volume dV in terms of the coordinates ρ, θ, and ϕ:

$$dV = (d\rho)(\rho \, d\theta)(\rho \sin\theta \, d\phi) \qquad (2.82)$$

Substitute Eq. (2.81) into the expression for the rate at which molecules leave the volume element and cross the reference plane. Integrate over the entire volume. This yields the excess number of molecules per second which cross the reference plane from right to left over those which cross from left to right.

$$\frac{dn_1}{dt} = \frac{\zeta_1 A}{4\pi} \int_0^\infty \int_0^\pi \int_0^{2\pi} (n_0 + \alpha_1\rho \cos\theta)\epsilon^{-\rho/\lambda_1} \cos\theta \sin\theta \, d\rho \, d\theta \, d\phi \qquad (2.83)$$

$$= \frac{\zeta_1 A}{4\pi} \int_0^\infty \left[0 + \frac{2}{3}\alpha_1\rho \right] \epsilon^{-\rho/\lambda_1} \, d\rho$$

$$\frac{dn_1}{dt} = \frac{1}{3} \zeta_1 A \lambda_1^2 \alpha_1 \qquad (2.84)$$

In a similar manner, the excess number of type 2 gas molecules that pass from right to left across the reference plane is given by

$$\frac{dn_2}{dt} = \frac{1}{3} \zeta_2 A \lambda_2^2 \alpha_2 \qquad (2.85)$$

In any unit volume of the gas mixture, the total number of molecules must remain constant if the pressure is to remain constant.

$$n = n_1 + n_2 = \text{constant} \qquad (2.86)$$

From Eq. (2.81), the coefficient α is

$$\alpha_1 = \frac{dn}{dz} \qquad (2.87)$$

but, from Eq. (2.86)

$$\frac{dn_1}{dz} = -\frac{dn_2}{dz}$$

or

$$\alpha_1 = -\alpha_2$$

In view of this, Eq. (2.85) may be written as

$$\frac{1}{3} \zeta_2 A \lambda_2^2 \alpha_2 = \frac{1}{3} \zeta_2 A \lambda_2^2 \alpha_1$$

The net diffusion of gas 1 and gas 2 molecules from right to left is found by adding Eqs. (2.84) and (2.85)

$$\frac{1}{3}(\zeta_1\lambda_1^2 - \zeta_2\lambda_2^2)\alpha_1 A$$

This net diffusion of gas molecules from right to left creates a diffusion potential (pressure) gradient that opposes the diffusion process. The result of this diffusion gradient is a return drift of gas molecules from left to right across the reference plane. The number of returning molecules of each gas is directly proportional to the concentration of each gas on the left-hand side of the reference plane. There are

$$\frac{1}{3}(\zeta_1\lambda_1^2 - \zeta_2\lambda_2^2)\frac{dn_1}{dz}\frac{n_1}{n} \quad \text{molecules/m}^2$$

of gas 1 and

$$\frac{1}{3}(\zeta_1\lambda_1^2 - \zeta_2\lambda_2^2)\frac{dn_1}{dz}\frac{n_2}{n} \quad \text{molecules/m}^2$$

of gas 2 that cross from left to right.

The total number per unit area, N_D, gas molecules that diffuse from right to left is

$$N_D = \frac{1}{3}\zeta_1\lambda_1^2\frac{dn_1}{dz} - \frac{1}{3}(\zeta_1\lambda_1^2 - \zeta_2\lambda_2^2)\frac{dn_1}{dz}\frac{n_1}{n} \tag{2.88}$$

Substitute $n_1 + n_2$ for n and place all terms over the common denominator $n_1 + n_2$ to obtain

$$N_D = \frac{1}{3}\frac{\zeta_1\lambda_1^2 n_2 + \zeta_2\lambda_2^2 n_1}{n_1 + n_2}\frac{dn_1}{dz} \tag{2.89}$$

or

$$N_D = D\frac{dn_1}{dz} \quad \text{particles/m}^2/\text{sec}$$

where

$$D = \frac{1}{3}\frac{\zeta_1\lambda_1^2 n_2 + \zeta_2\lambda_2^2 n_1}{n_1 + n_2} \tag{2.90}$$

is the *diffusion coefficient* for type 1 gas molecules in the mixture, under our original assumption that $\lambda_1 \approx \lambda_2$. An identical expression is obtained for type 2 molecules. One reason for this is our assumption that $\lambda_1 \approx \lambda_2$ when we originally set up our equations.

A coefficient of $8/\pi$ instead of $1/3$ is obtained from Eq. (2.90) if Maxwell-Boltzmann statistics are used in the derivations. Experimentally, the difference is not normally detectable. Considerable use of this concept of diffusion is made later in this text in discussions of the conduction of electricity in solids and gases.

PROBLEMS

1. A miniature receiving tube has an internal volume of 3 cm³. The operating pressure is 10^{-6} mm Hg at a temperature of about 100°C. How many gas molecules are in the tube? *Ans.* 7.8×10^{10}

2. The anode-to-cathode interelectrode spacing of a miniature receiving tube is 0.3 cm. The operating pressure is 7×10^{-7} mm Hg. What fraction of electrons traversing the cathode-to-anode space will collide with gas molecules if it is assumed that nitrogen is the only gas present? ($T = 400°$K.)

3. Plot the mean free path of nitrogen molecules in nitrogen gas and electrons in nitrogen gas. The temperature in each case is room temperature (300°K). Use log-log paper and the data from Table 2.1.

4. By application of Maxwell-Boltzmann statistics, develop the expressions for the average and rms velocities given in Eqs. (2.61) and (2.62).

5. By means of Maxwell-Boltzmann statistics, develop Eq. (2.20) for the mean pressure exerted by a gas upon the walls of its enclosing vessel. To do this, proceed in a manner similar to the derivation of Eq. (2.65). Recall that the force exerted by a molecule in colliding with a wall is because of the change in momentum, which is $2mv/t$ newtons. The pressure is the average force per unit area and is made up of the sum of the partial pressures caused by each velocity group of molecules. Each partial pressure is because of the number of molecules dN in the volume Svt corresponding to the velocity range v to $v + dv$. These all strike the surface in one second if $t = 1$, and the corresponding partial pressure is

$$Sp = NSvf(v) \, dv \, 2mv$$

Integrate over all positive velocities and use the Maxwell-Boltzmann distribution function for one degree of freedom to complete the problem. *Ans.* $P = 1/3 \, Nmv_m^2$

6. A vacuum tube has a volume of 5 cm³ and is originally filled with dry air at atmospheric pressure which is essentially composed of 78 % N_2, 21 % O_2, and 1 % Ar, by volume. A vacuum pump that pumps each constituent gas with the same efficiency is used to reduce the pressure to 10^{-4} mm Hg. What is the weight of each gas within the vessel? A chemical "getter" is employed to absorb all of the oxygen. To what pressure does this lower the residual gas within the tube?

7. A gas possesses a Maxwellian velocity distribution function. Show that the fraction of molecules in a given volume that possess a velocity ($+v_x$) in one direction only and whose magnitude is greater than some selected value v_0 is

$$\int_{v_0}^{\infty} f(v_x) \, dv_x = \frac{1}{2}\left[1 - \text{erf}\left(\frac{\frac{1}{2}mv_0^2}{kT}\right)^{1/2}\right]$$

Hint: Recall that

$$\int_0^\infty x^{n-1}\epsilon^{-x}\,dx = \Gamma(n) \quad \text{(gamma function)}$$

and that

$$\frac{2}{\sqrt{\pi}} \int_0^x \epsilon^{-x^2}\,dx = \text{erf } x \quad \text{(error function)}$$

Specifically, $\Gamma(\frac{1}{2}) = \sqrt{\pi}$ and tables of numerical values of the error function for explicit values of x are tabulated.

8. In Prob. 7 show that the fraction of molecules traveling in one direction only that travel a distance $v_0 t$ to cross a plane is given by

$$\frac{\displaystyle\int_{v_0}^\infty v_x f(v_x)\,dv_x}{\displaystyle\int_0^\infty v_x f(v_x)\,dv_x} = \epsilon^{-\frac{1}{2}mv_0^2/kT}$$

REFERENCES

1. J. Jeans, *The Dynamical Theory of Gases*, 4th ed., Cambridge University Press, London, 1925 (also Dover, New York, 1958).

2. L. B. Loeb, *Kinetic Theory of Gases*, 2nd ed., McGraw-Hill Book Company, New York, 1934.

3. J. D. Cobine, *Gaseous Conductors*, 2nd ed., Dover, New York, 1958.

4. A. van der Ziel, *Solid State Physical Electronics*, Prentice-Hall, Inc., Englewood Cliffs, N.J., 1957.

CHAPTER 3

Atomic structure

and quantum mechanics

In Chap. 2 we considered the translational or external energy of molecules in the gaseous state. In addition to translational kinetic energy, atoms possess an external energy associated with the extranuclear relationships existing between the nucleus and the electrons comprising the atom. There is also an internal energy associated with the structure of the nucleus, but to date no direct use of this energy is made in devices commonly classified in the realm of physical electronics and the subject is not considered in this text.

The extranuclear structure and energy of atoms, along with certain features of crystalline structure, govern the conduction of electricity in both conductors and semiconductors as well as the mechanics of electron emission. If these phenomena are to be understood, it will be necessary first to review those physical laws and methods of theoretical analysis applicable to atomic structure.

Any previous background in quantum mechanics is unnecessary; the few concepts required will be presented as needed. If the reader has been previously introduced to Maxwell's field equations and the wave equations, then Schrödinger's equation of quantum mechanics and its solution will not appear unfamiliar.

3.1   Development of the Bohr-Sommerfield model

It is always helpful to have a model of an item under analysis, and the atom is no exception. Following his identification of the electron in 1897, J. J. Thomson proposed an atomic model that consisted of a positive space-charge cloud of the diameter of an atom (known to be about 10^{-8} cm by previous experiments). Embedded in this cloud at equilibrium points were electrons. Electromagnetic radiation from this atomic model was supposed to result from oscillations of the electrons about their equilibrium positions. This model possessed several distinct drawbacks. For example, it did not explain satisfactorily the α-particle, which is a doubly ionized helium atom.

Following a series of experiments involving α-particle scattering, Ernest Rutherford in 1911 proposed a new atomic model that included a nucleus which contained most of the mass of the atom and a positive charge. The electrons were assumed to be negatively charged and scattered about the nucleus, thus filling the atomic volume. The early atomic model did not assign any real function to the electrons, yet there was work to be done. For instance, the mechanics of spectra emission, as determined by spectroscopy, required explanation. This led Niels Bohr to apply the quantum concepts of Max Planck to the Rutherford atomic model. The result, in 1913, was the early form of the modern atomic model.

Bohr's atomic model consisted of a nucleus which contained the majority of the mass of the atom plus all of the positive electric charge. The electrons moved about this nucleus in circular orbits. They carried the remaining mass of the atom and the total negative electric charge of the atom. This model explained most of the line spectra associated with the hydrogen atom and was found to apply to singly ionized helium, doubly ionized lithium, etc. In 1915–16, C. T. R. Wilson and A. Sommerfield improved upon the model by applying Kepler's laws of planetary motion to the electron orbits, with the result that the general electron orbit is elliptical (see Fig. 3.1).

The mass of the nucleus consists of the sum of the masses of all the protons and neutrons that combine to form the nucleus. In terms of the electron mass, m, the mass of a proton is $1836.13m$ and the mass of a neutron is $1836.66m$. The number of neutrons and protons included in any given element, as well as the atomic number, is given by the complete atomic symbol

$$_Z X^A_{A-Z}$$

where Z is the *atomic number*, A is the *mass number* (number of protons and neutrons present), and $A - Z$ is, therefore, the number of neutrons since there are as many protons as the atomic number. As an example, copper has an atomic number of 29, and about 70 per cent of all copper possesses a mass number of 63. Therefore, copper is written as

$$_{29}\text{Cu}^{63}_{34}$$

This represents only about 70 per cent of all naturally occurring copper. The majority of the remaining copper has a mass number of 65, which means that there are more neutrons present in the nucleus of these copper atoms. Such atoms are said to be *isotopes* of one another. There are three types of hydrogen atoms that are encountered:

$$_1\mathrm{H}_0^1 \qquad _1\mathrm{H}_1^2 \qquad _1\mathrm{H}_2^3$$

The isotopes of hydrogen are normal hydrogen, deuterium (heavy hydrogen), and tritium, respectively.

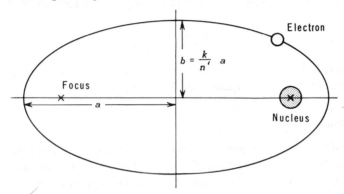

Fig. 3.1. Elliptical electron orbit of the Bohr-Sommerfeld atomic model.

Following this scheme, the symbol for the proton is $_1p^1$ and the neutron $_0n^1$. The neutron number is often omitted because it can easily be determined from the other two numbers.

A slight reduction in the net mass of the nucleus occurs because of the conversion of a finite amount of mass Δm into nuclear binding energy. The conversion of mass to energy is governed by Einstein's mass-energy equivalence formula

$$W = \Delta mc^2 \tag{3.1}$$

where c is the velocity of light (2.998×10^8 m/sec).

The potential energy existing between an electron and the nucleus can be written easily if any atomic nucleus with only one electron is considered. If other electrons are present, they tend to partially screen one another from the nucleus and thereby modify the energy relationship between a given electron and the nucleus.

According to the inverse square law of electrostatics, the force existing between an electron that possesses a charge, e, of 1.60×10^{-19} coulombs and a nucleus that possesses Z-protons is $Ze^2/4\pi\epsilon_0 r^2$ newtons. Take the center of the nucleus as origin. Then, if this force is integrated from $+\infty$

back to the location of the electron at r meters from the origin, the potential energy of the electron is obtained as

$$\text{P.E.} = -\frac{Ze^2}{4\pi\epsilon_0 r} \quad \text{joules} \tag{3.2}$$

The distance between the center of charges of the electron and the nucleus is r. The permittivity, ϵ_0, of free space is 8.854×10^{-12} farads per meter.

The total energy of an atomic system that consists of a nucleus and a single electron is the sum of the kinetic and potential energies.

It is possible to show that the *total energy* of the electron is given by

$$W = -\frac{e^2 Z}{8\pi\epsilon_0 a} \tag{3.3}$$

This result is interesting because it states that the total internal energy is dependent upon only the major axis of the elliptical orbit, $2a$.

3.2 Quantum concepts

The first quantum concept appeared in 1900, when Max Planck postulated that electromagnetic energy (specifically, light) could be radiated only in discrete amounts or integer multiples thereof. This hypothesis was necessary to bring the Stefan-Boltzmann radiation law and Wien's displacement law into accord when they are applied to the problem of electromagnetic radiation from a black-body radiator. Planck assumed that electromagnetic radiation of frequency f could be radiated only in integer mutiples of hf, where h is a universal constant.

Albert Einstein applied Planck's quantum hypothesis to the explanation of the photoelectric effect (1905) and to the calculation of the specific heats of solids (1907). The success of Planck's quantum concept led to Bohr's theory of atomic structure.

In 1913 P. Debye postulated the quantum condition that the integral of the momentum over one period of motion must be an integral multiple of Planck's constant h (6.624×10^{-34} joule-seconds). Two quantum conditions immediately arise from the elliptical motion of the electron about the nucleus. First, for the angular momentum p_θ:

$$\oint p_\theta \, d\theta = kh \tag{3.4}$$

The symbol $\oint$ is used here to indicate integration over a closed period of motion. The angular momentum p_θ is a constant and the integral reduces to

$$p_\theta = \frac{kh}{2\pi} \tag{3.5}$$

The second quantum condition refers to the radial momentum, which must also be quantized.

$$\oint p_r \, dr = n'h \tag{3.6}$$

The sum of the quantum numbers k and n', which specify respectively the angular and radial momentums of the electron, is set equal to the *principal quantum number*, n.

$$k + n' = n \tag{3.7}$$

With these results, it is easy to show that one-half of the major axis of the elliptical orbit of the electron is equal to

$$a = \frac{m + M}{mM} \times \frac{h^2 n^2 \epsilon_0}{\pi e^2 Z} \tag{3.8}$$

where M is the mass of the nucleus and m is the mass of the electron.

If Eq. (3.8) is substituted into Eq. (3.3), then the total energy of the quantized system is

$$W = -\frac{e^4 Z^2}{8\epsilon_0^2 h^2 n^2} \times \frac{mM}{m + M} \tag{3.9}$$

The quantity $mM/(m + M)$ is called the *effective mass* of the system. Because, in general, $M \gg m$, the effective mass is taken as simply m. By multiplying and dividing by ch, the expression for the total energy of the system may be written as

$$W = -R \frac{chZ^2}{n^2} \tag{3.10}$$

where R is called the *Rydberg constant* and has the numerical value of

$$R = 10,967,758 \quad \text{cycles/m} \tag{3.11}$$

The preceding equations are valid for the special case of a single electron moving about a nucleus which possesses an electronic charge eZ. Thus, these equations apply directly to the hydrogen atom, the singly ionized helium atom, the doubly ionized lithium atom, and so forth. The term "ionized" indicates that the normal atom has lost one or more electrons. It can also be applied to atoms that have attached one or more extra electrons. In either case, the ionized atom possesses a net electronic charge.

Equation (3.10) can also be applied to the *valence electrons* of any atom, provided that an effective reduced nuclear charge is used to replace eZ. This may be illustrated by considering the case of the lithium atom. Here, there are three electrons to the atom, with two of them moving about orbits close to the nucleus, while the third electron moves in an orbit that is considerably removed from the nucleus. This outermost electron is not as firmly bonded to the nucleus as are the others.

This electron provides the electrical and chemical characteristics of lithium. It forms the bonds with other atoms to form chemical compounds of lithium. In the case of lithium, the valence electron does not experience a force that arises from the three protons in the nucleus because the two inner-orbit electrons partially shield this valence electron from the charge in the nucleus. For this reason, a reduced nuclear charge must be used in the calculations (this subject is beyond the scope of this text).

The nature and behavior of the valence electrons in various crystalline elements is of primary importance in physical electronics; it will be treated in detail in subsequent chapters.

3.3 Atomic excitation and radiation

The energy expression (Eq. (3.10)) can be written for one electron associated with an atomic nucleus. The energy is a function of the principal quantum number alone; therefore, if the internal energy of the system is to change by ΔW, the electron must acquire a new value for the principal quantum number corresponding to a new orbit. Let n_1 prescribe the original orbit and n_2 prescribe the final orbit. Energy must be added to the atom in the amount of

$$W = -RchZ^2\left(\frac{1}{n_2^2} - \frac{1}{n_1^2}\right) \quad \text{joules} \tag{3.12}$$

This energy must be added by means of electromagnetic radiation which, according to Planck's theory, will have a frequency of

$$f = \frac{\Delta W}{h} = RcZ^2\left(\frac{1}{n_1^2} - \frac{1}{n_2^2}\right) \quad \text{cycles/sec} \tag{3.13}$$

In view of the increased energy of the atom because of the electron's moving in a larger orbit, the atom is said to be *excited*. After about 10^{-8} seconds the atom will revert to a lower energy level by radiating part or all of this acquired energy by electromagnetic (EM) radiation.

For the hydrogen atom ($Z = 1$), the lowest, or ground, energy level corresponds to $n_1 = 1$. Let n_1 describe the final energy level for a radiative transition and let n_2 describe higher energy levels ($n_2 > n_1$). The corresponding electromagnetic radiation will be at discrete sets of frequencies. Each frequency set or series will be determined by n_1 and bears the name of the early x-ray spectroscopist who identified the series. They are as follows:

Lyman series:

$$f = cR\left(\frac{1}{1^2} - \frac{1}{n_2^2}\right) \quad (n_2 = 1, 2, 3, \ldots, \infty)$$

Balmer series:

$$f = cR\left(\frac{1}{2^2} - \frac{1}{n_2^2}\right) \quad (n_2 = 2, 3, 4, \ldots, \infty)$$

the Paschen: $(n_1 = 3; n_2 = 3, 4, 5, \ldots, \infty)$, the Brackett: $(n_1 = 4; n_2 = 4, 5, \ldots, \infty)$, the Pfund: $(n_1 = 5; n_2 = 5, 6, \ldots, \infty)$; and the Humphreys: $(n_1 = 6; n_2 = 6, 7, \ldots, \infty)$.

These series of spectral lines may be shown on an energy level diagram such as Fig. 3.2. Three series are shown, the arrows indicating energy transitions from a higher to a lower level. In this plot the *vacuum level*, outside the atom, has been taken as the reference with zero energy. (Note that all energies are negative because the electron tries to "fall away" from the energy reference plane.) Therefore, the electron must possess negative potential energy. It requires 13.60 electron-volts' energy to ionize a hydrogen atom because this is equivalent to taking the electron from the ground state, $n = 1$, to the vacuum level, $n = \infty$.

In Fig. 3.2 the permitted energy levels and the corresponding permitted orbits are identified by the principal quantum number, n, and also by the spectroscopy notation:

n	1	2	3	4	5	6	7	$\cdots$
x-ray designation	K	L	M	N	O	P	Q	$\cdots$

A few atoms possess discrete energy levels from which radiative electron transitions to lower levels are forbidden. These levels are called *metastable levels* or *states*. When an electron is in a metastable level, it can leave by one of three processes:

1. The metastable atom can absorb electromagnetic radiation of sufficient energy content to raise the electron from the metastable level to a normal excited level. It can then return to the ground level by radiating this energy as a photon.
2. The metastable atom can make an inelastic collision with an electron or ion and obtain sufficient energy to raise the electron from the metastable level to an ordinary level from which a radiative transition is permitted.
3. The metastable atom can make a collision with another neutral atom, either free or part of a surface, and exchange energy so that the electron either drops to the ground state or is raised to a normal level that permits a radiative transition to the ground state.

Because of the small probability of any of these three mechanisms' occurring, the average lifetime of an atom in a metastable state is between 1 and 100 milliseconds. For this reason, although relatively few in number, atoms in a metastable state often play an important role in gaseous electronics. This subject will be treated in detail in Secs. 5.10 and 7.2 of Chap. 5 and 7, respectively.

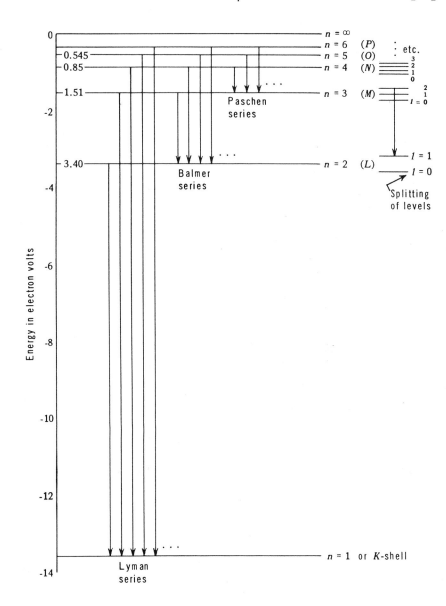

Fig. 3.2. Permitted electron orbits for hydrogen and the energy transitions for radiation of the characteristic spectra in field-free space.

3.4 Additional quantum numbers

Sommerfield has shown that it is necessary to distinguish between cases of similar principal quantum number n but different noncircular orbits according to the specific values of n' and k. In each case the energy is given by

$$W = -\frac{RchZ^2}{n^2} + f(n, k) \tag{3.14}$$

The term $f(n, k)$ was introduced by Sommerfield to account for the splitting of the energy levels. In other words, each transition from n_2 to n_1 may be broken up into a transition from any one of the split energy levels (n_2 and $k = 1$ or 2 or $\cdots$ or n_2) to the split level (n_1 and $k = 1$ or 2 or n_1). (See Fig. 3.2 for an approximate sketch of part of the fine structure of the hydrogen spectra.) A transition is shown from energy level $W(n, k) = W(3, 3)$ to $W(2, 2)$. Note that the fine structure lines are labeled in terms of a new *orbital quantum number* $l = k - 1$. Wave mechanics has shown that this new quantum number is proper and should replace k. Further, wave mechanics requires that the angular momentum be quantized according to

$$\mathbf{p}_\theta = \frac{h}{2\pi} \sqrt{l(l + 1)}\, \mathbf{i}_l \tag{3.15}$$

where $\mathbf{i}_l$ is a unit vector normal to the plane of the elliptical motion (see Fig. 3.3).

The orbital quantum number k was permitted to take on values from 1 to n inclusive. The new quantum number l is therefore permitted to take on the values 0 to $n - 1$ inclusive. The designation of the values of l follow x-ray notation as follows:

l	0	1	2	3	4	5	6
x-ray designation	s	p	d	f	g	h	i

A certain degeneracy exists with the model as developed thus far. The plane of an electron orbit can be completely random. To specify the plane of such an atomic orbit requires a coordinate system that has a physical significance. It cannot be perfectly arbitrary. The moving electron will set up a magnetic field perpendicular to the plane of the elliptical orbit. This magnetic field will react with any external magnetic field, and the magnetic field set up by the electron will make a discrete angle with the external field. As a result, the electron angular momentum vector $\mathbf{p}_\theta$, which is parallel to the magnetic field caused by the electron, will have a component parallel to the external magnetic field. Because of the reaction between the two magnetic fields, the angular momentum vector of the electron will precess about the external magnetic field, thereby giving rise to a third type of periodic motion:

i.e., the period of the precession (see Fig. 3.4). This motion is also quantized according to

$$m_l = 0, \pm 1, \pm 2, \ldots, \pm l \tag{3.16}$$

For instance, if $l = 3$, then $m_l = l$ indicates that **l** is parallel to the magnetic field, **H**. $m_l = +2$ would indicate an angle of 48 degrees between **l** and **H**. The number m_l is known as the *magnetic orbital quantum number*.

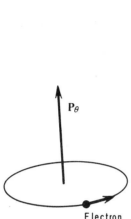

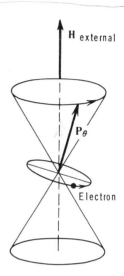

Fig. 3.3. Angular momentum of an electron moving in an elliptical orbit.

Fig. 3.4. The precessional motion of the angular momentum vector, P_θ, about an external magnetic field.

The electron itself spins about its own axis, establishing a small magnetic field which will react in a manner similar to that given above with any external field **H**. The associated vector spin momentum is

$$\mathbf{P}_s = \frac{h}{2\pi} \sqrt{s(s + 1)}\, \mathbf{i}_s \tag{3.17}$$

where $\mathbf{i}_s$ is a unit vector in the direction of the momentum (see Fig. 3.5). Quantum mechanically, the spin vector can only be parallel or antiparallel to the external field **H**, and can only have the value:

$$\mathbf{s} = s\mathbf{i}_s = \tfrac{1}{2}\mathbf{i}_s \tag{3.18}$$

The component of spin along **H** is, therefore

$$m_s = \pm s = \pm\tfrac{1}{2} \tag{3.19}$$

and m_s is the *magnetic spin quantum number*.

Five quantum numbers have been defined and these five numbers charac-
terize a *wave function* Ψ that describes the complete energy state of an
electron.

$$\Psi_{nlm_lm_s}$$

The last quantum number is the spin, and because it always has the magnitude
$+\frac{1}{2}$, it can be dropped without loss of
generality.

The Pauli exclusion principle states
that only one electron can occupy a given
energy state, as described by $\Psi_{nlm_lm_s}$.
Therefore, the number of energy
positions permitted for a given principal
quantum number n and orbital quantum
number l is

$$(2l + 1)(2) \qquad (3.20)$$

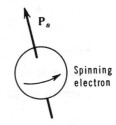

Fig. 3.5. Angular momentum because of
electron spin.

as determined by Eqs. (3.16) and (3.19). Accordingly, one may tabulate:

l	s	p	d	f	g	h	i
number of electrons	2	6	10	14	18	22	26

3.5   The complete Bohr-Sommerfield model

The Bohr-Sommerfield model may now be drawn for some of the lighter
elements because all the necessary information is available. The models for
atoms having an atomic number greater than 18 (argon) require a knowledge
of certain exceptions in the order of atomic structure; these exceptions will be
considered shortly.

The first rule in constructing a model for an atom in the normal or
ground energy state is to fill all permitted energy positions with electrons,
starting at the lowest energy positions (nearest the nucleus) and working out-
ward. To simplify the model, all electrons having a given value for n will
be considered to fall in a shell that surrounds the nucleus. Each value of l
will be interpreted as an energy position in a subshell of a given n-shell.
Figure 3.6 depicts the models of hydrogen ($Z = 1$), helium ($Z = 2$), nitrogen
($Z = 7$), and argon ($Z = 18$).

The applicable quantum numbers for each case are shown in Fig. 3.6
and are written in the order nlm_lm_s. The electronic formula is obtained by
writing down each occupied shell and subshell from the first out. The
superscripts indicate the number of electrons in each subshell.

The filling of the shells and subshells follows a pattern that is often given
as a complete chart or table in many references. It can be written down in a
simple chart as follows:

$$1s \quad 2s2p \quad 3s3p \quad 4s3d4p \quad 5s4d5p \quad 6s5d^{14}f5d^{9}6p$$

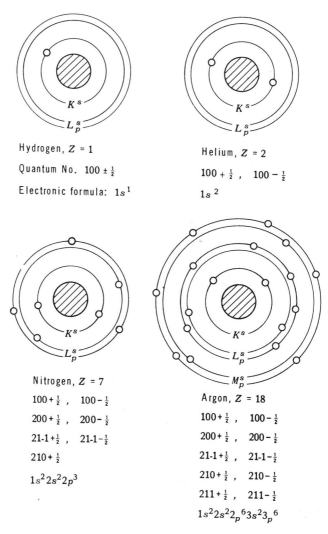

Fig. 3.6. The Bohr-Sommerfeld atomic model.

The superscripts indicate the number of electrons in a partially filled subshell; all other subshells are completely filled. There are several exceptions to the above pattern of filling the energy levels. They are as follows:

Chromium ($Z = 24$)	put 1 from $4s$ in $3d$
Copper ($Z = 29$)	put 1 from $4s$ in $3d$
Niobium ($Z = 41$) through	
Silver ($Z = 47$)	put 1 from $5s$ in $4d$
Gold ($Z = 79$)	put 1 from $6s$ in $5d$

atomic structure as conduction electrons; the single-valence electrons of each atom are much more readily available. The subject of conduction and emission will be treated in detail in Chap. 4.

The broadening of the energy levels that occurs when individual atoms combine to form a solid permits some of the valence electrons to have energies W_a that are lower than the energy of a valence electron in a single atom. For the same reason, other valence electrons can have energies as high as W_0 at $T = 0$ and much higher energies for $T > 0$.

For a valence electron to have an energy as low as W_a, it must yield all its kinetic energy, leaving only potential energy. Therefore, W_a represents the zero level for kinetic energy. The upper level, W_0, bears a thorough investigation which will be made subsequently. The vacuum level corresponds to the energy required for an electron to escape from the solid. Therefore, this energy represents the zero level for potential energy. Reference to the figure illustrates the effect of the shielding of the core electrons (those in the closed shells) on the valence electrons. The coulomb force experienced by the valence electrons is drastically reduced because of this shielding, with the result that the valence electron possesses only a small potential energy. Thus, the energy of the valence electrons in a metal is primarily kinetic.

Because of the relative proximity of the atomic centers, the valence electrons are moving in a net electric field that is approximately zero except for intense local irregularities near the atomic centers. The valence electrons, therefore, are moving in essentially field-free space. The total energy W of the valence electrons is because of kinetic energy, and at absolute zero $W_a < W < W_0$.

The electrons behave in a fashion quite similar to the behavior of molecules of a perfect gas. The coulomb repulsion force existing between electrons limits their space densities' increasing beyond a certain point in much the same manner as van der Waals' force governs the space density of a gas. In order to treat the valence electrons in the above manner, it is necessary to "adjust" their mass to an *effective mass*, which will appear in the equations that follow.

The electron in a metal sees several forms of boundaries limiting its motion. These boundaries exist in the form of potential barriers. One barrier is that enforced by quantum theory which limits the range of kinetic energies permissible to the valence electrons to a finite range. Another form of potential barrier is caused by the coulomb repulsion forces' limiting the degree of approach between electrons in the "electron gas."

It is apparent from the above discussion that the movement of an electron in a "potential well" is of theoretical interest because the conditions of motion approximate those experienced by electrons in a metal. To investigate this further, we will apply Schrödinger's equation to the motion of an electron in a "potential well."

3.7 Schrödinger's quantum equation

Two methods of analytic analysis have been developed to deal with the problems involving the behavior of an electron which is either bound to a nucleus or existing as a free electron in a solid. The first method was introduced in 1925 by Werner Heisenberg and employs matrix methods in its analytical approach. Several months later, Erwin Schrödinger presented a second form of the same basic quantum mechanics. Schrödinger employed operators in a wave equation in his analytical approach.

In view of the growing importance of a basic knowledge of quantum mechanics in the electron device field (see the Tunnel Diode, Sec. 6.4), we will introduce this subject at this point. The application of quantum mechanics to the motion of an electron in a space that is bounded by potential barriers is very similar to the conditions existing in a waveguide. The reader who has had an introduction to waveguide theory will find the similarities interesting.

L. de Broglie hypothesized the wave nature of the electron in 1925, and two years later C. Davisson, L. Germer, and G. P. Thomson verified this hypothesis experimentally. Schrödinger's contribution demonstrated mathematically that electrons obey the laws of wave motion as though they were photons. If this is the case, then the electron may be expected to satisfy Maxwell's wave equation

$$\frac{\partial^2 \Psi}{\partial x^2} + \frac{\partial^2 \Psi}{\partial y^2} + \frac{\partial^2 \Psi}{\partial z^2} = \frac{1}{c^2} \frac{\partial^2 \Psi}{\partial t^2} \tag{3.21}$$

where Ψ is the amplitude of the wave and c is the velocity of light. The probability of finding an electron at a point is proportional to the square of the amplitude Ψ at the point. According to the Einstein relation for the total energy W of a photon or electron,

$$W = hf = mc^2 = pc \tag{3.22}$$

where h is Planck's constant, f is the frequency, m is the effective mass of the electron, and p is the momentum of the electron. Substitution of Eq. (3.22) in Eq. (3.21) yields

$$\frac{\partial^2 \Psi}{\partial x^2} + \frac{\partial^2 \Psi}{\partial y^2} + \frac{\partial^2 \Psi}{\partial z^2} = \frac{p^2}{h^2 f^2} \frac{\partial^2 \Psi}{\partial t^2} \tag{3.23}$$

A satisfactory solution to this equation is

$$\Psi = \psi e^{-j2\pi f t} \tag{3.24}$$

where ψ is a function of x, y, and z. Substitute Eq. (3.24) into Eq. (3.23) and the wave equation becomes

$$\frac{\partial^2 \psi}{\partial x^2} + \frac{\partial^2 \psi}{\partial y^2} + \frac{\partial^2 \psi}{\partial z^2} = -\frac{4\pi^2 p^2}{h^2} \psi \tag{3.25}$$

The total energy W of the electron is equal to the sum of its kinetic energy T and its potential energy U, or

$$W = T + U$$

The kinetic energy can be written as

$$T = \frac{p^2}{2m} = (W - U) \tag{3.26}$$

Substitution of Eq. (3.26) in Eq. (3.25) yields the time-independent Schrödinger equation.

$$\frac{\partial^2 \psi}{\partial x^2} + \frac{\partial^2 \psi}{\partial y^2} + \frac{\partial^2 \psi}{\partial z^2} + \frac{8\pi^2 m}{h^2}(W - U)\psi = 0 \tag{3.27}$$

This is the most important equation in Schrödinger's quantum mechanics.

Equation (3.27) can be separated into three independent equations in x, y, and z, which facilitates a discussion of the boundary conditions imposed by a "potential well" upon an electron. In Eq. (3.24), $\psi = \psi(x, y, z)$. Hence assume that

$$\psi = X(x)\,Y(y)Z(z) \tag{3.28}$$

where $X(x)$ is a function of x alone, etc. This is the usual method of separation of variables employed in electromagnetic field theory, mechanical vibration analysis, heat flow, etc. Substitute into Eq. (3.27) and divide by XYZ to obtain

$$\frac{1}{X}\frac{\partial^2 X}{\partial x^2} + \frac{1}{Y}\frac{\partial^2 Y}{\partial y^2} + \frac{1}{Z}\frac{\partial^2 Z}{\partial z^2} + \frac{8\pi^2 m}{h^2}(W - U) = 0 \tag{3.29}$$

If the kinetic energy term $(W - U)$ is factored into three parts, each associated with the corresponding motion along the x, y, and z axes,

$$(W_x - U_x), \qquad (W_y - U_y), \qquad (W_z - U_z)$$

and if these results are substituted into Eq. (3.29), an equation is obtained that can be factored into three distinct parts. The first part is a function of x alone, the second a function of y alone, and the third a function of z alone.

$$\left[\frac{1}{X}\frac{\partial^2 X}{\partial x^2} + \frac{8\pi^2 m}{h^2}(W_x - U_x)\right] + \left[\frac{1}{Y}\frac{\partial^2 Y}{\partial y^2} + \frac{8\pi^2 m}{h^2}(W_y - U_y)\right]$$
$$+ \left[\frac{1}{Z}\frac{\partial^2 Z}{\partial z^2} + \frac{8\pi^2 m}{h^2}(W_z - U_z)\right] = 0 \tag{3.30}$$

If these parts are to remain independent, then

$$\frac{\partial^2 X}{\partial x^2} + \frac{8\pi^2 m}{h^2}(W_x - U_x)X = 0 \tag{3.31}$$

$$\frac{\partial^2 Y}{\partial y^2} + \frac{8\pi^2 m}{h^2}(W_y - U_y)Y = 0 \tag{3.32}$$

$$\frac{\partial^2 Z}{\partial z^2} + \frac{8\pi^2 m}{h^2}(W_z - U_z)Z = 0 \tag{3.33}$$

Consider the x-component of motion of an electron in the potential well. Because the electron moves in essentially field-free space, let

$$U_x = 0 \qquad (0 < x < a)$$

within the well. To establish the walls of the well let

$$U_x \to \infty$$

for all x outside the well. Obviously, the same condition would apply for the y- and z-components of motion. If the above conditions are applied to Schrödinger's equation (3.31) for the x-component of motion, then for $U_x = \infty$,

$$X(x) = 0 \tag{3.34}$$

for the equation to hold. It follows that

$$\frac{d^2X}{dx^2} = 0 \tag{3.35}$$

for $U = \infty$.

Equations (3.34) and (3.35) establish the boundary conditions at the sides of the well. Again, similar equations exist for the y- and z-components. For the region inside the well,

$$\frac{d^2X}{dx^2} + \frac{8\pi^2 m}{h^2} W_x X = 0 \tag{3.36}$$

The general solution is

$$X(x) = A e^{+j(2\pi/h)\sqrt{2mW_x}\,x} + B e^{-j(2\pi/h)\sqrt{2mW_x}\,x} \tag{3.37}$$

which can be written as

$$X(x) = (A + B) \cos \frac{2\pi}{h} \sqrt{2mW_x}\,x + (A - B) \sin \frac{2\pi}{h} \sqrt{2mW_x}\,x \tag{3.38}$$

When $x = 0$ or $x = a$, Eq. (3.38) must satisfy the condition (Eq. (3.34)) $X(x) = 0$ at the sides of the well. The first condition that $X(0) = 0$ requires that

$$(A + B) = 0 \tag{3.39}$$

The second condition that $X(a) = 0$ requires that the argument of the sine function be an integral multiple of π radians, or

$$\frac{2\pi}{h} \sqrt{2mW_x}\,a = n_x \pi \tag{3.40}$$

where n_x is a nonzero integer. (If n_x were permitted to be zero, then $X(x)$ would also be zero everywhere within the potential well as well as at the surface and the result would be without physical meaning.) Solve for the total electron energy:

$$W_x = \frac{n_x^2 h^2}{8ma^2} \qquad (n_x = 1, 2, 3, \ldots) \tag{3.41}$$

Thus, the energy associated with the x-component of motion of the electron is quantized according to Eq. (3.41). The associated *wave function* is obtained by substituting Eqs. (3.41) and (3.39) into Eq. (3.38).

$$X(x) = (A - B) \sin \frac{n_x \pi}{a} x \tag{3.42}$$

To solve for the coefficient $(A - B)$, square both sides of Eq. (3.42) and integrate between the walls of the well.

$$\int_0^a X^2(x)\, dx = (A - B)^2 \int_0^a \sin^2 \frac{n_x \pi}{a} x\, dx = \frac{a}{2}(A - B)^2 \tag{3.43}$$

The amplitude of the function $X(x)$ may be normalized by requiring that Eq. (3.43) be equal to unity, or

$$(A - B) = \sqrt{\frac{2}{a}} \tag{3.44}$$

The resultant x-component of the wave equation becomes

$$X(x) = \sqrt{\frac{2}{a}} \sin \frac{n_x \pi}{a} x \tag{3.45}$$

and the general solution to Schrödinger's wave equation for the amplitude of an electron moving in a "potential well" is

$$\psi(x, y, z) = X(x)Y(y)Z(z) = \sqrt{\frac{8}{abc}} \sin \frac{n_x \pi}{a} x \sin \frac{n_y \pi}{b} y \sin \frac{n_z \pi}{c} z \tag{3.46}$$

3.8   The electron in phase space

It follows from Eq. (3.41) that the total energy of an electron such as a valence electron is

$$W = \frac{h^2}{8m} \left[\frac{n_x^2}{a^2} + \frac{n_y^2}{b^2} + \frac{n_z^2}{c^2} \right] \tag{3.47}$$

where n_x, n_y, and n_z take on all values $1, 2, 3, \ldots, n$. The momentum associated with the x-component of motion of the electron is

$$p_x = \sqrt{2mW_x} = \frac{hn_x}{2a} \tag{3.48}$$

for $0 < x < a$. For each degree of freedom, a plot of momentum as a function of displacement may be constructed as shown in Fig. 3.9. Such a plot is called the *phase plane.*

For the sake of discussion, assume that an electron starts from the face of the "potential well" corresponding to $x = 0$ and moves with momentum

p_x in the $+x$ direction. This is the path shown from points 1 to 2. In this example it is assumed that $n = 3$; therefore,

$$p_x = \frac{hn_x}{2a} = \frac{3h}{2a}$$

When the electron reaches the "potential wall" at $x = a$, it must reverse direction, thus going from point 2 to point 3 along the momentum axis. The electron now moves in the direction of decreasing x with momentum $-p_x$ as depicted by motion from point 3 to point 4. When the electron reaches the first wall, it must again reverse its momentum from $-p_x$ to $+p_x$ corresponding to movement along the momentum axis from point 4 to point 1.

The area encompassed by this motion in phase space is given by

$$\oint p\,dx = \left(2\,\frac{3h}{2a}\right)(a) = 3h$$

or, in general,

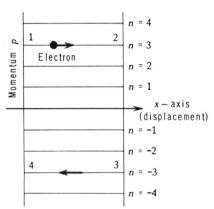

Fig. 3.9. Electron motion in phase space.

$$\oint p\,dx = nh \qquad (3.49)$$

where $n = 1, 2, 3, \ldots$.

The corresponding area of each of the three phase planes is

$$n_x h, \qquad n_y h, \qquad n_z h$$

respectively, according to Eq. (3.49). The six dimensions x, y, z, p_x, p_y, p_z define a volume in a *six-dimensional phase space*.

$$\text{phase space volume} = n_x h\, n_y h\, n_z h \qquad (3.50)$$

The maximum density of points corresponding to free electrons to be found in any given phase space occurs when the phase space volume is a minimum, or

$$n_x = n_y = n_z = 1$$

and

$$\text{minimum phase space volume} = h^3 \qquad (3.51)$$

Under these conditions, the exclusion principle indicates that only two electrons can possibly be present and these two electrons must have spins that are opposite. Therefore, the *maximum electron density* in phase space is

$$(N_p)_\text{max} = \frac{2}{h^3} \qquad (3.52)$$

electrons per unit volume of phase space.

The six-dimensional volume in phase space may be written

$$n_x h n_y h n_z h = 2p_x a 2 p_y b 2 p_z c$$
$$= (abc)(8 p_x p_y p_z)$$

$$\left(\begin{array}{c}\text{phase space} \\ \text{volume}\end{array}\right) = \left(\begin{array}{c}\text{volume in} \\ \text{ordinary space}\end{array}\right)\left(\begin{array}{c}\text{volume in} \\ \text{momentum space}\end{array}\right) \quad (3.53)$$

In ordinary space there is a certain *electron density* which may be called N; further in momentum space there exists a certain number of permitted electron momentum levels and therefore a *momentum level density M*. Obviously, M is a function of the specific metal under consideration. It follows from Eq. (3.53) that the electron density in phase space

$$N_p = NM = \left[\frac{\text{electrons}}{(\text{meter})^3}\right]\left[\frac{\text{momentum levels}}{(\text{momentum})^3}\right] \quad (3.54)$$

Equation (3.54) can be written in integral form as

$$N = \int\int\int N_p \, dp_x \, dp_y \, dp_z \quad (3.55)$$

electrons per unit volume. When the temperature of an atom is at absolute zero, then all the lower energy levels are filled and the electrons are filling permitted orbital positions nearest to the nucleus. *Thus, the ordinary space density and the momentum space level density are both a maximum; therefore, the phase space density is a maximum, or* $(N_p)_{max} = 2/h^3$ (see Eq. (3.52)). Under these conditions ($T = 0°K$)

$$N = \int\int\int \frac{2}{h^3} \, dp_x \, dp_y \, dp_z \quad (3.56)$$

The total kinetic energy of the system from Eq. (3.48) is

$$W = \frac{p^2}{2m} = \frac{p_x^2 + p_y^2 + p_z^2}{2m} \quad (3.57)$$

In momentum space Eq. (3.57) is the equation of a sphere of radius

$$p = \sqrt{2mW} \quad (3.58)$$

and the integral of Eq. (3.56) is the volume of this sphere in momentum space. The valence electron density in ordinary space is, therefore,

$$N_{max} = \frac{2}{h^3}\left[\frac{4\pi}{3}(2mW_0)^{3/2}\right] \quad (3.59)$$

electrons per unit volume at absolute zero. The associated energy at $T = 0$ is

$$W_0 = \frac{1}{2m}\left(\frac{3h^3 N_{max}}{8\pi}\right)^{2/3} \quad (3.60)$$

$$= 5.79 \times 10^{-38} N_{max}^{2/3} \quad \text{joules} \quad (3.61)$$

The energy W_0 is known as the *Fermi level*. It is different for each element inasmuch as N_{max} varies from element to element at $T = 0$.

The maximum density of electric charge at every point within the atomic structure can be obtained from Eq. (3.61). This density is approximately attained in actual atoms. Let ρ_{max} be the actual electric charge density; then,

$$\rho_{max} = -eN_{max} = -\frac{2e}{h^3}\left[\frac{4\pi}{3}(2mW_0)^{3/2}\right] \tag{3.62}$$

3.9 The Fermi distribution of electron energies

For any temperature above absolute zero, the electron density in phase space is no longer equal to $2/h^3$. The general differential expression for electron density in ordinary space at any temperature can be written as

$$dN = n(W)\,dW \tag{3.63}$$

The function $n(W)$ represents the number of electrons per unit range of energy. An explicit expression for this function will be developed.

In Chap. 2 we pointed out that whenever any particle is free to occupy any energy level in a large range of energy levels, Maxwell-Boltzmann statistics are applicable. This is true of a percentage of the valence electrons whose energies are somewhat higher than those of most of the valence electrons. These *conduction electrons* are discussed in detail in Chap. 4.

In Chap. 2 the probability of finding a particle in an energy state W was found to be given by

$$a(W) = Ae^{-W/kT} \tag{3.64}$$

Let the maximum number of electrons in each level be

$$dN_{max} = F(W)\,dW$$

and

$$dN'_{max} = F(W')\,dW'$$

where $F(W)$ or $F(W')$ represents the total number of available electron states in the interval dW or dW' (counting states of opposite spin as different).

The probability of a transition, in unit time, from a range of energy levels dW to a range dW' is

$b(W)$ if the range of levels contains vacant levels

0   if all the levels in the range are occupied

The probability of an electron's making an energy transition from an energy level in the range dW to a level in the range dW' is proportional to the probability $a(W')$ that the electron is to be found in the range dW'. It is also proportional to the number of electrons, dN, in the range dW and to the number of empty levels in dW'. The number of empty levels in dW' is

$$dN'_{\max} - dN' = F(W') \, dW' - n(W') \, dW'$$

The resultant probability may be written as

$$b(W) = A\epsilon^{-W'/kT} n(W) \, dW \, [F(W') \, dW' - n(W') \, dW']$$

In a similar manner, the probability of a transition from the energy range dW' to the range dW may be written

$$b'(W) = A\epsilon^{-W/kT} n(W') \, dW' \, [F(W) \, dW - n(W) \, dW]$$

Obviously, the system must be in thermal equilibrium. Therefore, the net number of systems in the various ranges does not vary with time and

$$b(W) = b'(W) \tag{3.65}$$

Upon substitution and division by $n(W)$ and $n(W')$, we obtain

$$\left[\frac{F(W')}{n(W')} - 1\right] A\epsilon^{-W'/kT} = \left[\frac{F(W)}{n(W)} - 1\right] A\epsilon^{-W/kT} \tag{3.66}$$

Equation (3.66) indicates that the function

$$\left[\frac{F(W)}{n(W)} - 1\right] \epsilon^{-W/kT} \tag{3.67}$$

is independent of any value of W because it must yield the same numerical value for W or W'. Therefore, the function (Eq. (3.67)) varies only with absolute temperature and it may be written as

$$\left[\frac{F(W)}{n(W)} - 1\right] \epsilon^{-W/kT} = D(T) \tag{3.68}$$

Solve for $n(W)$, which represents all of the occupied levels in the entire energy range W, and obtain

$$n(W) = \frac{F(W)}{D(T)\epsilon^{W/kT} + 1} \tag{3.69}$$

This is the *Fermi distribution function*.

To evaluate $D(T)$, let $T = 0°K$; then, the valence electrons occupy all of the lower energy levels so that the electron density in momentum space is a maximum. The maximum value permissible for W is W_0. All available energy levels $F(W)$ must be filled from $W = 0$ up through $W = W_0$. Beyond $W = W_0$, the energy levels $F(W) = 0$. The only function $D(T)$ that satisfies these conditions is the Boltzmann factor $\epsilon^{-W_0/kT}$. With this substitution the Fermi distribution becomes

$$n(W) = \frac{F(W)}{\epsilon^{(W - W_0)/kT} + 1} = F(W)f(W) \tag{3.70}$$

The function

$$f(W) = \frac{1}{\epsilon^{(W-W_0)/kT} + 1} \tag{3.71}$$

is called the *Fermi factor.*

To obtain the total number of electrons present per unit volume, it is necessary to integrate $n(W)$ over all possible energies, or

$$N = \int_0^{W_{max}} n(W)\, dW = \int_0^{W_{max}} \frac{F(W)}{e^{(W-W_0)/kT} + 1}\, dW \tag{3.72}$$

The functional expression $F(W)$ for the available energy levels is difficult

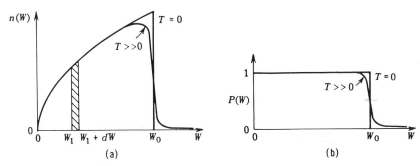

Fig. 3.10. Fermi-Dirac electron distribution functions. (a) Energy distribution function (the shaded area represents the number of electrons per unit volume having energies between W_1 and $W_1 + dW$) and (b) probability function $P(W) = n(W)/F(W) = f(W)$.

to obtain except for the case where $T = 0$. For this specific case, the electron density is known from Eq. (3.59).

$$N = \frac{2}{h^3}\left[\frac{4\pi}{3}(2mW_0)^{3/2}\right] = \int_0^{W_{max} = W_0} \frac{F(W)}{0 + 1}\, dW$$

where the term $e^{(W-W_0)/kT} \to 0$ for $T = 0$ because $W_0 > W$, thus making the exponent large but negative. It follows immediately that

$$n(W) = F(W) = \frac{8\pi}{h^3}\sqrt{2}\, m^{3/2} W_0^{1/2} \tag{3.73}$$

for $T = 0$.

Figure 3.10(a) is a plot of Eq. (3.73) for $T = 0$. It should be noted that the area under the curve is the electron density, N. The ratio $n(W)/F(W)$ is the probability $P(W)$ of a level's being filled and is equal to the Fermi factor $f(W)$. This is plotted in Fig. 3.10(b). Several important features of this distribution curve are worth noting. First, for any temperature $T > 0$, the distribution curve (Eq. (3.70)) has the value $n(W_0) = \frac{1}{2}F(W_0)$ for $W = W_0$. Therefore, a plot of several distribution curves representing different operating temperatures indicates that these curves all pass through the point $[\frac{1}{2}F(W_0), W_0]$.

For very high temperatures (much higher than those employed in thermionic emission), $W \gg W_0$ and $e^{W/kT} \gg 1$; hence,

$$n(W) = F(W)e^{-W/kT} \tag{3.74}$$

This is a Maxwell-Boltzmann distribution as obtained with an ordinary gas. Obviously, $n(W) \ll F(W)$, which indicates that a great number of available energy levels are not filled.

For a certain range of temperatures, the exponential term in the denominator of Eq. (3.70) becomes much greater than one,

$$e^{(W-W_0)/kT} \gg 1$$

yielding for the number of electrons

$$n(W) = F(W)e^{-(W-W_0)/kT} \tag{3.75}$$

When the energy $W < W_0$, then the number of electrons per unit volume per unit range of energy $n(W)$ equals $F(W)$, the number of available energy levels per unit volume. Mathematically, it would appear that $n(W)$ could exceed $F(W)$, but this is physically impossible.

When $W > W_0$, then $n(W) < F(W)$, indicating that there are unfilled levels in $F(W)$ and therefore some electrons have become "free electrons" in the metal; if W is sufficiently large, some of these electrons may be thermionically emitted from the metal. The subject of electron emission based upon Eq. (3.75) will be explored further in Chap. 4.

For $T = 0$, the Fermi level $W_0(0)$ was found to depend only upon the electron density N, as given in Eq. (3.60):

$$W_0(0) = \frac{h^2}{8m}\left(\frac{3N_{max}}{\pi}\right)^{2/3}$$

(In the literature the reader may encounter the symbol $\hbar$, which equals $h/2\pi$.) At temperatures above $0°K$ an expression for the Fermi level may be obtained for metals by making a series expansion of the probability function $P(W)$ in the neighborhood of $W = W_0$, yielding a temperature-dependent expression for the Fermi level.

$$W_0(T) = W_0(0)\left[1 - \frac{\pi^2}{12}\left(\frac{kT}{W_0(0)}\right)^2 + \cdots\right] \tag{3.76}$$

At room temperature ($300°K$), the term kT is 0.0258 electron-volts. Typical Fermi levels at $0°K$ are about 5 ev; hence the temperature-dependent term in Eq. (3.76) is negligible at low temperatures.

PROBLEMS

1. Sketch the Bohr-Sommerfeld model of the titanium atom ($Z = 22$).

2. Compute the second ionization potential of helium and the third ionization potential of lithium.

3. Compute the position of the Fermi level at absolute zero for copper. The density of atoms per cubic meter may be computed from a knowledge of the crystalline structure and the lattice constant. (Copper is face-centered cubic with a lattice constant of 3.61 angstroms.)

4. In Prob. 3, compute the position of the Fermi level at room temperature ($300°K$).

5. Plot an energy diagram similar to Fig. 3.2 for singly ionized helium.

6. What are the frequencies and wavelengths of the photons emitted corresponding to the Balmer series for hydrogen? Is this radiation in the visible spectrum?

7. Sketch the Bohr-Sommerfeld model of the oxygen atom ($Z = 8$) and suggest a physical explanation to describe the affinity displayed by an oxygen atom for picking up a free electron and thus becoming a negative ion.

8. Sketch the atomic models of an oxygen and a carbon atom and suggest a theory to describe the mutual bonding together of these two atoms to form CO (carbon monoxide). This is a very important type of atomic bonding known as *covalent* or *shared-pair* electron bonding.

9. Based upon the results of Probs. 7 and 8, make a two-dimensional sketch of the covalent bonding between tin atoms in gray tin (tin in the crystalline form). Tin (Sn, $Z = 50$) has a valence of 4. (*Hints:* It might help to make a sketch of the tin atom. If additional aid is required, refer to Fig. 4.7.)

10. The first metastable level for mercury (Hg) is 4.64 electron-volts and the first ionization potential is 10.38 ev. What threshold wavelength of light is required to raise a mercury atom from the ground state to the ionization level if a two-step process occurs?

REFERENCES

1. G. Herzberg, *Atomic Spectra and Atomic Structure*, Prentice-Hall, Inc., Englewood Cliffs, N.J., 1937 (also Dover, New York, 1958).

2. M. Born, *Atomic Physics*, 4th ed., Hafner Publishing Co., New York, 1946.

3. J. C. Slater and N. H. Frank, *Introduction to Theoretical Physics*, McGraw-Hill Book Company, New York, 1933.

4. H. Eyring, J. Walter, and G. E. Kimball, *Quantum Chemistry*, John Wiley & Sons, New York, 1944.

CHAPTER 4

Electronic conduction

in solids

The conduction of electricity is an electronic process when observed from a microscopic viewpoint. The outer orbit or valence electrons play a predominant role in electrical conduction. Most of these electrons possess energies that lie in the *valence energy band,* while some of the more energetic possess energies that lie in the *conduction energy band.* Those whose energies lie in the conduction energy band are often referred to as conduction electrons. Basically they are all valence electrons from the electro-chemical viewpoint. Their behavior in a metal is governed by the statistical Fermi-Dirac distribution and in a semiconductor by the Maxwellian distribution function. The medium may be a solid, liquid, or gas; however, in this chapter the discussion will be limited to crystalline solids. Gaseous conduction (including vacuums) will be covered in Chap. 7. Liquid conductors will not be considered because they are of limited interest in the electronics field at this time.

4.1 Crystalline structure

Typical crystalline structures of electronic importance are the face-centered cubic structure and the diamond lattice structure. The diamond structure is actually an extension of the face-centered cubic structure, as is seen by comparing Figs. 4.1(a) and (b). The noble metals such as copper,

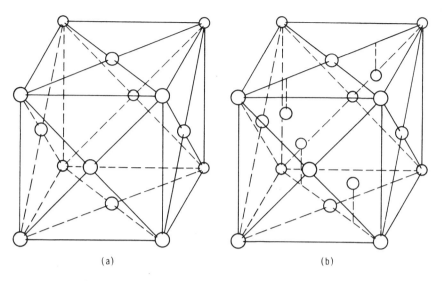

(a)   (b)

Fig. 4.1. Crystalline structures of special interest in electronics. (a) Face-centered cubic lattice and (b) diamond lattice.

silver, and gold are of the face-centered cubic structure, whereas the two important semiconductors, germanium and silicon, are of the diamond structure (see Table 4.1). Carbon in the diamond state is an excellent electrical insulator. Although it has no commercial application, it will be used

Table 4.1

Physical properties of common conductors and semiconductors

Element	Crystal structure	Mass number and abundance (approx. %)	Atomic weight	Common valence electrons	Lattice constant (angstroms)
$_{13}Al^{27}$	FCC	27(100)	26.98	3	4.04
$_{14}Si$	D	28(93), 29(4), 30(3)	28.09	4	5.42
$_{28}Ni$	FCC	58(68), 60(26), 62(4)	58.69	2	2.66
$_{29}Cu$	FCC	63(70), 65(30)	63.54	1	3.61
$_{32}Ge$	D	74(37), 72(27), 70(20)	72.60	4	5.62
$_{47}Ag$	FCC	107(51), 109(49)	107.88	1	4.08
$_{73}Ta^{181}$	BCC	181(100)	180.95	5	3.28
$_{74}W$	BCC	184(30), 186(29), 182(26)	183.92	6	3.16
$_{78}Pt$	FCC	195(34), 194(33), 196(25)	195.23	2	3.91
$_{79}Au^{197}$	FCC	197(100)	197.0	1	4.07

for illustrative purposes in the following discussion. (Most of our commercial insulators are complex compounds that occur naturally, such as mica and the porcelain clays, or are manufactured plastics of numerous types.) Figure 4.2

is another sketch of the diamond crystalline lattice that shows "rods" which represent the covalent (shared electron-pair) bonds that hold this class of crystalline structure together rather than the artificial construction lines employed in Fig. 4.1(b) to give the illusion of three-dimensional construction.

The dimension of the cube is 3.56*A* for diamond, 5.42*A* for silicon, and 5.62*A* for germanium. Of the total 18 atoms shown, each corner atom is shared by eight adjacent cubes and thus $\frac{1}{8}$ of each atom belongs to the cube

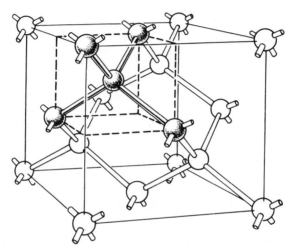

Fig. 4.2. The diamond crystalline lattice structure showing the shared-pair valence electron bonds as connecting rods. (By permission of the *Bell Telephone System Technical Journal.*)

shown. Each face-centered atom is shared with an adjacent cube and thus counts $\frac{1}{2}$. The four atoms inside the cube each count 1. Therefore, the equivalent number of atoms actually within the cube is 8. From this information, it is a simple matter to compute the density of atoms in each crystal. For silicon there are 5.00×10^{28} atoms per cubic meter; for germanium, 4.52×10^{28}.

The Bohr-Sommerfeld atomic models of carbon, copper, silicon, and germanium are sketched in Fig. 4.3. Approximate energy-level diagrams of these atoms are shown in Fig. 4.4. A *metal* such as copper is an excellent conductor because of the single valence electron found in the $4s^1$ ground state. Copper possesses an energy-level diagram as shown at the top of Fig. 4.4 (see also Fig. 3.8). The valence electron energy band for copper is about 7 ev wide; the remaining continuum of permitted energy levels corresponding to the overlapping 4*p*, 4*d*, 4*f*, 5*s*, 5*p*, etc. energy levels is about 4.4 ev in width.

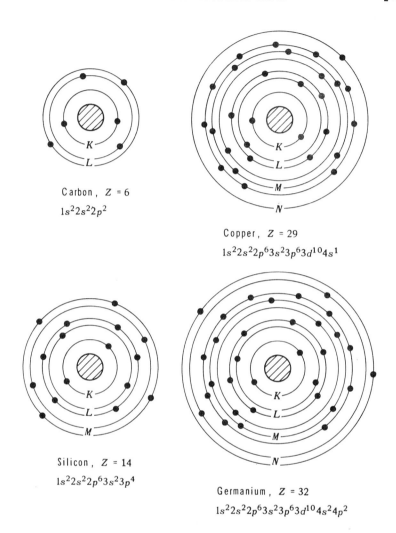

Carbon, $Z = 6$
$1s^2 2s^2 2p^2$

Copper, $Z = 29$
$1s^2 2s^2 2p^6 3s^2 3p^6 3d^{10} 4s^1$

Silicon, $Z = 14$
$1s^2 2s^2 2p^6 3s^2 3p^4$

Germanium, $Z = 32$
$1s^2 2s^2 2p^6 3s^2 3p^6 3d^{10} 4s^2 4p^2$

Fig. 4.3. Bohr-Sommerfeld models of atoms of electronic interest.

In a metal, all the valence electron energy levels, plus the remaining permitted levels above the Fermi level, are available in electrical conduction, and therefore the *conduction band* in a metal is sometimes defined to include this entire range of energies (see Fig. 4.4). However, from a practical standpoint, only those electrons having energies near or above the Fermi level participate in normal electrical conduction, which will be discussed in detail in Sec. 4.3. For this reason, the conduction band in a metal is thought of as penetrating a limited amount into the valence band.

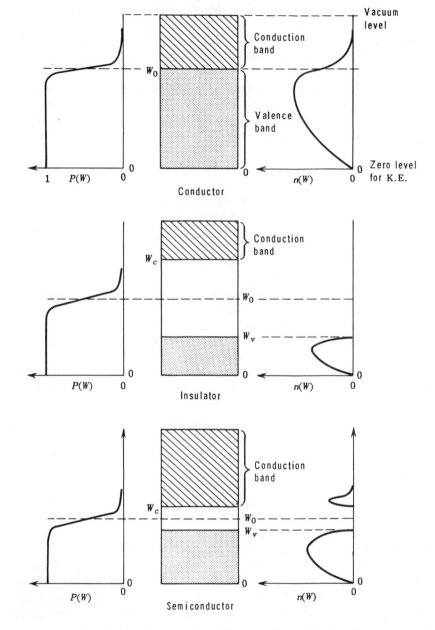

Fig. 4.4. Typical energy-level diagrams showing the Fermi-Dirac probability distribution, the energy levels, and the electron level density.

An *insulator*, such as carbon in the crystalline state (diamond), has an energy level diagram as shown in the middle of Fig. 4.4. In this case the valence band is separated from the conduction band by a band of *forbidden electron energy levels*. For diamond the *forbidden band* is about 6.5 ev in width.

A *semiconductor* possesses an energy level diagram similar to the bottom figure of Fig. 4.4. The semiconductor energy level diagram is identical to that of the insulator, except that the width of the forbidden band is relatively narrow—about 1.09 ev for silicon and 0.72 ev for germanium.

4.2   Random electron motion

In crystalline solids the valence electron energy levels (shown shaded dark in Fig. 4.4.) are available to all the atoms. One atom may have one of its valence electrons at an energy level lying at the top of the valence band; another atom may have one of its valence electrons possessing an energy corresponding to the bottom of the band. However, at $T = 0$ the valence energy levels $F(W)$ are all filled.

The valence electrons are not bound to the individual atoms because their orbits overlap those of the neighboring atoms and make it possible for these electrons to move about from atom to atom in a perfectly random fashion. In other words, *it is unimportant to associate a given valence electron with a given atom.* For drift motion to take place, it is necessary that the electrons be free to increase their energy, thus moving to a higher energy level. This is impossible at $T = 0$ because all the available and permitted energy levels $F(W)$ are filled (see Eq. (3.70)). For $T > 0$, those electrons near the Fermi level, W_0, in a metal may acquire increased energy from the thermal vibrations of the crystalline lattice. This leaves empty levels in the valence band which permit other valence electrons to acquire slightly increased energies and, thereby, acquire a drift velocity.

This picture of the conduction process does not mean that a given electron remains at a certain energy level for any extended length of time. Actually, the electrons continually randomize their energies, because of collisions, with the result that any given electron may at one moment possess an energy near the top of the conduction band only to be scattered a moment later to some energy level near the bottom of the valence band, following an inelastic collision. Because it is not important to identify individual electrons, we may speak of the concentration and behavior of electrons at certain energy levels. This approach will be used in the following discussion of the electrical conduction process.

Only those electrons whose energy levels lie near the Fermi brim may actually participate in electrical conduction. This occurs because only empty energy levels are to be found near the Fermi brim at ordinary temperatures.

To demonstrate this, consider the probability of an energy level's being filled. From Eq. (3.70) we may write for the probability

$$P(W) = n(W)/F(W) = \frac{1}{\epsilon^{(W-W_0)/kT} + 1} \qquad (4.1)$$

When the energy level, W, in question lies below the Fermi brim ($W < W_0$), then

$$P(W) = \frac{1}{\epsilon^{-\eta} + 1}$$

and if $\eta > 2$ or 3, then

$$P(W) \approx 1$$

or the probability, $P(W)$, of locating a filled level reaches unity. As previously seen, when this occurs electron drift is impossible because there are no vacant energy levels. In view of this and because

$$\eta = \left| \frac{W - W_0}{kT} \right|$$

we may assume that for W within 2 or $3kT$ of W_0, then $P(W) < 1$ and some of the valence band electrons near the Fermi brim can increase their energy and form an electrical current.

Those electrons that lie above the Fermi brim have a probability

$$P(W) = \frac{1}{\epsilon^{+\eta} + 1}$$

of filling an energy level W where $W > W_0$. If $\eta > 2$ or 3, then

$$P(W) \approx \epsilon^{-\eta}$$

and the probability $P(W)$ of finding a free electron approaches zero as η increases beyond 2 or 3. In view of this, it may be assumed that for W within 2 or $3kT$ of W_0, conduction band electrons are found in reasonable quantity. These electrons are also available to form the electrical current.

The total current is thus borne by electrons lying immediately on both sides of the Fermi brim. The majority of these electrons probably lie within $\pm 2kT$ of the Fermi brim.

For insulators and semiconductors, the valence electrons cannot easily increase their energy because of the forbidden energy levels between the valence band and the conduction band of permitted energy levels. For temperatures slightly above $T = 0$ only a very few valence electrons can obtain sufficient energy to jump the forbidden gap in a semiconductor, and essentially none is able to jump the gap in an insulator.

The net energy of all the valence electrons remains constant for a given temperature and the probability of finding an electron occupying a given energy range dW is given by the Fermi-Dirac probability function, $P(W)$.

If the temperature is raised, then the crystalline lattice spacings vibrate more energetically. More of this energy is transferred to the electrons, a reasonable number of which can increase their kinetic energies considerably as evidenced by the high energy tail in the Fermi-Dirac probability function (see Figs. 4.4 and 3.10). This increased energy permits more valence electrons to enter the conduction band in both metals and semiconductors. At very high temperatures, even insulators may begin to have a detectable number of conduction electrons. The increased lattice vibrations also increase the scattering of the random valence electron motion.

In a given solid sample, the random motion of the valence electrons is such that the concentration of electrons remains uniform when averaged over any sufficiently long time interval. For instance, if an ordinary resistor is placed in the grid-to-cathode circuit of a Class A_1 (the subscript 1 indicates that no grid current flows) vacuum-tube voltage amplifier (Fig. 4.5), no voltage would be expected to appear across this resistor in the absence of an input signal. However, if the output of this stage is further amplified and carefully analyzed, especially at the higher frequencies, there is a pronounced noise signal present because of the instantaneous unbalance in the volume density distribution of electrons throughout the resistor. This momentary unbalance arises from the random thermal motion of the electrons. In other words, at any given instant of time more electrons are found toward one end of the resistor than toward the opposite end and a resulting noise voltage appears across the resistor.

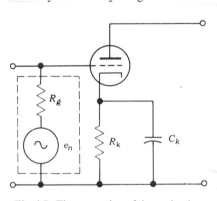

Fig. 4.5. The generation of thermal noise voltage in the grid resistor, R_g.

It has been shown experimentally and theoretically[*] that the rms noise voltage is given by

$$e_n = \sqrt{4kTRB} \qquad (4.2)$$

where k is Boltzmann's constant, T is the temperature of the resistor in °K, R is the ohmic resistance of the resistor, and B is the frequency bandwidth of the following voltage amplifier in cycles per second.

It might seem odd at first that the bandwidth of the amplifier should enter into the magnitude of the noise appearing across R. Actually, the noise voltage possesses components at all frequencies; in other words, it is "white" noise. Obviously, the wider the frequency spectrum the electronic system

* J. B. Johnson, *Phys. Rev.*, **32**, 97–109 (July 1928); H. Nyquist, *Phys. Rev.*, **32**, 110–113 (July 1928); J. R. Pierce, *Proc. I.R.E.*, **44**, 601–608 (May 1956).

passes, the greater the number of noise components that appear in the output; and because the output rms value of noise is composed of the phasor sum of all these individual frequency components, the greater is the magnitude of the noise voltage in the output. This, in turn, makes it appear that the noise source is dependent upon the bandwidth of the system.

4.3 The conduction of electricity

An electric current is the flow or time rate of change of electric charge. There is only one known basic unit of electric charge, the charge on the electron, which is -1.60×10^{-19} coulombs. There are four extranuclear common charge carriers:

1. The *electron*, either as a *free electron* in a gas or high vacuum and as a *conduction electron* in a solid.
2. The *hole*, which is the absence of an electron in the covalent bonds of a crystalline structure such as germanium or silicon. The hole possesses one positive electronic charge. (A more detailed discussion of the hole will be given subsequently.)
3. *Positive gas ions* derived from gas atoms in the case of monatomic gases or from gas molecules in the case of diatomic gases. The most abundant ions are singly ionized molecules which have lost one outer-orbit electron and therefore carry a net charge of one electronic charge. Double-ionized molecules are not uncommon, and experimental work with more highly ionized particles is possible.
4. *Negative gas ions* obtained from certain gas molecules that display an affinity for attaching free electrons to themselves. Oxygen is outstanding in its ease of forming single-, double-, and triple-charged negative ions.

In this chapter our attention will be confined to the conduction electron and the hole. A discussion of the free electron and positive and negative ions will follow in Chap. 5. The subject of superconductivity will not be treated.

It was pointed out earlier that we cannot tag, and thereby identify, individual electrons; therefore we cannot assume that a certain group of electrons remains in any given incremental volume element, dV. Actually, the electrons within a volume element are scattered continually by collisions with the thermally vibrating lattice structure of the microscopic crystals that comprise the conductor. Electrons continually diverge out of and into the volume element. On the average, the net divergence from any particular volume element is zero, which permits us to consider each volume element, dV, as containing an average electric charge of $eN\, dV$ coulombs. N is the electron density per unit volume.

With reference to Fig. 4.6, if an electric field is set up throughout the conductor or semiconductor, then a force $q\mathbf{E}$ is exerted upon the charge carriers and they drift parallel to the electric field $\mathbf{E}$ with an average or *drift velocity*, $\mathbf{v}_d$. If the charge carriers are electrons, then $\mathbf{v}_d$ is directed opposite to $\mathbf{E}$; if the carriers are holes, then $\mathbf{v}_d$ is directed with the field $\mathbf{E}$. Each electron possesses an instantaneous velocity that is the vector sum of a velocity imparted to the electron by virtue of the presence of the applied electric field and a thermal velocity obtained from the crystal.

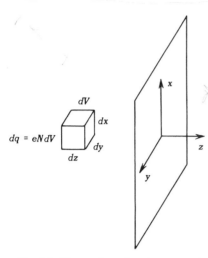

Dynamically, in free space each electron continues to accelerate indefinitely under the force $e\mathbf{E}$. In a crystalline conductor or semiconductor, the continual inelastic collisions of the electrons with the potential barriers surrounding the atoms that comprise the crystal prevent the electron from ever attaining average energies greater than the energy corresponding to the drift

Fig. 4.6. The motion of an incremental electric charge.

velocity $\mathbf{v}_d$. The drift velocity is a type of average terminal velocity for the electron. Only by increasing the accelerating field $\mathbf{E}$ can this terminal velocity be increased. In view of this, we may write

$$\mathbf{v}_d = \mu\mathbf{E} \qquad (4.3)$$

where μ is a coefficient of proportionality called the *mobility*.

The mobility is a unique characteristic of the conducting material and depends upon the direction of drift relative to the crystalline axes and upon the macroscopic composition of the material. Lattice forces in single crystals are never completely isotropic; therefore, the electron scattering, and thus mobility, both vary along different crystal axes. Large single crystals normally are used only in semiconductor devices; common metallic conductors consist of mosaics of microscopic crystals randomly oriented. Because of this random orientation of the constituent crystals, the mobility through a metal is essentially independent of the direction of drift. Mobility is also affected by the presence of lattice defects in single-crystal semiconductors. Such defects tend to scatter the charge carriers and thereby decrease the mobility.

An electric charge $eN\,dV$ passes through the incremental volume dV of Fig. 4.6 in a time dt. The current through the surface $d\mathbf{s}$ is $\mathbf{J} \cdot d\mathbf{s}$ amperes, where **J** is the *current density* in amperes per square meter. This current is equal to the time rate of change or flow of charge; therefore,

$$\mathbf{J} \cdot d\mathbf{s} = \frac{dq}{dt} = eN\frac{dV}{dt} \quad \text{amp} \tag{4.4}$$

Set the incremental surface $|d\mathbf{s}| = dx\, dy$ and the incremental volume $dV = dx\, dy\, dz$. Then

$$\mathbf{J} \cdot d\mathbf{s} = eN\, dx\, dy\, \frac{dz}{dt}$$

$$\mathbf{J} \cdot d\mathbf{s} = eN\, d\mathbf{s} \cdot \mathbf{v}_d$$

The current density is therefore

$$\mathbf{J} = eN\mathbf{v}_d \quad \text{amp/m}^2 \tag{4.5}$$

whereas the total current passing through a conductor of finite cross section is

$$I = \int_s \mathbf{J} \cdot d\mathbf{s} = e\int_s N\mathbf{v}_d \cdot d\mathbf{s} \tag{4.6}$$

The current flowing through any conductor with a cross-sectional area S, when V volts difference in potential exist across a length L, follows from Eq. (4.6):

$$I = eNSv_d$$

$$I = eNS\mu\left(\frac{V}{L}\right) \tag{4.7}$$

where V/L has been substituted for the magnitude of the electric field, $|E|$.

According to Ohm's law, the resistance of this conductor is V/I or

$$R = \left(\frac{1}{Ne\mu}\right)\frac{L}{S} \quad \text{ohms} \tag{4.8}$$

The term $1/Ne\mu$ is called the *resistivity*, ρ, of the material.

$$\rho = \frac{1}{Ne\mu} \quad \text{ohm-meters} \tag{4.9}$$

The reciprocal of the resistivity is termed the *conductivity*, σ.

$$\sigma = Ne\mu = \frac{1}{\rho} \quad \text{mho/m} \tag{4.10}$$

Detailed tables are available in the literature that cover the resistivity and conductivity of the pure metals and alloys, as well as certain semiconductor compositions (see Table 4.2).

Each inelastic collision of a conduction electron with the potential barrier of the lattice structure results in an energy transfer to the lattice

Table 4.2

Electrical properties of common conductors and semiconductors

Element	Mobility m²/volt-sec (20°C) electron	hole	Hall coefficient volt-meter³/amp · weber or meter³/coulomb	Resistivity ohm-meter (20°C)
Al	0.10×10^{-2}		-3.0×10^{-11}	2.7×10^{-8}
Si	0.12	0.05	$1 \times 10^{-3}*$	600*
Cu	0.35×10^{-2}		-5.5×10^{-11}	1.72×10^{-8}
Ge	0.36	0.17	$-0.15*$	0.6*
Ag	0.56×10^{-2}		-8.4×10^{-11}	1.64×10^{-8}
Au	0.30×10^{-2}		-7.2×10^{-11}	2.44×10^{-8}

* Intrinsic material.

structure. The structure vibrates more energetically and thus represents an increased temperature. These collisions represent a continual energy loss, and therefore electrical power is consumed. This is the familiar *joule heating*. The instantaneous power dissipated is given by the product of the instantaneous current and voltage.

$$p = ei$$

The average power dissipated over a time interval T is

$$P = \frac{1}{T} \int_0^T ei \, dt \quad \text{watts} \tag{4.11}$$

4.4   Sources of charge carriers

There is an important difference between metals and semiconductors that remains to be discussed. This is the source of free charge carriers and the nature of these charge carriers.

A two-dimensional sketch of a diamond-type crystalline lattice structure that shows the shared-pair valence electron bonds can be drawn as shown in Fig. 4.7(a). The atomic cores, as shown, contain the nucleus plus all of the inner-shell electrons. The four valence electrons are shown as forming the covalent or shared-pair bonds that hold the lattice structure together. Compare this sketch with that of Fig. 4.2. Both silicon ($Z = 14$) and germanium ($Z = 32$) possess four valence electrons; thus this model applies equally well to each material. The valence electrons of silicon lie in the $3p^4$ subshell; those of germanium lie in the $4s^2$ and $4p^2$ subshells (see Fig. 4.3).

Several items of interest are apparent from this simplified sketch of a semiconductor crystalline structure. First of all, it is obvious that at the surface of the crystal there must be incompleted valence bonds. This gives rise to surface effects, which constitute a broad field for research and which will not be treated here. It is easy to visualize the manner in which these unsatisfied bonds can trap foreign matter such as adsorbed gases in an effort to satisfy the valence bonds.

Second, this crystalline sketch enables us to visualize the creation of the charge carrier called the *hole*. The manner in which a small fraction of the valence electrons are able to gain sufficient energy at room temperature to jump the forbidden energy gap and enter the conduction band has already been discussed. These free electrons can be obtained only at the expense of the valence bonds. Each free electron obtained means that a broken valence bond is left somewhere in the crystal, and this means that an empty energy level exists in the valence band.

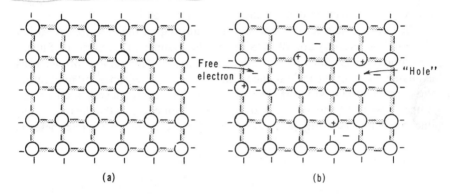

(a)   (b)

Fig. 4.7. Two-dimensional sketch of the diamond-type crystalline structure of silicon and germanium showing the shared-pair valence electron bonds. (a) All bonds intact and (b) several bonds broken, freeing electrons and producing holes.

Figure 4.7(b) shows the same crystalline structure, but several valence bonds have been broken by elevating these electrons to the conduction band. The free electrons that are obtained are shown moving freely throughout the crystal. The broken valence band represents a missing electron. There is an unsatisfied positive charge at the atomic center, and thus the "hole" where the valence electron is missing appears to have a positive electronic charge. The *hole* is, therefore, a place in the valence bonds of an ordered crystalline structure where a valence electron is missing.

If an electric field is established throughout the semiconductor by the application of an external potential, then the free electrons drift in a direction opposite to this field with a mobility μ_n. The *holes* also *appear* to move. A valence electron neighboring the hole can now increase its energy slightly and drift into the hole to satisfy the valence bond. However, a hole now exists at the point where this valence electron originated. Thus, the hole has apparently drifted with the applied electric field. This process will continue and the hole can traverse the crystal. When the hole reaches the metallic connection at the end of the crystal, a conduction electron from the metal falls into the hole and eliminates it.

The mobility, μ_p, of the hole is considerably smaller than that of the conduction electron because the motion of the hole depends upon the complicated shifting of valence band electrons from one atom to another. The holes will move with a random thermal motion and a superimposed drift motion if an electric field is present in the same manner as free electrons. The conductivity of the semiconductor depends upon both charge carriers, or

$$\sigma = e(\mu_n n + \mu_p p) \tag{4.12}$$

where n is the electron density and p is the hole density.

Obviously, the electron concentration must equal the hole concentration if the charge carriers are all obtained in the manner just described. Such a semiconductor is called an *intrinsic semicondutor*. The number of electrons available from an intrinsic semiconductor can be determined by integrating the expression $n(W)$ for the number of occupied energy levels in an energy range between W and $W + dW$ over the range of energies that lie in the conduction band* (see Fig. 4.4). The result for n electrons per cubic meter is

$$n = 2\left(\frac{2\pi m_n kT}{h^2}\right)^{3/2} \epsilon^{-(W_c - W_0)/kT}$$

$$= 4.83 \times 10^{21} T^{3/2} \epsilon^{-(W_c - W_0)/kT} \tag{4.13a}$$

where W_c is the bottom of the conduction band and W_0 is the Fermi level.

In a similar manner, the number of holes p per cubic meter can be determined:

$$p = 2\left(\frac{2\pi m_p kT}{h^2}\right)^{3/2} \epsilon^{-(W_0 - W_v)/kT}$$

$$= 4.83 \times 10^{21} T^{3/2} \epsilon^{-(W_0 - W_v)/kT} \tag{4.13b}$$

W_v is the top of the valence band.

Because p is equal to n for an intrinsic semiconductor, Eqs. (4.13a) and (4.13b) must be equal. If these two equations are solved simultaneously for the Fermi level, then

$$W_0 = \frac{1}{2}(W_c + W_v) + \frac{3}{4} kT \ln\left(\frac{m_p}{m_n}\right) \tag{4.14a}$$

or, if the Fermi level is *measured up from the top of the valence band*, as is often done, then

$$W_0' = \frac{1}{2}(W_c - W_v) + \frac{3}{4} kT \ln\left(\frac{m_p}{m_n}\right) \tag{4.14b}$$

* See W. Shockley, *Electrons and Holes in Semiconductors*, D. Van Nostrand Co., Princeton, N.J., 1950, p. 240; C. Kittel, *Introduction to Solid State Physics*, John Wiley & Sons, New York, 1953, pp. 275–276.

The quantities m_p and m_n are the effective masses of the hole and the electron, respectively.

The mass of the hole is the effective imaginary mass required to account for the kinetic energy, $\frac{1}{2}m_p(\mu_p E)^2$ of the hole. Although the hole acts as a

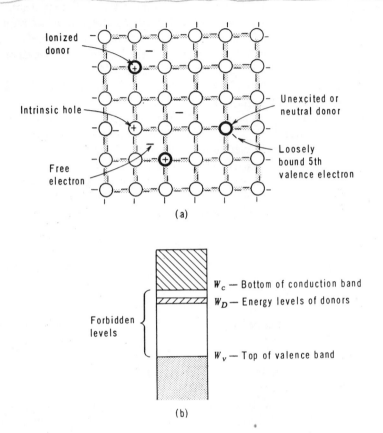

Fig. 4.8. *n*-type semiconductor. (a) Model and (b) energy-level diagram.

real particle, we must remember that it is in reality only the apparent movement of a missing valence bond electron. The approximate mobilities of the free electrons and holes are given in Table 4.2.

Intrinsic conduction is not the most important form of conduction in semiconductors. Intrinsic conduction is highly temperature-dependent and is usually limited to relatively small current densities at room temperatures. *Extrinsic semiconductors* can be formed by artificial introduction of charge carriers into the crystal, which is accomplished in an interesting manner. In Fig. 4.8(a), *substitutional impurities* from the valence V group of the periodic chart have replaced some of the silicon or germanium atoms of the crystal. This replacement can be accomplished in several ways. For instance, it can occur during the growing of the single crystal from a melt. The impurities are added to the melt.

The useful valence V elements are arsenic (As), antimony (Sb), and phosphorus (P). In each case, one of the five valence electrons is not required to complete the covalent crystal bonds. The fifth electron is loosely bound to the parent atom. It possesses an energy level that lies much nearer to the conduction band than the valence electrons (see Fig. 4.8(b)).

At temperatures slightly above absolute zero, sufficient thermal energy can be transferred to these impurity atoms to *activate* a fraction of them and to permit the fifth uncompensated electron to become free of the parent atom. These valence V impurity atoms thus become free electron *donors*. Upon activation the donor electrons jump the small gap into the conduction band where they are free to participate in electrical conduction. The activated donor atoms have become *positive ions*. These ions are locked in the crystal structure and therefore cannot participate in conduction.

Silicon or germanium that is *doped* with valence V impurities is said to be an *n-type semiconductor*, and the electrons are the *majority charge carriers*.

If valence III elements are added to the melt instead of valence V elements, then a different situation results, as shown in Fig. 4.9(a). Typical valence III impurity elements are boron (B), aluminum (Al), indium (In), and gallium (Ga). Only three valence electrons are available to form bonds with the neighboring valence IV atoms, resulting in an unsatisfied bond or *hole*. Depending upon the temperature, a fraction of these unsatisfied bonds will be filled by neighboring valence electrons that have gained the necessary activation energy.

Upon activation, these valence III impurity atoms become negative ions locked in the crystalline structure. They are *acceptors* of electrons. The accepted electrons come from the energy range of the valence electrons, as shown in Fig. 4.9(b). The acceptor impurity level lies only a little above the top of the valence band.

At room temperature, a reasonable number of these acceptors are ionized, which means that the associated holes have moved to the position previously occupied by the ionizing electrons. There is a continual random motion of other valence electrons filling the holes and in turn leaving holes at their previous locations. If an external electric field is applied, then those valence electrons that are filling the holes display a tendency to drift opposite to the field. The holes they leave behind thereby appear to drift in the direction of the electric field and constitute a hole current.

Silicon or germanium that has been doped with valence III impurities is said to be *p-type* semiconductor material, and the holes are the *majority charge carriers*.

The net number of impurity-provided charge carriers governs the conductivity in a semiconductor. Let the density of donor impurities be N_d and that of acceptors be N_a. It is difficult to produce a semiconductor that is doped solely with one type of impurity. When donors and acceptors are both

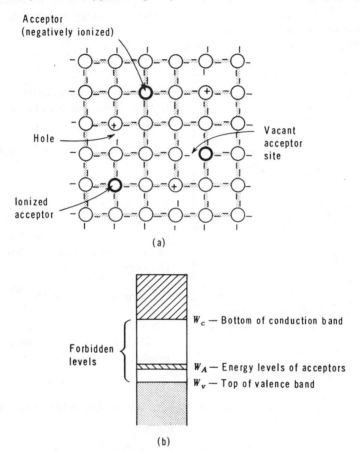

(a)

(b)

Fig. 4.9. p-type semiconductor. (a) Model and (b) energy-level diagram.

present, they tend to compensate one another and only the net unbalance is effective in the conduction process.

If the operating temperatures are held close to room temperature, then the net concentration of conduction band electrons donated varies in the following manner:

$$n = A N_d T^{3/2} \epsilon^{-(W_c - W_D)/kT} \tag{4.15a}$$

where A is a coefficient that depends to some extent upon the number of compensating acceptors that are present.

In the case of holes injected into the valence band, the relationship is similar.

$$p = BN_a T^{3/2} \epsilon^{-(W_A - W_v)/kT} \qquad (4.15b)$$

In each case the density of charge carriers is proportional to the Boltzmann factor $\epsilon^{-W/kT}$ where W represents the activation energy required to ionize a donor site or an acceptor site.

Either Eq. (4.15a) or (4.15b) is of the form

$$N = CT^{3/2} \epsilon^{-W/kT} \qquad (4.16)$$

where N is the charge carrier concentration. Take the logarithm of Eq. (4.16).

$$\log N = \log C + \frac{3}{2} \log T - 0.434 \frac{W}{kT} \qquad (4.17)$$

The term $\log T$ varies only slightly compared to the term W/kT for operating temperatures in the vicinity of room temperature. Thus, Eq. (4.17) may be written as

$$\log N = K - 0.434 \frac{W}{kT} \qquad (4.18)$$

where K is a constant.

In Sec. 4.3 it was shown that conductivity could be written as

$$\sigma = Ne\mu \qquad (4.19)$$

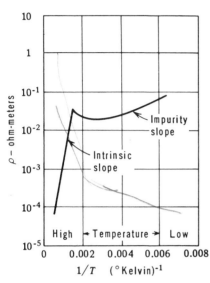

Fig. 4.10. Typical resistivity characteristics of an impurity semiconductor as a function of absolute temperature.

Take the logarithm of this expression and substitute Eq. (4.18) into the result.

$$\log \sigma = \log e\mu + \log N$$

$$\log \sigma = \log e\mu + K - 0.434 \frac{W}{kT} \qquad (4.20)$$

A sketch of the variation of resistivity as a function of $1/T$ for a typical semiconductor is shown in Fig. 4.10. Over a restricted range of temperature, the mobility μ may be treated as a constant and Eq. (4.20) becomes the equation of a straight line on semilogarithmic paper. The slope of the experimental curve for low temperatures satisfies the analytical slope $0.434 W/k$. In this manner, the activation energy may be determined experimentally.

As the temperature is raised, a transitional region is reached and, finally, the intrinsic range of conductivity. In this range the number of intrinsic carriers is far greater than those provided by donors or acceptors. The slope of the curve in this range yields the energy width of the forbidden gap. Because any valence electron can have an energy up to the Fermi level at absolute zero, it is necessary only to supply the additional energy between the Fermi level and the conduction band to cause an electron to jump the entire forbidden gap. The Fermi level lies approximately in the middle of the forbidden gap; therefore the slope of the conductivity curve in the intrinsic range is $0.434(W_c - W_v)/2k$. For a more complete analysis on this subject, consult the references at the end of the chapter.

4.5 Electrical conductivity

The general concept of electrical conductivity was reviewed in Sec. 4.3. At this point we will discuss electrical conductivity from a statistical viewpoint.

Under certain conditions the velocities of the charge carriers in a semiconductor follow a Maxwell-Boltzmann type of distribution function in the same manner as do neutral gas molecules. In other words, the density of charge carriers, N, in a velocity range between v and $v + dv$ is temperature-dependent. Such a gas of electric charge carriers (electrons or holes) is said to be *nondegenerate*, and the material is termed a *nondegenerate semiconductor*.

On the other hand, metals or semiconductors (which possess a large impurity concentration) have a charge carrier density in any given velocity range between v and $v + dv$ that is essentially independent of temperature. Such a group of charge carriers obviously does not behave in a manner similar to a gas. In fact, we have previously shown that the velocity distribution function for the charge carriers in a metal is of the Fermi-Dirac type. Thus, the charge carriers in metals and highly doped semiconductors are *degenerate* and these materials are termed *degenerate semiconductors* or *metals*.

In a metal the conduction electrons all lie close to the Fermi level. The density of charge carriers in this energy range is quite large and governed entirely by the Fermi-Dirac distribution function,

$$n(W) = \frac{F(W)}{\epsilon^{(W - W_0)/kT} + 1} \tag{4.21}$$

as sketched in Fig. 4.4.

A semiconductor, on the other hand, possesses free charge carriers in the bottom of the essentially empty conduction band if donor impurities are present, or holes in the top of the valence band if acceptor-type impurities are present (see Fig. 4.11). In the case of the n-type semiconductor, there are so few electrons in the conduction band and their energies are so much greater than the Fermi level that $\epsilon^{(W - W_0)/kT} \gg 1$ and the distribution function becomes

$$n(W) = F(W)\epsilon^{-(W - W_0)/kT} \tag{4.22}$$

which is a Maxwell-Boltzmann type of distribution.

If p-type semiconductor material is used, then the energies of the holes lie considerably below the Fermi level, and again the distribution function is of the Maxwell-Boltzmann type.

Instead of expressing an electric current density by means of an average drift velocity v_d as in Eq. (4.5), it can be expressed in terms of the integral of the velocity of each individual charge carrier over the entire distribution of velocities.

$$J = -e \int v_x f'(v) \, dv \qquad (4.23)$$

where $f'(v)$ expresses the number of electrons per cubic meter possessing velocities between v and $v + dv$. It is assumed that v may depend upon the

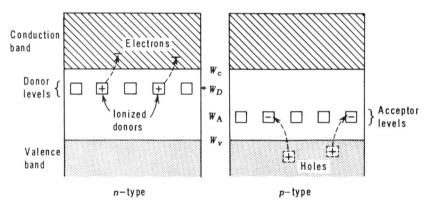

Fig. 4.11. Impurity levels in semiconductors.

position coordinates x, y, and z. Notice the difference between Eq. (4.22) and Eq. (2.33). Equation (2.33) requires the use of a normalized velocity distribution function $f(v)$ and therefore yields an average velocity only. Equation (4.23) does not use a normalized distribution function and thereby the integral yields the product Nv_d where N is the charge carrier density and v_d is the average drift velocity.

The correct velocity distribution function $f'(v)$ for use in Eq. (4.23) must be some modified form of $f'_0(v)$. The modification is necessary because of the presence of the externally applied electric field $\mathbf{E}_x$ that establishes the net flow of charge carriers. H. A. Lorentz* suggested that in the presence of an electric field, but under isothermal conditions, the velocity distribution function could be represented by

$$f'(v) = f'_0(v) + v_x f'_x(v) \qquad (4.24)$$

The term $v_x f'_x(v)$ is a modifying function that arises from the application of the electric field parallel to the x-axis.

* H. A. Lorentz, *The Theory of Electrons*, G. E. Stechert and Co., New York, 1923.

Before Eq. (4.24) can be used, $f'_x(v)$ must be determined. To accomplish this, it is first necessary to develop *Boltzmann's equation of state*. Let a represent the number of electrons per unit volume whose velocity changes from v_x, v_y, v_z to some other value in a unit of time. Also, let b represent the number whose velocities change to v_x, v_y, v_z from other values. The difference $(b - a)$ is then the *change* in the number of electrons to be found in a given velocity range. We may write

$$\frac{df'(v)}{dt} = b - a \tag{4.25}$$

This expression may be expanded mathematically to

$$\frac{\partial f'(v)}{\partial x}\frac{dx}{dt} + \frac{\partial f'(v)}{\partial y}\frac{dy}{dt} + \cdots + \frac{\partial f'(v)}{\partial v_x}\frac{dv_x}{dt} + \cdots = b - a \tag{4.26}$$

This is *Boltzmann's equation of state*.

As an example of the physical meaning of Boltzmann's equation of state, consider a metal with no externally applied electric fields and a constant temperature throughout the sample. Under these conditions the velocity distribution function is the same everywhere in the sample and there is no acceleration of electrons. Therefore,

$$\frac{\partial f'(v)}{\partial x} = 0$$

and similar expressions exist for y and z. Also,

$$\frac{\partial v_x}{\partial t} = \frac{\partial v_y}{\partial t} = \frac{\partial v_z}{\partial t} = 0$$

The result is that $a = b$ under these conditions.

If an external field E_x is applied, then $a \neq b$ because extra energy is imparted to the x-component of motion of the electrons. The acceleration of the electrons is

$$\frac{dv_x}{dt} = -\frac{eE_x}{m}$$

With this substitution, Boltzmann's equation of state reduces to

$$\frac{\partial f'(v)}{\partial x}v_x - \frac{\partial f'(v)}{\partial v_x}\frac{eE_x}{m} = b - a \tag{4.27}$$

Lorentz's solution (Eq. (4.24)) may be substituted into this equation. However, first note that the drift term, $v_x f'_x(v)$, is very small compared to the normal velocity distribution function, $f'_0(v)$, and may be neglected. With these substitutions Eq. (4.27) yields

$$\frac{\partial f'_0}{\partial x}v_x - \frac{eE_x}{m}\frac{\partial f'_0}{\partial v_x} = b - a \tag{4.28}$$

Equation (4.28) expresses the rate of change in $f'(v)$ caused by inelastic collisions of the electrons with the atomic structure of the crystal. The term $v_x f'_x(v)$ in Lorentz's equation expresses the number of electrons per cubic meter in a velocity range between v and $v + dv$ because of electron drift under the influence of an applied electric field. Let the collision rate per unit volume be

$$\zeta = \frac{v}{\lambda} \quad \text{collisions/sec} \tag{4.29}$$

where λ is the electron mean free path. The rate of change in $f'(v)$ caused by inelastic electron collisions is then $-v_x f'_x(v)\zeta$. Equation (4.28) may be written as

$$\frac{\partial f'_0}{\partial x} v_x - \frac{eE_x}{m} \frac{\partial f'_0}{\partial v_x} = -v_x f'_x \frac{v}{\lambda} \tag{4.30}$$

This equation permits us to solve for the unknown drift velocity function, f'_x.

$$f'_x = -\frac{\lambda}{v} \left[\frac{\partial f'_0}{\partial x} - \frac{eE_x}{mv_x} \frac{\partial f'_0}{\partial v_x} \right] \tag{4.31}$$

The first term $\partial f'_0/\partial x$ in the brackets can exist only if there is a temperature gradient present. The second term is due to the applied electric field exclusively.

If an isothermal problem is considered, then Eq. (4.24) may be written as

$$f'(v) = f'_0 + eE_x \lambda \frac{\partial f'_0}{\partial W} \frac{v_x}{v} \tag{4.32}$$

where the variable ∂v_x has been replaced by $\partial W/mv_x$ and $W = mv_x^2/2$. The current density, as expressed by Eq. (4.23) now becomes

$$J = -e \int_{-\infty}^{\infty} \int_{-\infty}^{\infty} \int_{-\infty}^{\infty} v_x f'_0(v) \, dv_x \, dv_y \, dv_z$$
$$-e^2 E_x \int_{-\infty}^{\infty} \int_{-\infty}^{\infty} \int_{-\infty}^{\infty} \frac{\lambda v_x^2}{v} \frac{\partial f'_0(v)}{\partial W} \, dv_x \, dv_y \, dv_z \tag{4.33}$$

The first integral yields the mean x-component of electric current because of thermal diffusion velocity, which is, of course, zero. The second term represents electron drift and may be placed in a form to be integrated by eliminating the x-component of velocity in favor of the speed v because the distribution function $f'(v)$ is a direct function of the speed. If a spherical volume in momentum (or velocity) space is taken, then

$$v_x^2 + v_y^2 + v_z^2 = 3v_x^2 = v^2 \tag{4.34}$$

and

$$dv_x \, dv_y \, dv_z = 4\pi v^2 \, dv \tag{4.35}$$

With these substitutions and integrating from 0 to ∞ because of the spherical volume, the integral expression for electrical current may be written as

$$J = -\frac{4\pi e^2}{3} E_x \int_0^\infty v^3 \lambda \frac{\partial f_0'(v)}{\partial W}\, dv \qquad (4.36)$$

By definition, conductivity is the ratio

$$\sigma = \frac{J}{E} \quad \text{amp/volt-meter} \qquad (4.37)$$

In view of Eq. (4.36) the conductivity may be written as

$$\sigma = -\frac{4\pi e^2}{3} \int_0^\infty v^3 \lambda \frac{\partial f_0'(v)}{\partial W}\, dv \qquad (4.38)$$

It can be shown that the distribution function, $f_0'(v)$, may be written in terms of energy. The relationship is

$$f_0'(v) = \frac{2m^3}{h^3} f(W)$$

If W is substituted for $mv^2/2$, then

$$\sigma = -\frac{16\pi e^2 m}{3h^3} \int_0^\infty \lambda \frac{\partial f_0(W)}{\partial W} W\, dW \qquad (4.39)$$

To integrate Eq. (4.39), first recognize the fact that only electrons very close to the Fermi level can participate in the conduction process. Thus the energy, W, of the conduction electrons remains nearly equal to W_0. Also, the mean free path, λ, of the electrons is essentially a constant, λ_0, for electrons that have energies near W_0.

The partial derivative of the distribution function is zero everywhere except in the immediate vicinity of W_0 (see Fig. 4.12). Upon substitution,

$$\frac{\partial f_0(W)}{\partial W} = -\frac{1}{kT} \epsilon^{(W-W_0)/kT} \left[\epsilon^{(W-W_0)/kT} + 1 \right]^{-2}$$

$$\frac{\partial f_0(W)}{\partial W} = -\frac{1}{kT} f(W)[1 - f(W)] \qquad (4.40)$$

From this equation it follows that

$$\int_0^\infty \frac{1}{kT} f(1 - f)\, dW = -\int_0^1 df(W) = 1 \qquad (4.41)$$

because $f(W)$ has the value 1 below and the value 0 above the narrow transition region centered about the Fermi level.

In view of these substitutions, Eq. (4.39) becomes

$$\sigma = \frac{16\pi e^2 m}{3h^3} \lambda_0 W_0 \qquad (4.42)$$

which may be written as

$$\sigma = \frac{16\pi e^2 m}{3h^3} \lambda_0 \frac{W_0^{3/2}}{W_0^{1/2}} \tag{4.43}$$

The Fermi level varies very little with temperature (see Eq. (3.76)), which enables us to employ Eq. (3.60) for W_0 at $T = 0$.

$$W_0^{3/2} = \left(\frac{1}{2m}\right)^{3/2} \frac{3h^3 N_{\max}}{8\pi}$$

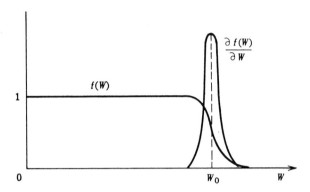

Fig. **4.12.** The Fermi factor and its derivative as a function of energy.

For $W_0^{1/2}$, substitute $v_0\sqrt{m/2}$. With these substitutions Eq. (4.43) becomes

$$\sigma = \frac{e^2 \lambda_0 N_{\max}}{m v_0} \quad \text{mho/m} \tag{4.44}$$

for the conductivity of a metal or degenerate semiconductor.

The same basic expression for conductivity (Eq. (4.38)) also applies to *nondegenerate* semiconductors. The proper velocity distribution function is of the Maxwell-Boltzmann type rather than of the Fermi-Dirac type. From Eq. (2.52) the Maxwell-Boltzmann distribution may be written as

$$f(v) = \left(\frac{m}{2\pi kT}\right)^{3/2} \epsilon^{-mv^2/2kT} \tag{4.45}$$

The number of free electrons per unit volume that have a velocity between v and $v + dv$ is ΔN. The probability of finding electrons in this velocity range is

$$\Delta P = \frac{\Delta N}{N} = f(v)\,\Delta v \tag{4.46}$$

$$\Delta N = N f(v)\,\Delta v = n(W)\,\Delta W \tag{4.47}$$

where $n(W)\,\Delta W$ is the number of free electrons in the energy range ΔW.

The number of free electrons per unit volume, N, is temperature-dependent. Take an incremental volume shell $4\pi v^2 \, dv$ in velocity space; then

$$4\pi N f(v) v^2 \, dv = n(W) \, dW$$

Change the variable on the left-hand side of this equation to energy by means of

$$W = \frac{mv^2}{2}$$

This yields

$$4\pi N f(v) \frac{1}{m} \sqrt{\frac{2}{m}} \sqrt{W} \, dW = n(W) \, dW \qquad (4.48)$$

Substitute Eq. (4.45) into Eq. (4.48) and solve for the density $n(W)$ of free electrons in the energy range W.

$$n(W) = \frac{2N}{\sqrt{\pi}} \frac{\sqrt{W}}{(kT)^{3/2}} \epsilon^{-W/kT} \qquad (4.49)$$

It is again emphasized that $N = f(T)$ for a *nondegenerate semiconductor*.

With $n(W)$ known, it is now possible to evaluate the expression $f'(v)$ for the number of electrons per cubic meter that have velocities in a certain range. The number of electrons in the incremental volume shell $4\pi v^2 \, dv$ is

$$4\pi f'(v) v^2 \, dv = n(W) \, dW \qquad (4.50)$$

Again set $v = \sqrt{2W/m}$ and substitute Eq. (4.49) for $n(W)$. When terms are rearranged, the electron density velocity distribution function becomes

$$f'(v) = \frac{1}{4\pi} \left(\frac{2}{\pi}\right)^{1/2} \left(\frac{m}{kT}\right)^{3/2} N\epsilon^{-W/kT} \qquad (4.51)$$

The conductivity of the nondegenerate semiconductor is obtained by substituting Eq. (4.51) into the general expression for conductivity (Eq. (4.38)).

$$\sigma = -\frac{4\pi e^2}{3} \int_0^\infty v^3 \lambda \frac{\partial f_0'(v)}{\partial W} \, dv$$

If the mean free path for electrons with energies near W_0 is treated as a constant, λ_0, then the conductivity is

$$\sigma = \frac{4N e^2 \lambda_0}{3\sqrt{2\pi m kT}} \quad \text{mho/m} \qquad (4.52)$$

4.6   Minority charge carriers

If a semiconductor has charge carriers opposite to the majority carriers normally present, these injected carriers are termed *minority carriers*. For example, let holes be injected into an n-type semiconductor. The electrons are the *majority carriers* and the holes are the *minority carriers*. The practical use of injected minority carriers is discussed in Chap. 6.

There is always a small percentage of minority carriers present in any semiconductor sample. As previously pointed out, these arise from the impurities of a type opposite to that supplying the majority carrier and also from the thermal formation of electron-hole pairs as in the case of intrinsic conductivity. Let p_n be the normal equilibrium hole concentration in n-type material and let p_m be the injected hole concentration. If the normal equilibrium electron concentration is n_n, then the *time rate of electron-hole pair recombination* is proportional to the concentration of holes and electrons within the material and may be written as $rp_n n_n$ (for p-type material, it would be written as $rp_p n_p$). The *recombination coefficient r* is a proportionality constant.

In general, in germanium and silicon recombination occurs at points throughout the crystalline structure where there are local discontinuities in the periodic electrical potential structure of the lattice. Electrons and holes are *trapped* at these points of potential discontinuity. The neutral *trap* captures either an electron or a hole, thus becoming ionized. The ionized trap then traps a charge carrier of the opposite sign, whereupon the trapped hole and electron recombine, leaving a neutral trap. Upon being trapped, a charge carrier releases its excess energy by radiation to the surrounding crystal lattice structure. Direct recombination of holes and electrons is also possible, and this process is believed to play an important role in semiconductor materials such as indium antimonide (InSb), which has a relatively small energy gap of forbidden levels.

The average time that an electron or hole can exist as a charge carrier before capture at a trap or direct recombination is termed the *lifetime* of the carrier. When recombination by the two-step trap process is predominant, the lifetimes of the electrons and holes are different. When direct recombination is present, the lifetimes of the electrons and holes must be equal.

The formation of electron-hole pairs by thermal excitation is independent of the concentration of the electrons or the holes. Let g be the *time rate* of *electron-hole* pair formation. The net time rate of change of hole concentration in n-type semiconductors *without minority carrier injection* is

$$\frac{dp}{dt} = g - rpn \tag{4.53}$$

Under equilibrium conditions dp/dt is zero, and the rate of formation of electron-hole pairs is equal to the rate of recombination. Thus

$$g = rp_n n_n \tag{4.54}$$

Let the additional holes be injected into the n-type sample prior to time $t = 0$. The hole concentration p now consists of the normal equilibrium hole concentration p_n plus the injected hole concentration p_m.

$$p = p_n + p_m \tag{4.55}$$

The semiconductor must remain electrically neutral at all times with respect to the other parts of the circuit. Therefore, electrons must also enter the semiconductor from the external circuit in the same concentration as that of the injected holes. The over-all electron density is, therefore,

$$n = (n_n + p_m) \tag{4.56}$$

In this case of injected holes, the rate of change of over-all hole density is

$$\frac{dp}{dt} = g - r(p_n + p_m)(n_n + p_m) \tag{4.57}$$

The rate of formation of electron-hole pairs does not change from that normally present, and Eq. (4.54) may be used to replace g in the above equation.

$$\frac{dp}{dt} = r[p_n n_n - (p_n + p_m)(n_n + p_m)]$$

$$\frac{dp_m}{dt} = -r[p_m(p_n + n_n) + p_m^2] \tag{4.58}$$

where
$$\frac{dp}{dt} = \frac{d}{dt}(p_n + p_m) = \frac{dp_m}{dt}$$

because p_n is a constant.

The injected carrier density is normally small compared to the equilibrium hole and electron concentrations p_n and n_n. To a good approximation, this permits dropping the term p_m^2. The resultant differential equation

$$\frac{dp_m}{dt} = -rp_m(p_n + n_n) \tag{4.59}$$

is satisfied by
$$p_m = p_{m0}\epsilon^{-t/\tau_p} \tag{4.60}$$

where p_{m0} and τ_p are integration constants. Substitute Eq. (4.60) in Eq. (4.59) and

$$\tau_p = \frac{1}{r(p_n + n_n)} \text{ sec} \tag{4.61}$$

Equation (4.61) expresses the *lifetime*, τ_p, of the holes.

The initial injected hole density is p_{m0}, and after τ_p seconds it has decreased one time constant or *lifetime*.

Consider the more general case when a component of current is established because of continuously injected holes in *n*-type material. From Eqs. (4.59) and (4.61)

$$\frac{dp_m}{dt} = -rp_m(p_n + n_n)$$

$$\frac{dp_m}{dt} = -\frac{p_m}{\tau_p}$$

It is not proper to distinguish between injected holes and those normally present in the equilibrium concentration p_n; therefore replace p_m with $(p - p_n)$ according to Eq. (4.55).

$$\frac{dp}{dt} = -\frac{(p - p_n)}{\tau_p} \qquad (4.62)$$

This equation only expresses the change in hole distribution in the case of no continuous hole injections. If the holes are continually injected, then a hole current density $\mathbf{J}_p$, is established. The density of these minority carriers is very small compared to the density of the majority carriers (electrons in this case). For this reason, the minority carriers diffuse as a free gas within the semiconductor, and the results of the kinetic theory of gases may be applied.

The diffusion of minority electric charge carriers in a semiconductor is very similar to the interdiffusion of two species of gas molecules (Sec. 2.10) and to the diffusion of electrons or ionized gas molecules in an electron tube (Sec. 7.7). Only the basic concept of diffusion in a semiconductor will be introduced at this point. The subject will be developed by application in more detail in Sec. 6.1 and 6.3.

Without recourse to a statistical approach, it should be apparent that any ensemble of particles that are free to move in a random fashion tends to distribute itself in a manner that results in its spatial density's being constant. For the sake of discussion, suppose that the spatial density, p, of holes in n-type material is not uniform; then a concentration gradient exists ($\nabla p \neq 0$). If the density in one region is considerably greater than that found in the immediate surroundings, a large negative gradient is encountered when moving in a positive direction away from the region of high hole concentration. The movement or diffusion of holes away from this region of high concentration will be proportional to the magnitude of the gradient. This diffusion of particles (holes) constitutes a *particle current density* that may be written as

$$\text{particle current density} = -D_p \nabla p$$

where the minus sign is required to cancel the negative value of the gradient, yielding a positive material current that moves away from the region of high concentration. The proportionality coefficient D is termed the *diffusion coefficient*. In the case of holes moving as minority charge carriers in n-type material, an electric diffusion current density $-eD_p\nabla p$ is established. If the minority charge carriers are electrons in p-type material, then the electric diffusion current density is $+eD_n\nabla n$ amperes per square meter.

In general, any current that arises from the motion of minority charge carriers can be expressed as the sum of two components. One arises from the *drift* of the charge carriers in an applied electric field, $\mathbf{E}$. The other component is the *diffusion* current that is present as long as any concentration gradient exists. In the case of holes, the net electric current density is

$$J_p = ep\mu_p E - eD_p\nabla p ,$$
(4.63)

The minus sign is associated with the hole diffusion coefficient D_p and indicates that the diffusion is directed away from regions of high hole concentration as expressed by the gradient ∇ of p. For values of the diffusion coefficient, see Table 4.3.

Table 4.3

Diffusion coefficients
(m²/sec)

Element	D_n (electrons)	D_p (holes)
Si	3.8×10^{-3}	1.3×10^{-3}
Ge	9.0×10^{-3}	4.5×10^{-3}

The divergence of Eq. (4.63) divided by the electronic charge e yields the time rate of change of hole concentration caused by hole current flow.

$$\frac{1}{e}\nabla \cdot J_p = \nabla \cdot (\mu_p p E) - D_p\nabla^2 p$$
(4.64)

Combining Eqs. (4.62) and (4.64) yields the *continuity equation for holes* in n-type semiconductor material.

$$\frac{dp}{dt} = \frac{p_n - p}{\tau_p} - \frac{1}{e}\nabla \cdot J_p$$
(4.65)

The minus sign on the term arises from the flow of current and is necessary because it opposes the time decay of the hole density.

Similar equations can be written for minority electrons in p-type material. The continuity equation for electrons in p-type semiconductor material is

$$\frac{dn}{dt} = \frac{n_p - n}{\tau_n} + \frac{1}{e}\nabla \cdot J_n$$
(4.66)

4.7 The Hall effect

There are a series of electrical effects that are sufficiently pronounced in semiconductors to make them of possible practical importance. Most of these effects are direct functions of temperature; however there exists an *isothermal Hall effect* that is very important. This phenomenon will be investigated from an average behavior viewpoint, although it can also be treated from a statistical approach. The Hall effect applies to both conductors and semiconductors; however, in general it is sufficiently pronounced to be of major interest only in semiconductors.

Let a current density $\mathbf{J}_z$ flow through the rectangular sample of material because of an applied electric field $\mathbf{E}_z$, as shown in Fig. 4.13. The sample is placed in a uniform magnetic field of density $\mathbf{B}_y$ webers/meter². The current density is given by Eq. (4.5), which is presented here in vector form.

$$\mathbf{J}_z = Nq\mathbf{v}_d = Nq\mu\mathbf{E}_z \tag{4.67}$$

The carrier charge is q, which would be $-e$ for an electron or $+e$ for a hole.

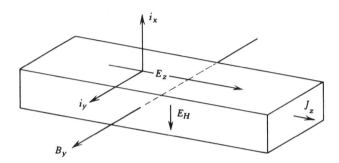

Fig. 4.13. The isothermal Hall effect.

The drifting charge carriers experience a force because of the presence of the magnetic field. In general, the force on any charge moving with a velocity $\mathbf{v}$ in a combined electric and magnetic field is

$$\mathbf{F} = q(\mathbf{E} + \mathbf{v} \times \mathbf{B}) \tag{4.68}$$

In the absence of external forces the net force on the charge carriers must be zero. Equation (4.68) reduces to

$$q\mathbf{E}_H = -q\mu\mathbf{E}_z \times \mathbf{B}_y \tag{4.69}$$

for this particular problem. An electric field

$$\mathbf{E}_H = -\mathbf{E}_x = -\mu E_z B_y \mathbf{i}_x \tag{4.70}$$

is established laterally across the sample, where $\mathbf{i}_x$ is a unit vector along the x-axis. This is the *Hall field*, $\mathbf{E}_H$, and its establishment is the *Hall effect*. By means of Eq. (4.67), the magnitude of the Hall field can be written as

$$E_H = \frac{J_z B_y}{Nq} \tag{4.71}$$

or as

$$E_H = RJ_z B_y \tag{4.72}$$

where

$$R = \frac{1}{Nq} \tag{4.73}$$

is the *Hall coefficient*.

Equation (4.72) agrees with statistical theory and experimental data for metals. For extrinsic semiconductors and low magnetic field densities, theory requires that

$$R = \frac{3\pi}{8} \frac{1}{Nq} \tag{4.74}$$

The magnetic field B_y forces the drifting charge carriers that form J_z to one side of the sample. This distribution of electric charge across the sample sets up the Hall field. Electrons drift against the externally applied electric field $\mathbf{E}_z$. Hence, the force $(-e\mathbf{v}_d \times \mathbf{B})$ on the electrons is directed in the negative x-direction. Holes drift with the externally applied electric field and, therefore, the force $(e\mathbf{v}_d \times \mathbf{B})$ on the holes is also directed in the negative x-direction. Normally, the material is either n- or p-type. Thus, the transverse Hall field is caused by the crowding of the net majority carriers to one side of the sample. The varying density of charge carriers across the sample gives rise to the Hall field, which in turn prevents more charge carriers from crowding to one side of the sample. In this manner, an equilibrium condition is established.

The net electric field within the sample is

$$\mathbf{E} = \mathbf{E}_H + \mathbf{E}_z \tag{4.75}$$

The angle θ formed between $\mathbf{E}$ and $\mathbf{E}_z$ is the *Hall angle*.

$$\tan \theta = \frac{E_H}{E_z} \tag{4.76}$$

In general, the Hall effect is weak and $E_H \ll E_z$ so that

$$\theta \approx \tan \theta = \frac{E_H}{E_z} \tag{4.77}$$

From Eq. (4.72),

$$E_H = RJ_z B_y$$
$$= RNq\mu E_z B_y$$

or

$$\frac{E_H}{E_z} = RNq\mu B_y \tag{4.78}$$

For a semiconductor, R is $3\pi/8Nq$, or

$$\theta = \frac{E_H}{E_z} = \frac{3\pi}{8} \mu B_y \tag{4.79}$$

$$\theta = \mu_H B_y \tag{4.80}$$

$$\mu_H = \frac{3\pi}{8} \mu \tag{4.81}$$

where μ_H is the *Hall mobility*. The ratio μ_H/μ is not a constant but has the value of $3\pi/8$ for small values of magnetic field density. This ratio approaches a value of unity for very large magnetic field densities.

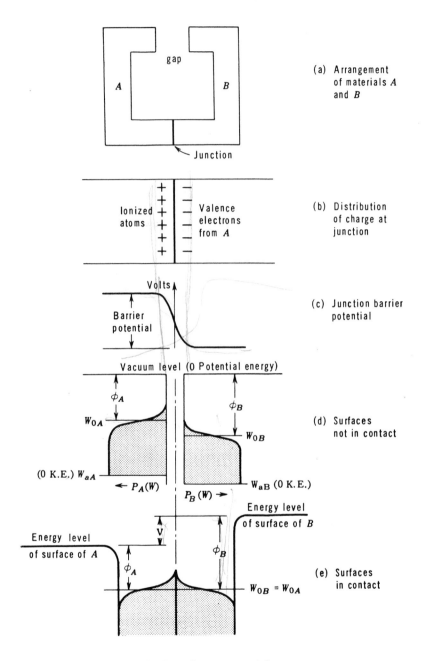

Fig. 4.14. Contact potential.

4.8   Contact potential

When two dissimilar materials are brought into intimate electrical contact so that a free exchange of valence electrons can occur between the atoms of each material within the region of contact, an electrical potential difference is found to exist. In general, this contact potential (Volta effect) cannot be measured by the use of conventional instruments; attempts to do so yield the thermal Seebeck potential at the junction instead of the contact potential. In general, contact potential is an open-circuit phenomenon and can be detected by measuring the electric field strength in the region of the open circuit. For instance, suppose that two dissimilar materials, A and B, are joined as shown in Fig. 4.14(a). The contact potential will appear across the gap and may be ascertained by measuring the electric field within the gap.

The number of valence electrons having an energy W in material A is given by the Fermi-Dirac distribution (Eq. (3.71)) as

$$n_A(W) = \frac{F_A(W)}{e^{(W - W_{0A})/kT} + 1}$$

where $F_A(W)$ represents all available valence energy levels in A and W_{0A} is the Fermi level in material A. The probability of a level's being filled is

$$P_A(W) = \frac{n_A(W)}{F_A(W)}$$

$$= \frac{1}{e^{(W - W_{0A})/kT} + 1} \tag{4.82}$$

Upon joining the two materials electrically, electrons from the material having the higher Fermi level will tend to spill across the junction into the material of lower Fermi level (see Fig. 4.14(b)). An equilibrium condition will be reached when those valence electrons from material A (assuming that $W_{0A} > W_{0B}$) drifting across to material B create a sufficiently high potential barrier to inhibit the further drift of electrons across the junction (Fig. 4.14(c)). The probability of a valence electron from A diffusing across to B is proportional to the probability $P_A(W)$ of an energy level W being filled with electrons in material A and also proportional to the probability $[1 - P_B(W)]$ of the corresponding energy level's not being filled in material B. Similarly, the probability of a valence electron from B diffusing across to A is proportional to $P_B(W)$ and $[1 - P_A(W)]$. At equilibrium the probability of electron diffusion must be the same in either direction at any given energy level and

$$P_A(W) [1 - P_B(W)] = P_B(W) [1 - P_A(W)] \tag{4.83}$$

Substituting Eq. (4.82) into Eq. (4.83) and simplifying yields

$$e^{-W_{0A}/kT} = e^{-W_{0B}/kT}$$

or the Fermi levels in materials A and B (Fig. 4.14(d)) will be adjusted by the potential barrier, V, so that

$$W_{0A} = W_{0B}$$

measured from any energy reference level (Fig. 4.14(e)).

If the Fermi levels are equal, then it follows that in the gap the vacuum energy level of material B is higher than that of material A. (The surface work function of material B is assumed greater than that of material A.) The potential barrier at the junction has charged material B negative relative to material A; therefore the electric field in the air gap is directed from material A to B. The difference in potential will be

$$_AV_B = \phi_B - \phi_A \tag{4.84}$$

If one of the materials is a semiconductor or insulator and the other is a metal, some of the energy levels $n(W)$ of the valence electrons may find themselves in equilibrium with forbidden levels in the semiconductor or insulator. As above, some of the electrons from the metal having energies within ranges forbidden within the semiconductor or insulator will penetrate to a probable depth of several angstroms in the region of the junction.

This transfer of electrons to an insulator or semiconductor by a conductor can be detected experimentally by carefully separating the materials at the junction. The semiconductor or insulator will obtain a negative charge. This is one aspect of an effect called *triboelectricity* or *contact electricity*. It is more familiar to us in everyday life when the contact and separation of insulators is involved—such as the rubbing of a plastic bag over a piece of dry cloth to produce static electricity. This is a unique field of growing importance about which relatively little is known.

PROBLEMS

1. From a knowledge of the lattice constant and electron mobility of copper, compute its conductivity.

2. From a knowledge of the lattice constant and electron and hole mobility of germanium, compute the effective density of intrinsic charge carriers if the measured conductivity is 1.67 mho/m.

3. What potential difference must be maintained across a certain copper conductor of rectangular cross section if a current of 150 amp passes through the bar? The bar is 4 ft long and has a cross section of 1 by 1.5 in. What is the drift velocity of the electrons?

4. The intrinsic resistivities of germanium and silicon are given by the empirical relations:

$$(\rho_i)_{Ge} = (2.3 \times 10^{-7})\epsilon^{4350/T} \quad \text{ohm-meters}$$
$$(\rho_i)_{Si} = (2.9 \times 10^{-7})\epsilon^{6450/T} \quad \text{ohm-meters}$$

Use the measured mobilities and determine the effective number of charge carriers in each material as a function of temperature. Plot the results for a range of 300–400°K.

5. Based upon the empirical relations for resistivity given in Prob. 4 and a knowledge of the theoretical equations, show that electron and hole densities in intrinsic germanium and silicon can be written as

$$n = p = (9.7 \times 10^{21})T^{3/2}\epsilon^{-4350/T}$$

carriers per cubic meter for Ge and

$$n = p = (2.8 \times 10^{22})T^{3/2}\epsilon^{-6450/T}$$

for Si.

6. An ingot of intrinsic germanium has a rectangular slab cut from it by means of a diamond saw. The slab measures 0.250 by 0.250 in. in cross-section and is 1 in. long. Assume that the above empirical relationships apply. Compute the current through the sample if 30 v is applied across it. The temperature of the sample is 310°K.

7. The sample of Prob. 6 is assumed to contain 10^{21} ionized arsenic atoms per cubic meter. What will the current be now?

8. At approximately what temperature would the intrinsic conductivity overshadow the impurity conductivity in Prob. 7?

9. Compute the Hall coefficient for the sample of Prob. 7. If this sample is placed in a magnetic field that has a flux density of 0.7 webers/m², what will be the Hall voltage for the current calculated in Prob. 7?

10. Show that the diffusion equation in the absence of any externally applied electric field may be written as

$$\frac{dp}{dt} = -\frac{p}{\tau} + D_p \nabla^2 p$$

by selecting a reference level for measuring hole density such that $p_n = 0$.

11. For the case where there is no recombination ($\tau \to \infty$), the continuity equation reduces to the form of the familiar heat equation

$$\frac{dp}{dt} = D_p \nabla^2 p$$

Show that a satisfactory solution to this equation for the case of an impulse of holes injected at $x = 0$ into a large, semi-infinite sample is

$$p(x, t) = \frac{p_0}{\sqrt{4\pi Dt}} \epsilon^{-x^2/4Dt}$$

12. Does the solution given in Prob. 11 satisfy the boundary condition that as $x \to \infty$, the hole density $p(z, t) \to 0$?

13. A sample of n-type germanium measures 1 mm by 1 mm by 2 cm. An input pulse of holes is injected at one end of the sample (see Prob. 11). If $p_0 = 10^{20}$ holes/m³, what will be the density of holes halfway along the sample and 1 millisecond after injection of the pulse? After 0.1 seconds?

14. Show that

$$p(x, t) = \frac{p_0}{\sqrt{4\pi D_p t}} \epsilon^{-x^2/4Dt} \epsilon^{-t/\tau}$$

is a satisfactory solution to the diffusion equation for the case where volume recombination is included and the sample is semi-infinite in length.

15. Recalculate Prob. 13 including the effects of volume recombination. Assume a lifetime for holes of 370 microseconds.

16. Show that the following expression in the case of a semi-infinite sample including the effects of volume recombination and carrier drift in an applied electric field satisfies the differential diffusion equation.

$$p(x, t) = \frac{p_0}{\sqrt{4\pi Dt}} \epsilon^{-(x - \mu Et)^2/4Dt} \epsilon^{-t/\tau}$$

REFERENCES

1. F. Seitz, *The Modern Theory of Solids*, McGraw-Hill Book Company, New York, 1940.

2. W. Shockley, *Electrons and Holes in Semiconductors*, D. Van Nostrand Co., Princeton, N.J., 1950.

3. F. J. Blatt, *Solid State Physics*, Vol. 4, Academic Press, New York, 1957, pp. 199–366.

4. C. Zwikker, *Physical Properties of Solid Materials*, Pergamon Press, London, 1954.

5. E. Spenke, *Electronic Semiconductors*, McGraw-Hill Book Company, New York, 1958.

6. N. B. Hannay, *Semiconductors*, Reinhold Publishing Corp., New York, 1959.

CHAPTER 5

Electron emission

A commonly observed and very important phenomenon is the emission of electrons from the surface of a body. Because of limitations in instrumentation, it is difficult to measure directly currents below about 10^{-15} amperes, although by integration methods* or by the use of electron multipliers it is possible to measure currents on the order of 10^{-18} amperes. This technological limitation on current measurement makes it impractical to detect electron emission except when relatively high excitation energies are employed. However, it does not imply that emission is not present at lower excitation energies.

The phenomenon of electron emission depends upon the transfer of sufficient kinetic excitation energy to some of the conduction band electrons that are found near the emission surface. This permits these electrons to overcome a natural potential energy barrier that exists at the surface and be emitted. This potential barrier is known as the *surface work function*. Values of the surface work function for several materials are listed in Table 5.1.

Electron emission can be identified by the method by which energy is transferred to the electrons. There are six basic methods:

1. *Thermionic emission.* This method utilizes elevated temperatures (1500–2700°K) to provide the energetic thermal vibrations of the lattice bonds of the emitter. These vibrations transfer energy to the conduction band electrons.

* See G. R. Partridge, *Principles of Electronic Instruments*, Prentice-Hall, Inc., Englewood Cliffs, N.J., 1958; R. L. Ramey and R. L. Overstreet, *I.R.E. Trans. on Instrumentation*, Vol. I-8, No. 2, pp. 46–51 (Sept. 1959).

2. *Photoelectric emission.* The necessary electron energy for emission is obtained from incident electromagnetic radiation of energy content *hf* joules according to Einstein's theory.

3. *Secondary emission.* The required energy for emission of electrons is obtained from the kinetic energy of incident primary electrons.

4. *High field emission.* Extremely high electric field strengths ($>10^9$ volts/meter) in the immediate vicinity of the surface of the emitter can reduce the effective surface barrier and permit relatively low energy electrons to *tunnel* through the remaining barrier. This form of emission is often called *auto-* or *cold-cathode* emission.

5. *Emission due to ion bombardment.* The necessary energy for electron emission is obtained from the potential and/or kinetic energy of incident positive ions. This is a very inefficient process, but it plays an important role in gas discharge tubes.

6. *Emission due to metastable atoms.* Some elements possess certain atomic excitation levels known as *metastable levels.* Radiative release of energy from these levels is forbidden quantum-mechanically. The atom in a metastable state must either gain more energy to reach an ordinary excitation level from which radiation of energy is permitted or it must exchange this energy in a two-body collision or transfer it to the free electrons in a surface. In this way target electrons can gain the energy necessary to be emitted.

A case of electron emission may be caused by one or more of the above processes. The emission of electrons is of primary importance in all electron tubes, photoelectric cells, and gas discharge tubes—to name a few applications. Each of these devices depends upon electron emission for the continuous supply of electrons necessary to sustain a continuous current.

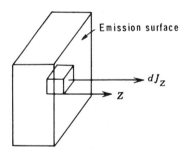

Fig. 5.1. Electron emission from a heated surface.

5.1 Thermionic emission from metals

The most important electron emission process is that caused by the addition of energy to the free electrons by means of energetic lattice vibrations which occur at elevated temperatures. Let the $+z$-direction be taken as normal to the surface of the metallic crystal shown in Fig. 5.1. If electron emission occurs from the surface, then the *differential emission current density* is

$$dJ_z = ev_z \, dN \quad \text{amp/m}^2 \tag{5.1}$$

The differential charge carrier density, dN, is given in terms of the Fermi factor $f(W)$ by Eq. (4.21) as

$$dN = \frac{2}{h^3} f(W)\, dp_x\, dp_y\, dp_z \tag{5.2}$$

The differential current density is then

$$dJ_z = \frac{2e}{mh^3} f(W) p_z\, dp_x\, dp_y\, dp_z \tag{5.3}$$

where the term p_z/m has been substituted for v_z.

The *emission current density* is found by integrating the momenta p_x and p_y over all possible values $(-\infty$ to $+\infty)$ and the momentum p_z from a minimum positive value p_z' to $+\infty$. Obviously, only those electrons that possess a finite positive momentum p_z' can escape the surface potential barrier that tends to attract the electrons to the atomic centers. The value of p_z' remains to be determined. The current density is the integral of Eq. (5.3).

$$J = \frac{2e}{mh^3} \int_{p_z'}^{\infty} \int_{-\infty}^{\infty} \int_{-\infty}^{\infty} \frac{p_z}{\epsilon^{(W-W_0)/kT} + 1}\, dp_x\, dp_y\, dp_z \tag{5.4}$$

For energies $W > W_0$ and of several kT in magnitude, the exponential term is much larger than unity and Eq. (5.4) may be written

$$J = \frac{2e}{mh^3} \epsilon^{W_0/kT} \int_{p_z'}^{\infty} \int_{-\infty}^{\infty} \int_{-\infty}^{\infty} p_z \epsilon^{-(p_x^2 + p_y^2 + p_z^2)/2mkT}\, dp_x\, dp_y\, dp_z \tag{5.5}$$

which has been written in terms of momentum by setting

$$W = \frac{p_x^2 + p_y^2 + p_z^2}{2m}$$

Equation (5.5) is relatively simple to integrate because the three components of momentum are independent of each other. Recall that

$$\int_{-\infty}^{\infty} \epsilon^{-x^2}\, dx = \sqrt{\pi} \tag{5.6}$$

and set x equal to $p_x/\sqrt{2mkT}$ and integrate. Repeat for p_y and obtain

$$J = \frac{2e}{mh^3} \epsilon^{W_0/kT} (2mkT\pi) \int_{p_z'}^{\infty} p_z \epsilon^{-p_z^2/2mkT}\, dp_z \tag{5.7}$$

This integral is of the form

$$\int x \epsilon^{ax^2}\, dx = \frac{1}{2a} \epsilon^{ax^2}$$

which yields $\quad \int_{p_z'}^{\infty} p_z \epsilon^{-p_z^2/2mkT}\, dp_z = mkT\epsilon^{-(p_z')^2/2mkT}$

In reference to Fig. 5.2, the minimum momentum of an electron corresponds to the zero level of kinetic energy which is W_a joules below the vacuum level. Each emitted electron must acquire an energy W_a or $(p_z')^2 = 2mW_a$ and

$$\int_{p_z'}^{\infty} p_z \epsilon^{-p_z^2/2mkT} \, dp_z = -mkT\epsilon^{-W_a/kT} \tag{5.8}$$

Electrons lying at this low energy level are useless, as previously seen, because only filled energy levels lie above them. Only those electrons with energies

Energy range of emitted electrons

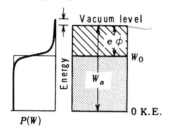

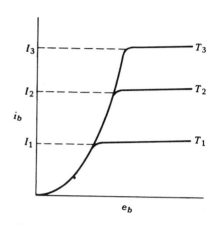

Fig. 5.2. Energy levels in thermionic emission.

Fig. 5.3. Typical plot of the volt-ampere characteristics of a diode vacuum tube showing saturation currents I_1, I_2, and I_3 corresponding to emission surface temperatures of T_1, T_2, and T_3 degrees Kelvin. $T_1 < T_2 < T_3$.

very near the Fermi level have vacant energy levels above them and may therefore thermally increase their energy. Thus, the necessary added energy to raise one of these electrons to the vacuum level is

$$e\phi = W_a - W_0 \quad \text{joules} \tag{5.9}$$

The quantity ϕ is called the *surface work function* and is commonly expressed in electron-volts.

The substitution of Eqs. (5.8) and (5.9) in Eq. (5.7) yields the Richardson-Dushman equation for thermionically emitted current density.

$$J = \left(\frac{4\pi mek^2}{h^3}\right) T^2 \epsilon^{-e\phi/kT} \quad \text{amp/m}^2 \tag{5.10}$$

This equation is often written as

$$J = AT^2 \epsilon^{-e\phi/kT} \tag{5.11}$$

and the symbol b is occasionally substituted for $e\phi/k$. In the preceding calculations, the effective mass of the electron is employed. The theoretical value for A is 120.4×10^4 amp/m²/(°K)². It must be emphasized that the current density predicted by Eq. (5.10) is the *saturation current density* determined by the temperature of the emission surface. This can be illustrated by considering the plot of the volt-ampere characteristic of a diode tube containing a directly heated tungsten filament, as shown in Fig. 5.3. The anode-to-cathode voltage is e_b and the anode current is i_b. The volt-ampere characteristic is a function of the tube geometry up to the point where further increases in anode voltage fail to produce a corresponding change in anode current. This is the saturation current I. If the anode saturation current is divided by the area of the emitting surface, then the saturation current density J is obtained and fairly accurate correspondence between this and the value predicted by the Richardson-Dushman equation should result provided that experimentally measured values for the "A-factor" are employed (see Table 5.1). Changing the emission surface temperature changes the saturation current, as shown in Fig. 5.3.

Table 5.1

Electron emission characteristics of metals

Element	Surface work function (electron-volts)	"A-factor" (amp/m²/°K²)	Melting point (°K)
Ni	4.6	30×10^4	1725
Cu	3.9	65×10^4	1356
Ta	4.2	55×10^4	3123
W	4.5	60×10^4	3655
Pt	5.3	32×10^4	2047

The discrepancy between the theoretical value of A and the experimental values is felt to be caused by the wave nature of the electron. Even though a given electron may possess the required escape energy, there is still a finite probability that it may be reflected back into the material from a surface atom or, more probably, that it may be reflected back from surface contamination such as adsorbed gas layers. The effective A-factor can be expressed in terms of an electron reflection coefficient γ, such that

$$A_{\text{eff}} = A(1 - \gamma) \tag{5.12}$$

If exacting comparisons are desired between the Richardson-Dushman equation and experimental results, then it is necessary to consider the effect of an electron accelerating electric field at the emission surface upon the surface work function. This is the *Schottky effect*.

The emitted electron sees an electrostatic force of attraction between itself and the emission surface caused by the image charge appearing within the conducting surface when the electron is emitted (see Fig. 5.4). The magnitude of the image force is

$$F = \frac{e^2}{4\pi\epsilon_0(2z)^2} \quad \text{newtons} \tag{5.13}$$

If an external electric field is applied, then it will also exert a force on the electron, and at some critical position z_m these two forces are in equilibrium and yield

$$eE = \frac{e^2}{16\pi\epsilon_0 z_m^2} \tag{5.14}$$

$$z_m = \frac{1}{2}\sqrt{\frac{e}{4\pi\epsilon_0 E}} \tag{5.15}$$

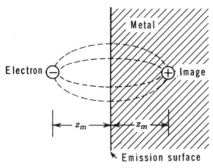

Fig. 5.4. The image force existing between an emitted electron and the emission surface.

In moving the electron from the emission surface to the critical position z_m, the external electric field does work amounting to eEz_m joules. For electron positions beyond this point, the net potential barrier is decreasing (see Fig. 5.5). To guarantee complete escape for an electron, the external field must remove it a considerable distance from the emission surface (theoretically an infinite distance). The total energy supplied to the electron by the external field in overcoming the image force is the sum of the energy required to move the electron from the emission surface to the critical point z_m plus the energy required to remove the electron an infinite distance from the point z_m, or

$$eEz_m + \int_{z_m}^{\infty} \frac{-e^2}{16\pi\epsilon_0 z^2}\,dz = eEz_m + \frac{e^2}{16\pi\epsilon_0 z_m} \tag{5.16}$$

If Eq. (5.15) is substituted into Eq. (5.16), then the energy supplied by the external field is

$$\Delta e\phi = e\sqrt{\frac{eE}{4\pi\epsilon_0}} \tag{5.17}$$

The effective work function is then

$$\phi' = \phi - \sqrt{\frac{eE}{4\pi\epsilon_0}} \quad \text{electron-volts} \tag{5.18}$$

If these results are substituted into the Richardson-Dushman equation, the result is a corrected equation for the current density.

$$J' = AT^2\epsilon^{-e\phi'/kT} \tag{5.19}$$

$$J' = J\epsilon^{0.44E^{1/2}/T} \tag{5.20}$$

amperes per square meter.

Reference to Eq. (5.20) indicates that increasing the electric field strength at the cathode results in a slightly increased emission current density. This is evidenced in Fig. 5.3, where the volt-ampere characteristics display a slight positive slope beyond the saturation knee.

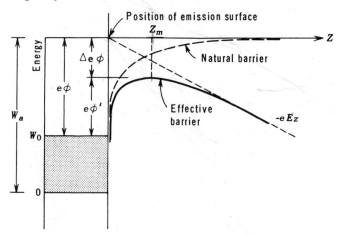

Fig. 5.5. The reduction of the surface work function caused by externally applied electron-accelerating fields. (The Schottky effect.)

Experimentally, the data on saturation current of an emitter for various temperatures can best be handled by means of a plot on special graph paper known as *power emission paper** (see Fig. 5.6).

The concept behind the power emission plot is based on the fairly accurate assumption that very little molecular cooling of the cathode is possible in a high-vacuum tube; so, if corrections are made for thermal loss through the heater loads, then the input power density to the emitter must equal the radiated power density, P_r. Thus

$$P_r = \frac{V_f I_f}{S} \quad \text{w/m}^2 \tag{5.21}$$

where S is the emission surface area, V_f is the rms heater voltage, and I_f is the rms heater current. This radiated power density must satisfy the Stefan-Boltzmann law,

$$P_r = K e_t T^4 \quad \text{w/m}^2 \tag{5.22}$$

where the coefficient K is 5.673×10^{-8} w/m²/°K⁴ and e_t is the electromagnetic radiation emissivity and is a function of the temperature.

Equate Eqs. (5.21) and (5.22) and take the logarithm

$$\log P_r = \log \frac{I_f V_f}{S} = \log K e_t + 4 \log T \tag{5.23}$$

* This paper is available from the Keuffel and Esser Company.

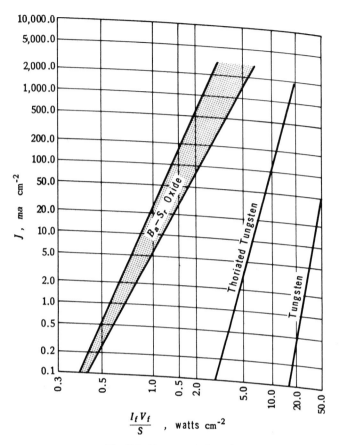

Fig. 5.6. Power-emission plot.

The Richardson-Dushman equation may also be written in logarithmic form as

$$\log J = \log A + 2 \log T - 0.434 \frac{e\phi}{kT} \tag{5.24}$$

If the temperature is eliminated between these two equations, there results

$$\log J = \log A(Ke_t)^{-\frac{1}{2}} + \frac{1}{2} \log \frac{I_f V_f}{S} - \frac{0.434 e\phi}{k} \left(\frac{I_f V_f}{SKe_t}\right)^{-\frac{1}{4}} \tag{5.25}$$

If $\log J$ is plotted as a function of $\log I_f V_f / S$ and if the term

$$- \frac{0.434 e\phi}{k} \left(\frac{I_f V_f}{SKe_t}\right)^{-\frac{1}{4}}$$

is treated as a coordinate skewing factor, the plot becomes a straight line. Davisson made use of this in the development of power emission paper.

Plotted in Fig. 5.6 are the power emission curves for tungsten, thoriated tungsten, and barium-strontium oxide coated emitters.

5.2 Thermally emitted electrons

In the preceding section we developed the expression for the emission current density from a heated metal. The velocity distribution of these emitted electrons will be investigated and the energy that they remove from the emission surface will be accounted for.

Before the integration indicated in Eq. (5.7) is carried out, the differential current density may be written as

$$dJ = \frac{AT}{mk} \epsilon^{-(e\phi - W_a)/kT} \epsilon^{-p_z^2/2mkt} p_z \, dp_z \tag{5.26}$$

or, if the momentum is replaced by the energy $(W_z + W_a)$ associated with the z-component of motion (motion normal to the emission surface), we obtain

$$dJ = \frac{AT}{k} \epsilon^{-(e\phi - W_a)/kT} \epsilon^{(-W_z - W_a)/kT} dW_z \tag{5.27}$$

where $p_z^2/2m = W_a + W_z$ and $p_z \, dp_z = m \, dW_z$. Equation (5.27) can be written in terms of the total emission current density J by multiplying and dividing by T.

$$dJ = (AT^2 \epsilon^{-e\phi/kT}) \frac{1}{kT} \epsilon^{-W_z/kT} dW_z$$

$$\frac{dJ}{J} = \frac{1}{kT} \epsilon^{-W_z/kT} dW_z = \frac{mv_z}{kT} \epsilon^{-mv_z^2/2kT} dv_z \tag{5.28}$$

Equation (5.28) states that the fraction of emitted electrons having energies between W_z and $W_z + dW_z$ is proportional to a modified one-dimensional Maxwell distribution function (see Eq. (2.52)).

The ratio dJ/J may be written as $d(eN)/eN$, where e is the electronic charge and N is the number of electrons per unit volume. The probability of an emitted electron's having an energy between W_z and $W_z + dW_z$ because of its component of motion normal to the emission surface is

$$\Delta P = \frac{\Delta N}{N} = \frac{1}{kT} \epsilon^{-W_z/kT} \Delta W_z \tag{5.29}$$

$$= f(v) \, \Delta v$$

according to Eqs. (2.29) and (5.28). The net kinetic energy due to motion normal to the emission surface of all the emitted electrons is

$$W_{\text{total}} = \frac{1}{2} Nmv_m^2 \tag{5.30}$$

joules per unit volume. According to Eq. (2.35), the root-mean-square velocity v_m is written in terms of an integral of the probability function. Thus

$$W_{\text{total}} = \frac{1}{2} Nm \int_0^\infty v_z^2 f(v)\, dv_z$$

$$W_{\text{total}} = \frac{1}{2} Nm \int_0^\infty \frac{1}{kT} \epsilon^{-mv_z^2/2kT} v_z (mv_z\, dv_z) = kT \tag{5.31}$$

where $dW_z = mv_z\, dv_z$.

This is an interesting result because it states that the electron energy associated with motion normal to the emission surface is equal to kT joules, which is twice that specified by the equipartition law for particles obeying Maxwell-Boltzmann statistics; this is because of the skewed velocity distribution function caused by the electric field's increasing the proportion of high-velocity electrons over that found in a normal Maxwellian distribution.

For the x- and y-components of motion (motion tangential to the emission surface), a true Maxwellian velocity distribution exists. This can be seen by solving for the energies $W_x = W_y = \frac{1}{2}kT$ in a manner similar to the preceding approach. In general, when electrons are accelerated by an electric field, their velocity distribution is no longer Maxwellian.

5.3   Filament considerations

The mean energy of each emitted electron is

$$\frac{1}{2}mv_m^2 = \frac{1}{2}m(v_x^2 + v_y^2) + \frac{1}{2}mv_z^2$$
$$= \frac{1}{2}kT + \frac{1}{2}kT + kT$$
$$= 2kT \tag{5.32}$$

The number of electrons per second emitted under saturation conditions is I_s/e. The power in watts required to liberate I_s/e electrons per second is $I_s 2kT/e$. The *total useful power extracted* from the filament is

$$P_e = I_s\phi + I_s\frac{2kT}{e} \tag{5.33}$$

The product $I_s\phi$ represents the power expended in overcoming the surface work function, ϕ, of the emitter. (*Note:* It is necessary to deal with the saturation current density to avoid space charge limiting effects.)

If a directly heated filamentary emitter is raised to a temperature $T_1{}^\circ$K by a current of I_{f1} amperes, and if the resistance of this filament is R_f ohms at temperature T_1, then the electrical power delivered to the emitter is

$$P_{f1} = I_{f1}^2 R_f \quad \text{watts} \tag{5.34}$$

Now let the anode-to-cathode accelerating potential be applied and increased until emission saturation current is drawn. The total power that must now be applied to the filament in order to maintain the temperature, T_1, is

$$P_{f2} = P_{f1} + P_e$$

or
$$I_{f2}^2 R_f = I_{f1}^2 R_f + I_s\left(\phi + \frac{2kT_1}{e}\right) \tag{5.35}$$

If accurate methods are provided for measuring the temperature and the filament resistance, then it is possible to compute the surface work function ϕ from Eq. (5.35). The variation of the resistivity of tungsten with temperature is plotted in Fig. 5.7.

In the absence of the drawing of emission current, the filament temperature rises to T_2 if P_{f2} watts are supplied. Thus, the drawing of emission current has a cooling effect upon the filament.

By convention, the *cathode efficiency* is defined as

$$\text{cathode efficiency} = \frac{I_s\,(\text{ma})}{P_f\,(\text{w})} \tag{5.36}$$

The ratio of the actual cathode current, I_k, to the saturation current, I_s, is defined as the *employment factor*.

$$\text{employment factor} = \frac{I_k}{I_s} \tag{5.37}$$

It is difficult to guarantee that exactly the correct filament or heater voltage will always be supplied to an electron tube. The operation of the emitter must be designed so that saturation does not occur even though the emitter temperature is low because of low heater voltage. This requires an *emission reserve factor*:

$$\text{emission reserve factor} = \frac{I_s - I_k}{I_k} \tag{5.38}$$

Oxide-coated cathodes operate with an emission reserve factor of between 0.01 and 0.001 for receiving tubes and 0.1 to 0.01 for high-power tubes.

Tungsten is the most popular material for use as either a filamentary emitter or as a heater in an indirectly heated emitter. This is primarily because it can be operated in the neighborhood of 2500°K to obtain reasonable emission. The only other pure metal that is of any importance is tantalum, which can be operated at similar temperatures. Tantalum has the disadvantage of being very easily poisoned by residual gases with an attendant large reduction in electron emission. Tungsten crystallizes at high temperatures and becomes very brittle.

Any heated filament suffers from evaporation, and the rate is a direct function of the temperature. This plays an important role in the design of filaments with long life expectancies. It is interesting to note that not only must the operating temperature be kept as low as possible to enhance long life but, in addition, care must be exercised to avoid localized suface damage that may result in *hot spots* on the filament. Hot spots may be accompanied by localized, above-normal rates of evaporation which increase the temperature further, thereby increasing the rate of evaporation. The result is a

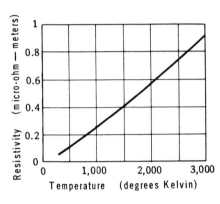

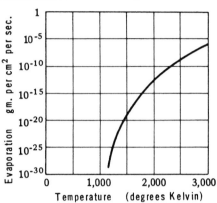

Fig. 5.7. The resistivity of tungsten as a function of temperature. The curve is typical for a filament in a high vacuum and with only radiation cooling. (From data by H. A. Jones and I. Langmuir, "The Characteristics of Tungsten Filaments," *Gen. Elec. Rev.*, vol. 30, pp. 312–313, 1927.)

Fig. 5.8. The evaporation of tungsten from a filament. (From data by H. A. Jones and I. Langmuir, "The Characteristics of Tungsten Filaments," *Gen. Elec. Rev.*, vol. 30, pp. 312–313, 1927.)

runaway situation that reduces the life of the filament. Jones and Langmuir have tabulated the rate of evaporation of tungsten. This is plotted in Fig. 5.8.

5.4 High temperature measurement

The temperature of a filament can be computed from a knowledge of the resistivity-temperature characteristics of the metal and a knowledge of the heat losses present. For instance, for a tungsten filament, if corrections are made for all heat losses, then the information of Fig. 5.7 may be used to obtain the temperature from a knowledge of the filament resistance as measured by Kelvin double bridge methods.

Another very satisfactory method of high temperature measurement is the use of an optical pyrometer. This instrument is basically a telescope fitted with a red filter which permits the eye to receive only a narrow bandwidth of radiation centered about a wavelength of 6500 Angstroms. A special lamp bulb with a tungsten filament that is calibrated in such a manner that the temperature of the filament is known as a function of filament current is included in the instrument. Optically, the image of the filament of this standard lamp is viewed simultaneously with the image of the object that the telescope is trained on. The standard lamp filament current is varied until the brightness of the lamp equals the brightness of the filament under measurement.

The standard lamp is calibrated in true temperature based upon blackbody radiation. The filament under measurement usually does not act as a black body but has a spectral response at 6500 Angstroms that depends upon the material and the surface finish of the filament. The true temperature, T, of the filament in °K is given by

$$\frac{1}{T} = \frac{1}{T_b} + \frac{C}{\lambda} \ln \epsilon \tag{5.39}$$

where T_b is the brightness temperature, C is 1.438 cm°K, and λ is the wavelength in cm. The spectral emissivity is ϵ.

For a wavelength of 6500 Angstroms, Eq. (5.39) becomes

$$\frac{1}{T} = \frac{1}{T_b} + 45 \times 10^{-6} \ln \epsilon \tag{5.40}$$

The spectral emissivity at 6500 Angstroms of several metals and a typical barium-strontium oxide coating is given in Table 5.2.*

Table 5.2

Spectral emissivity of several emitters
at 6500 Angstroms

Material	Emissivity
Ta	0.49
W	0.43
Pt	0.30
Ba-Sr Oxide	∼0.30

5.5 Surface conditions and emission

The electron emission current density from an emitter is dependent upon the condition of the surface. The presence of any atomic films of foreign elements can have a pronounced effect upon emission. The film may be a sorbed gas. Depending upon the chemical nature of the film relative to the emitter material, the emission may either be enhanced or almost completely eliminated.

The film is usually monatomic in thickness because of the elevated temperatures used in thermionic emission. A film of electropositive ions tends

---

* The reader will find comprehensive tables on spectral emissivity available in the literature. See *Temperature—Its Measurement and Control in Science and Industry*, Reinhold Publishing Corp., New York, 1941, p. 1313; *American Institute of Physics Handbook*, McGraw-Hill Book Co., New York, 1957, pp. 6–73.

to reduce the effective surface work function, whereas electronegative ions increase it. This may be seen by considering the effect of the surface dipole layer caused by these ions on the effective work function.

Let the number of atoms per square meter forming the monatomic film be N. Because each atom can form an electric dipole with the surface, N is also the number of dipoles per square meter. The moment, M, of each dipole is the product of the electric charge e multiplied by the effective charge spacing, d. The change in potential in volts experienced in passing through a dipole layer with a moment of MN coulombs per meter is MN/ϵ_0, where ϵ_0 is the permittivity of free space (8.85×10^{-12} farads/meter).

If the surface work function of an emitter is ϕ_0 electron-volts when the emission surface is clean and ϕ is the surface work function of the same surface possessing a monatomic film, then

$$\phi = \phi_0 - \frac{NM}{\epsilon_0} \tag{5.41}$$

For electropositive ions, the dipole moment $M > 0$ and $\phi < \phi_0$ and the effective surface work function is reduced.

The only atomic film of commercial value used to enhance emission is *thorium*. Other elements usually prove to be unstable over periods of extended operation. About one and one-half per cent thorium oxide, ThO_2, is introduced into the tungsten melt prior to the forming of the ingots that are swaged into filament wire. The thorium oxide is reduced to metallic thorium by heating the filament to $2800°K$ for several minutes. All thorium on the surface of the tungsten is evaporated at this temperature; so, after reduction is complete, the temperature is reduced to $2100°K$ for one-half hour to permit more thorium to diffuse to the surface. When this has been accomplished, the temperature is further reduced to between 1900 and $2100°K$ for continuous operation (see Fig. 5.6 for a comparison of a thoriated tungsten filament with other emitters).

Because of the comparative simplicity, pure tungsten filaments are usually used in experimental electron devices instead of thoriated tungsten filaments. The reader interested in the details of thoriated tungsten filaments should consult the references.*

Electron tubes operating with anode-to-cathode potentials in excess of about 1000 volts use tungsten or thoriated tungsten filaments. These emitters can withstand bombardment by the high-energy positive ions produced in the tubes by ionization of the residual gas. According to Eq. (2.15) there are

$$n = 9.70 \times 10^{18} \frac{P}{T} \quad \text{molecules/m}^3$$

* K. R. Spangenberg, *Vacuum Tubes*, McGraw-Hill Book Co., New York, 1948.

in any near-ideal gas. The pressure in this equation is to be in mm Hg and T is in °K. Assume an equilibrium temperature of 400°K and a pressure of 10^{-7} mm Hg in the operating electron tube and there are about 2400 molecules/cm³ between the cathode and the anode. Some of the electrons ionize a small percentage of these molecules and the resulting positive ions bombard the filament. This subject is treated in more detail in Chap. 7.

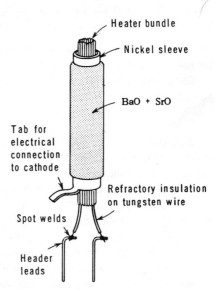

5.6   The oxide-coated emitter

The most important thermionic emitters are those coated with oxides of the alkaline-earth metals. Such a cathode is often called a *Wehnelt cathode* in honor of its inventor. Barium and strontium oxide are usually used, although calcium oxide can also be used. An equal mixture of BaO and SrO possesses a surface work function of about one electron-volt. The oxide coatings are applied and heated in two ways:

Fig. 5.9. Typical construction of an indirectly heated Wehnelt cathode.

1. For the *directly heated filamentary-type emitter*, powdered barium hydroxide aud strontium hydroxide are mixed with an organic binder, or sometimes a nitrocellulose binder, and applied directly to the tungsten filament wire by repeated dipping and drying to build up a coating of 0.010–0.020 in.
2. For the *indirectly heated cathode*, a nickel sleeve several thousandths of an inch in wall thickness is coated with a mixture of barium and strontium carbonate by spraying or brushing. Repeated applications alternated with drying cycles permit the building of uniform coatings between 0.010–0.050 in. in thickness.

Only a small fraction of low-voltage electron tubes are constructed today using directly heated filaments; therefore the second method is the most important and will be discussed in detail. Either method is relatively easy to carry out and may be used with success in the experimental laboratory.

Figure 5.9 is a sketch of the typical construction used for the indirectly heated cathode. The tungsten heater wire is coated with a refractory insulating material and folded into a compact bundle, which slides freely into the hollow nickel cylinder that supports the oxide coating and provides the electrical contact to the latter.

The oxide coating is unstable in the general atmosphere; therefore the oxides are formed during the pumping stage of construction, when there is little chance of contamination. The process may be summarized as follows:

1. *Coating:* The cathode is sprayed or painted with a 50-50 mixture of barium and strontium carbonates plus a binder. Careful attention is given to cleanliness. The cathode is then mounted along with the rest of the structure of the electron tube.

$$BaCO_3 + SrCO_3 + binder$$

2. *Reduction:* The glass, ceramic, or metal envelope of the electron tube is sealed in place and the mechanical vacuum pump is started. This reduces the pressure within the tube to 10^{-3} to 10^{-4} mm Hg. Reduced filament power is applied and the binder breaks down at about 400–500°K.

The decomposition of the binder produces large quantities of gas, as evidenced by a momentary rise in pressure on the pressure-monitoring gauges of the pumping equipment. Free carbon remains behind and gives the cathode a slightly gray color by visual observation.

There is some evidence that a noticeable amount of free carbon may be evaporated from the heated cathode and condensed upon any cooler surfaces —such as on the walls of the envelope. Later, when the electron tube is placed in normal operation, these surfaces become heated and the carbon is evaporated. Some of this carbon condenses on the cathode when the tube is shut down for the first time. It is possible that enough carbon can condense on the oxide coating to reduce electron emission materially. Heating the anode by radio-frequency induction heating and flame heating the glass envelope during the decomposition of the binder may lessen this problem.

Upon completion of the decomposition of the binder, the heater current is raised until the temperature of the film is about 1400°K. At this temperature chemical reduction occurs according to the reaction formula:

$$BaCO_3 + SrCO_3 + heat \longrightarrow (Ba, Sr)O + 2 CO_2$$

where the BaO and SrO exist as a mixed crystal of (Ba, Sr)O. At this elevated temperature the carbon dioxide combines chemically with the free carbon on the surface of the coating.

$$2 C + 2 CO_2 \longrightarrow 4 CO$$

The carbon monoxide is pumped out of the envelope. About one-half minute is required for the reduction process, as indicated by a corresponding rise in pressure during the liberation and pumping of the carbon monoxide. The heater current tends to drop at the end of the reduction process and indicates that the cathode temperature is rising because of the cessation of the chemical process and the attendant cooling by the liberated carbon monoxide. Care should be exercised to keep the cathode temperature below about 1600°K to prevent damage to the coating.

A word of caution is in order for experimental work. Suitable cold traps that employ solid carbon dioxide, or preferably liquid nitrogen, or sorption traps that use activated charcoal or copper wool should be placed between any high-vacuum oil diffusion pumps and the tube being processed. This is necessary to prevent pump oils from diffusing back into the tube where they would crack chemically on the hot cathode and contaminate it.

3. *Activation:* The crystalline barium-strontium oxide coating is a semi-conductor. Any excess metallic barium atoms (not forming oxides) distributed throughout the (Ba, Sr)O crystal act as electron donors. The formation of these donors greatly increases the electron emission of the coating and the oxide coating is said to be *activated*.

The free barium is obtained by a process that probably proceeds in a manner as follows: During the high-temperature reduction phase, silicon that is present in the nickel sleeve as an impurity (0.03 to 0.10 per cent) reacts with the barium oxide according to

$$Si + 4\,BaO \longrightarrow Ba_2\,SiO_4 + 2\,Ba$$

and forms free barium and a glassy layer of barium orthosilicate (Ba_2SiO_4). The free barium acts as a solute with the BaO and SrO acting as solvents. The presence of the free barium in the (Ba, Sr)O crystal donates free electrons, some of which are emitted. The electron tube is outgassed by radio-frequency induction heating of the elements and simultaneous flame heating of the glass envelope. This can usually be accomplished in less than a minute, and then the tube is sealed off.

If anode-to-cathode potential is applied and emission current drawn, then further activation proceeds according to

$$\text{(thermal heating + drawing of emission current)} + 2\,BaO + 2\,SrO$$
$$\longrightarrow Ba + Sr + BaO + SrO + O_2$$

The oxygen liberated is trapped by flashing a *getter* in the envelope.

Gettering consists of evaporating a small amount of a metal such as barium or magnesium inside the envelope and permitting it to condense out on the relatively cool walls of the envelope. The getter absorbs gases such as oxygen and traps them permanently on the walls of the envelope. The pressure is between 10^{-3} and 10^{-4} mm Hg within the sealed-off tube when the getter is flashed. After about 24 hours the getter has "pumped" the cold tube down to a pressure approaching 10^{-8} mm Hg. During operation the pressure rises to between 10^{-6} to 10^{-7} mm Hg. A tube is gaseous when the pressure is about 10^{-5} mm Hg.

The total amount of free barium and strontium produced is about 0.01 per cent. The tube is fully activated and the emission is quite high. The approximate power emission characteristics are indicated in Fig. 5.6. However, it should be mentioned that emission measurements on oxide-coated emitters are difficult to perform. The oxide-coated cathode is capable of supplying instantaneous emission current densities as high as 100 amp/cm². Such current densities can only be drawn for a few milliseconds. This feature makes this type of cathode very important in the design of pulsed tubes in high-power radar transmitters.

5.7 The interface layer

The barium orthosilicate layer formed over the surface of the nickel sleeve is an *n*-type semiconductor possessing a typical net resistance of about one ohm for a new receiving-type tube. During operation the free barium within this interface layer is probably slowly lost to the (Ba, Sr)O matrix. This loss of free barium raises the resistance of the semiconducting interface layer. The interface resistance may rise as high as 100–150 ohms.

The presence of the interface resistance confronts the circuit designer with a unique problem. Here is a resistance in series with the cathode that cannot be bypassed as can the usual cathode bias resistor. The result is negative feedback around the stage, whether desired or not. The equivalent circuit of a voltage amplifier including the interface resistance, r_i, is shown in Fig. 5.10.

The effective grid signal voltage is

$$e_g = e_{g0} - r_i i_p \qquad (5.42)$$

where e_{g0} is the grid signal voltage in the absence of any feedback. According to Kirchhoff's laws,

$$\mu e_g = i_p[r_i + r_p + R_L] \qquad (5.43)$$

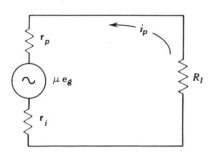

Fig. 5.10. The equivalent circuit of a vacuum tube amplifier including the effect of cathode interface resistance, r_i.

Substitute Eq. (5.42) into Eq. (5.43) and the actual driving voltage in the equivalent circuit is

$$\mu e_{g0} = i_p[r_i(1 + \mu) + r_p + R_L] \qquad (5.44)$$

By inspection of Eq. (5.44), the apparent effective plate resistance is

$$r'_p = r_i(1 + \mu) + r_p \qquad (5.45)$$

The transconductance of the tube in the absence of any feedback ($r_i = 0$) is

$$g_m = \frac{\mu}{r_p}$$

With feedback ($r_i \neq 0$) the effective transconductance is

$$g'_m = \frac{\mu}{r'_p} = \frac{\mu}{r_p + r_i(1 + \mu)} \qquad (5.46)$$

This may be written as

$$g'_m \approx \frac{g_m}{1 + g_m r_i} \quad \text{mhos} \qquad (5.47)$$

According to Eq. (5.47) the transconductance of a tube decreases as the interface resistance builds up. This buildup of interface resistance is slow but may play a very important role in determining the extended life operation of high-reliability tubes. Equation (5.47) may be solved for the interface resistance

$$r_i = \frac{g_m - g'_m}{g_m g'_m} \quad \text{ohms} \qquad (5.48)$$

As an example, the transconductance of a certain triode designed for high reliability was 5300 micromhos when the tube was new. After 5000 hours of operation, the transconductance was 4100. Assuming that the original interface resistance was negligible, the interface resistance after 5000 hours can be calculated by Eq. (5.48) to be 55 ohms.

There is some evidence that the interface resistance can be lowered to a certain extent and the subsequent growth rate reduced if the quiescent cathode current is appreciably increased.*

5.8 Photoelectric emission

The photoelectric effect was discovered by H. Hertz in 1887—two years before J. J. Thompson postulated the existence of the electron. The photoelectric emission of electrons from metals is not a very pronounced phenomenon and, for this reason, the technical applications of the photoelectric effect are usually concerned with electron emission from semiconductors. However, the reader who has made very low current measurements (less than 10^{-12} amp) in a vacuum has probably experienced the photoelectric effect from the metals and insulators (such as glass) of his apparatus. As a result, it is usually necessary to completely shield such experiments from any light.

To obtain electron emission from a metal, it is necessary to raise the energy of those electrons which possess an energy near the Fermi level to the vacuum energy level. In photoelectric emission this additional energy is obtained from electromagnetic light photons' penetrating the surface and making inelastic collisions with Fermi level electrons.

If the depth of penetration into the crystal is about one hundred Angstroms (a distance of ten to twenty lattice constants) and if any electrons are

* See Ref. 2 at the end of this chapter.

emitted, the effect is commonly referred to as a _volume photoelectric effect._ The probability of photoexcited electrons' being able to reach the surface before losing most of their acquired energy is low, and thus the volume photoelectric effect is weak. The volume photoelectric effect is not sensitive to the angle of incidence of the light source.

If the emitted electrons originate near the surface, then the _surface photoelectric effect_ is present. There is very little opportunity for these electrons to lose much of their acquired energy by collision, and therefore the photoelectric emission yield is high. The surface photoelectric effect varies as the cosine of the angle of incidence.

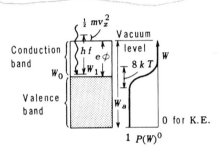

Figure 5.11 is a sketch of the energy diagram of a metal. The Fermi level W_0 is probably 5 to 6 electron-volts below the vacuum level. It was shown in Chap. 4 that only those electrons that possess an energy within several kT of the Fermi level can materially change their energy levels. Photoelectric emission yields only very small emission current densities at best, and therefore every electron counts. Even the relatively few with energies up to $\pm 4kT$ each side of the Fermi level are important. This is an energy of about 0.1 electron-volts either side of the Fermi level. Let the energy of an electron be W_1 and,

Fig. 5.11. The energy diagram of a metal and the associated probability function for finding an electron in any energy range between W and $W + dW$. An incident photon with energy hf causes electron emission provided $(hf + W_1) > W_a$. Any excess energy appears as initial velocity v_z of the electron.

further, suppose that it lies within $\pm 4kT$ of the Fermi level. If photoelectric emission is to occur, the energy content, hf_0, of the photon must be such that

$$hf_0 + W_1 = W_a \tag{5.49}$$

The coefficient h is Planck's constant, and f_0 is the lowest frequency that will satisfy the equation. Thus, f_0 is the threshold frequency.

Upon substitution,

$$hf_0 + W_1 = W_0 + e\phi \tag{5.50}$$

where ϕ is the surface work function in electron-volts. The initial energy W_1 of the electrons can vary a total of $4kT$; therefore the threshold frequency, f_0, is not sharply defined by these equations. For the case when $(hf + W_1) < W_a$, electron emission is unattainable and the photon energy may be used to excite a bound electron (see Sec 3.3).

The usual case of photoemission occurs when the incident photon transfers more than the threshold energy to the electron. In this case

$$hf + W_1 = W_0 + e\phi + \tfrac{1}{2}mv^2 \tag{5.51}$$

where v is the emission velocity. This equation neglects any energy lost by the electron by collision before escaping from the surface.

For a metal, the mechanism of photoelectron emission is identical to that encountered in thermionic emission. The only major difference is that, in addition to thermal energy, kT, the electron can also obtain electromagnetic energy, hf, from the photons. The electromagnetic energy appears to reduce

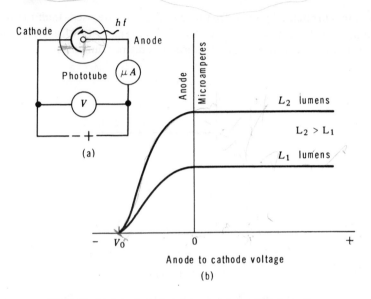

Fig. 5.12. (a) A typical phototube circuit and (b) tube voltage characteristics. L_1 and L_2 are of the order of hundredths of a lumen.

the surface work function, ϕ, that must be overcome by supplying thermal energy. The photoemission current density from a metal may be written as

$$J = KT^2F\left(-\frac{\phi - hf}{kT}\right) \tag{5.52}$$

The function

$$F\left(-\frac{\phi - hf}{kT}\right)$$

is not a simple exponential function as in the case of thermionic emission.

A typical experimental arrangement for observing the photoelectric effect is shown in Fig. 5.12(a) and the results are sketched in Fig. 5.12(b). The light intensity is maintained constant in each case. Where a retarding field is established between anode and cathode, the anode current decreases as the anode potential is made more negative relative to the cathode. At a potential V_0 the anode current ceases. The fact that some of the emitted electrons can overcome retarding potentials up to V_0 volts indicates that the velocities of emission of these photoelectrons range up to this potential. From Eqs. (5.50) and (5.51) the difference in energy between that supplied by the photons, hf, and the threshold energy, hf_0, is

$$hf - hf_0 = \tfrac{1}{2}mv_z^2 = eV_0 \qquad (5.53)$$

If monochromatic lights of frequencies f_1 and f_2 are used, then the results are similar to those shown in Fig. 5.13.* The sensitivity of a typical high-vacuum phototube approaches 50 microamperes per lumen.

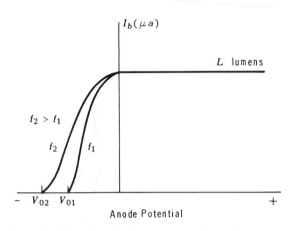

Fig. 5.13. The effect of photon energy, hf, on tube current.

The *photoelectron yield* of any surface is the ratio of emitted electrons to incident photons. The yield is always very much less than 1 and is a function of the frequency of the incident photons, according to Eq. (5.51). Metals have a very low yield because it is impossible to transfer all of the energy of the photon to the free electrons and satisfy the laws of conservation of energy and momentum. For instance, in Eq. (5.51) the initial energy of the electron is W_1 and its initial momentum is $\sqrt{2mW_1}$. For simplicity, assume that momentum hf/c of the photon is in the same direction as the momentum of the electron. The net initial momentum is then $\sqrt{2mW_1} + hf/c$. The electron has increased its energy from W_1 to $W_1 + hf$ and, therefore, the final momentum of the electron is $\sqrt{2m(W_1 + hf)}$, which is greater than the initial momentum. The necessary additional momentum can be gained from the lattice structure.

* *Note:* The *lumen* is the unit of luminous flux. It is equal to the luminous flux passing through a spherical surface of unit radius surrounding a point source of one candle. The *candle* is 1/60 of the intensity of radiation from 1 cm² of a black-body radiator which is at the temperature of solidification of platinum, or 2042°K.

The conduction band electrons in metals are relatively free, and for this reason it is difficult for these electrons to gain the required additional momentum from the lattice structure to permit the emission process to be fulfilled. The conduction band electrons in a semiconductor are more closely associated with the lattice structure and find it easier to obtain the required additional momentum to permit their being emitted. For this reason and also because there is much less loss of incident photons by reflection at the surface, semiconductors possess a relatively high yield.

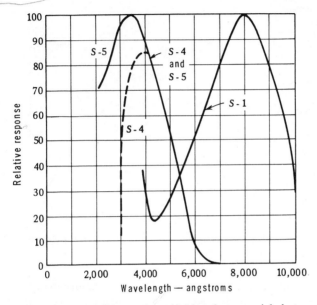

Fig. 5.14. Several spectral sensitivities of commercial photo-tubes. Tubes with quartz windows to pass ultraviolet have an *S*-5 sensitivity.

The preparation and chemistry of most technical photoemitting surfaces are complex. Certain surfaces and their frequency response characteristics have been standardized and denoted as *S*-1 *Response*, *S*-2 *Response*, etc. Several typical curves are shown in Fig. 5.14.

5.9 Secondary electron emission

Secondary electron emission is the liberation of electrons from a crystalline surface that is being bombarded by a stream of primary electrons. The primary electrons provide the necessary energy to permit other electrons within the surface to overcome the surface energy barrier and escape. A complete theory of secondary emission that explains all of the experimentally observed phenomena is not available; however, the better-known and more commonly accepted concepts will be presented here.

The problem of distinguishing between true secondary electrons and primary electrons that have been rediffused or reflected must be considered in any theoretical development and also in any experimental approach. Let the primary current density be j_p, the true secondary current density be j_s,

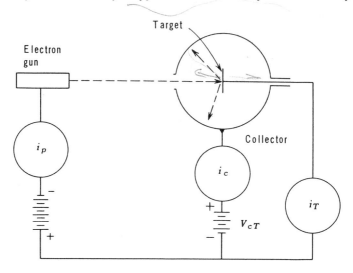

Fig. 5.15. The measurement of secondary electron emission from a target.

and the rediffused current density be j_r. The exact definition of the coefficient of secondary emission, δ, of a given surface is then

$$\delta = \frac{j_s - j_r}{j_p - j_r} \tag{5.54}$$

The phenomenon of secondary emission is quite pronounced from insulators and semiconductors as well as from metals. The basic measurement technique is the same for all these materials; however, there are certain unique details that are worth mentioning. Figure 5.15 is the sketch of a typical experimental arrangement for measuring the secondary emission from metals and semiconductors of relatively good conductivity.

The emission of secondary electrons from a flat and technically smooth target surface is nearly independent of the angle of incidence of the primary electrons, and the current density in any angular direction from the point of incidence of the primaries follows a cosine distribution (see Fig. 5.16). For this reason, it is experimentally desirable to surround the target electrode with a collector electrode. To permit keeping the electric field strength uniform in the region between the target and the collector, it is desirable to provide a small target located at the center of a spherical collector.

The primary electrons are usually obtained from a simple electron gun (see Chap. 11) because this permits controlling the size and intensity of these electrons and enables the experimenter to obtain essentially monoenergetic electrons. The collector potential relative to the target is usually varied from

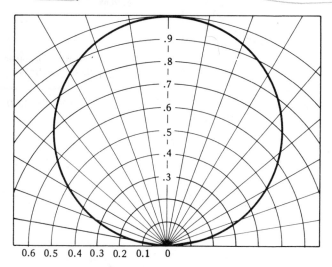

Fig. 5.16. The cosine distribution.

positive accelerating potentials to negative retarding potentials. A retarding potential V permits determining those secondary electrons that possess a kinetic energy $W > eV$.

A typical plot of collector current as a function of collector potential is shown in Fig. 5.17. For large retarding potentials, the only electrons that reach the collector are the relatively high-energy primary electrons that are rediffused at, or slightly within, the surface of the target. As the retarding potential is decreased, relatively high-energy secondary electrons begin to reach the collector. Thus, the shaded incremental area in the figure represents those secondary electrons that possess an energy between eV and $e(V + dV)$. For small positive collector potentials, all the secondaries are collected as indicated by a flat volt-ampere characteristic. The difference between the maximum and the minimum collector currents is very nearly the true secondary current.

Another plot that is of interest is one of target current i_T as a function of target voltage, V_T, measured relative to the cathode of the electron gun (see Fig. 5.18). These characteristics should be familiar to the reader who has plotted the volt-ampere characteristics of a tetrode tube. The collector

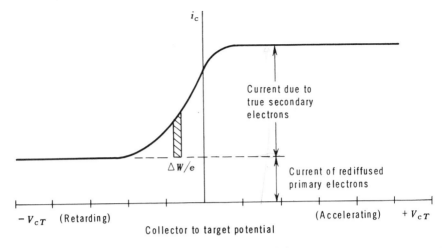

Fig. 5.17. Collector characteristics.

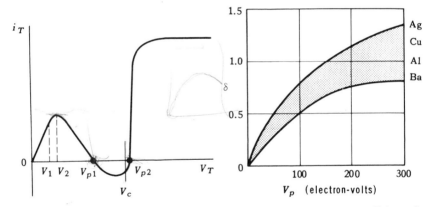

Fig. 5.18. Typical target characteristics.

Fig. 5.19. Variation in the coefficient of secondary emission as a function of the energy of the primary electrons in electron volts. The relative position of several target materials is indicated.

potential (measured relative to the gun cathode this time) is held constant at some selected value, V_c.

As the target potential is increased, the energy of the primary electrons increases and so does the primary current. The net target current is the difference between the arriving primary and departing secondary currents. At a potential V_1, the effects of secondary emission become noticeable and at a greater potential, V_2, the rate of increase of secondary electrons with increasing potential is equal to the rate of increase of the primary target current. Still further increases in target potential result in a net target current that decreases almost linearly and may even go negative if the secondary emission coefficient is greater than unity ($\delta > 1$).

Where the target potential approaches the collector potential, then some of the secondary electrons are returned to the target instead of being collected by the collector. The result is an increasing target current. As $V_T > V_c$, the target collects all the electrons and the target current saturates at a value determined by the design and operation of the electron gun. The points (i_T, V_T), where i_T is 0, occur for target potentials of 0, V_{P1} and V_{P2} volts. The point $(0, 0)$ is, of course, stable; however the point $(0, V_{P1})$ is not stable because a small increase ΔV in target potential causes the target current to reverse, which in turn drives the target more positive. The third point $(0, V_{P2})$ is stable by the same reasoning.

The target characteristics of Fig. 5.18 are quite valuable in predicting the operation of an experiment on secondary emission from the surface of an insulator or a semiconductor having a very poor conductivity. Obviously, if the conductivity of the surface is very low, then for all practical instrumentation purposes a steady-state target current is impossible and i_T is 0. Thus, the target must be at either cathode potential or the potential V_{P2} because it has just been argued that point $(0, V_{P1})$ is unstable.

An initial transient target current can flow. If the coefficient of secondary emission, δ, is less than unity, then the transient primary current to the non-conducting target cannot pass to the point $(0, V_{P2})$ and the surface of the target must charge to the potential of the cathode. If $\delta > 1$, then the transient target current can pass to the stable point $(0, V_{P2})$ and the surface of the target will charge to a potential of V_{P2} volts.

During the time of existence of the transient target current, secondary electrons are emitted and collected by the collector. The collector current can be read by means of an oscilloscope.

Figure 5.19 is a plot of the limits of variation in the secondary emission coefficient of most metals as a function of the energy of the primary electrons. In the special case of single crystal surfaces, the particular crystal face bombarded has a noticeable effect upon the emission. Detailed data may be found in the references, especially Ref. 7. The general trend of the data as given in Fig. 5.19 is probably the most important information for the reader to remember because there is reasonable variation in the data even for one material, depending upon target surface preparation, the presence of impurities, etc.

As a primary electron penetrates the surface of a target, localized interactions occur with the valence electrons of the atoms in the crystalline structure of the target. The probability of a primary electron's making an inelastic collision with these valence electrons varies inversely with the energy of the primary electron. Thus, the primary electron transfers little energy to the first few valence electrons it encounters. However, because each inelastic collision slows it down, the amount of energy transferred per inelastic collision increases steadily. If the depth of penetration normal to the target surface is z, then

$$\frac{dW_p(z)}{dz} = -\frac{a}{W_p(z)} \tag{5.55}$$

When z is 0, let W_p be W_{p0}.

The energy of a primary electron, as it penetrates into the crystal, is formed by solving Eq. (5.55) for W_p between the energy limits W_{p0} and W_p.

$$\int_{W_{p0}}^{W_p} W_p \, dW_p = -\int_0^z a \, dz$$

$$W_p^2 = W_{p0}^2 - 2az \tag{5.56}$$

This equation expresses *Whiddington's energy law* of secondary electron emission. The coefficient a is proportional to the density of the material. Let the mean depth of penetration be d, and when W_p is 0 let $z = d$. Thus

$$W_{p0}^2 = 2ad$$

and Eq. (5.56) may be written as

$$W_p^2 = W_{p0}^2(1 - z/d) \tag{5.57}$$

By means of Whiddington's law and a general approach as followed by Bruning[7] it is possible to derive a universal curve for the secondary emission from a metal. Several assumptions are required, so that the derivation is not as rigorous as might be desired. However, the results are instructive and serve as a guide to the direction further efforts must take. The reader interested in other recent theories should consult Ref. 6.

The number of secondary electrons, dN_s, produced per square meter in the layer between z and $z + dz$ is proportional to the total energy given up by the primary electrons, N_p, crossing this layer:

$$dN_s = -\left(\frac{k}{e}\right)\frac{dW_p}{dz} N_p \, dz \tag{5.58}$$

The proportionality coefficient is k and e is the charge of the electron.

The increment of emission current issuing from the surface because of the secondary electrons produced in the layer z to $z + dz$ is equal to the number produced in the layer, according to Eq. (5.58), times an assumed probability function $\epsilon^{-\alpha z}$. This function expresses the probability of a secondary electron's reaching the surface with sufficient energy to escape. Interestingly enough, the surface work function apparently plays only a minor role in influencing secondary emission.

With these assumptions, the incremental secondary emission current contributed by a layer between z and $z + dz$ is

$$di_s = \tfrac{1}{2}kai_p\epsilon^{-\alpha z}(W_p^2 - az)^{-\frac{1}{2}} \, dz \tag{5.59}$$

From Whiddington's law, the maximum depth of penetration of the primary electrons is

$$z_{max} = \frac{W_p^2}{a} = \frac{(eV_p)^2}{a} \tag{5.60}$$

The total secondary emission current is then

$$i_s = \frac{1}{2} kai_p \int_0^{z_{max}} (e^2 V_p^2 - az)^{-\frac{1}{2}} \epsilon^{-\alpha z} \, dz \tag{5.61}$$

This may be written as

$$i_s = ki_p \sqrt{\frac{a}{\alpha}} \, \epsilon^{-r^2} \int_0^r \epsilon^{y^2} \, dy \tag{5.62}$$

Equation (5.62) can be solved numerically, and by a suitable choice of the coefficients a and α, a curve that agrees with experimental data may be obtained for primary voltages up to $V_{p_{max}}$. Beyond this point the actual secondary emission slumps up to 10 or 20 per cent and then remains relatively constant. Equation (5.62), on the other hand, predicts a constantly decreasing secondary emission coefficient.

If Eq. (5.62) is divided by the maximum secondary emission current obtainable, corresponding to $V_{p_{max}}$, then the ratio δ/δ_{max} is a function of $V_p/V_{p_{max}}$.

$$\frac{\delta}{\delta_{max}} = F\left(\frac{V_p}{V_{p_{max}}}\right) \tag{5.63}$$

Table 5.3 lists the maximum value of the coefficient of secondary emission as a function of the energy of the primary electrons for several metals.

Table 5.3

Secondary emission from metals

Element	δ_{max}	$V_{p_{max}}$
Si	1.1	250
Cu	1.3	600
Ge	1.2	200
Ag	1.5	300
Pt	1.8	800

The limitation of δ_{max} to about 1.5 for most metals makes it desirable to utilize metallic compounds that offer substantially higher coefficients of secondary emission. Table 5.4 covers several compounds of technical interest, as well as glass or quartz. With reference to the earlier discussion on secondary emission from insulators, the potentials V_{p1} and V_{p2} corresponding to zero steady-state emission current and a unity yield are listed.

Table 5.4

Secondary emission from insulators and semiconductors

Material	δ_{max}	$V_{p_{max}}$	V_{p_1}	V_{p2}
Cs_2O	2.3–11	low	..	..
KI	5.5	low	..	..
$SbCs_3$	5–8.3	375	..	..
MgO	2.4–4.0	400–1500	..	..
Al_2O_3	1.5–4.8	350–1300	20	1200–1700
Glass or quartz	1.9–3.1	300–440	30–60	900–3800

5.10   High field emission

The phenomenon of high electric field emission is entirely different in character from thermionic emission, including the Schottky effect. In the case of thermionic emission, the emitted electron must gain sufficient energy

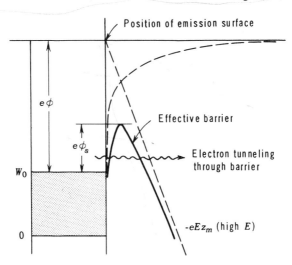

Fig. 5.20. Electron emission by tunneling. Electrons within several kT of the Fermi level have a small but finite probability of tunneling through the narrow potential barrier at the surface. The height of the barrier is $e\phi_s$ joules.

to pass over the energy barrier at the surface and the presence of an electric field (usually up to about 10^5 v/m) serves to reduce the effective height of the barrier (Fig. 5.5). In contrast, the mechanism of high field emission (field strength above 10^9 v/m) depends entirely upon the ability of a very small percentage of electrons to *tunnel* through the barrier at the surface (Fig. 5.20).

Tunneling is strictly a quantum phenomenon and its experimental existence furnishes strong support for quantum mechanics. The growing importance of electronic devices that utilize tunneling phenomena warrants a discussion of this matter. For instance, the operation of the *tunnel diode* described in Chap. 6 is based entirely upon this phenomenon.

In Sec. 3.7, Schrodinger's quantum equation was introduced and the time-independent form of this equation (3.27) was found to be

$$\frac{\partial^2 \psi}{\partial x^2} + \frac{\partial^2 \psi}{\partial y^2} + \frac{\partial^2 \psi}{\partial z^2} + \frac{8\pi^2 m}{h^2}(W - U)\psi = 0 \tag{5.64}$$

Upon application of the method of separation of variables, three independent differential equations are obtained (Eqs. (3.31), (3.32), and (3.33)). For motion normal to the emission surface the equation in z may be used (Eq. (3.33)).

$$\frac{\partial^2 Z}{\partial z^2} + \frac{8\pi^2 m}{h^2}(W - U)Z = 0 \tag{5.65}$$

Equation (5.65) expresses the wave behavior of an electron that possesses a z-component of motion. In Chap. 3, a solution to Eq. (5.65) (Eq. (3.33)) was obtained when the electron was confined to a potential well whose sides were infinitely high. The problem of interest is now one where the sides of the potential well that bounds an electron are still too high for the electron to climb over but are far from infinite in height. Further, the sides of this potential well are not very wide. Seek a solution to Eq. (5.65) that answers these questions: Is there any probability that an electron might penetrate this barrier? If so, could it tunnel through a relatively thin barrier and escape the potential well?

The general solution to Eq. (5.65) for an electron within the well is

$$\psi = Z(z) = C_1 \cos \frac{2\pi}{h}\sqrt{2mW}\,z + C_2 \sin \frac{2\pi}{h}\sqrt{2mW}\,z \tag{5.66}$$

where the potential energy, U, of the electron is zero and only the kinetic energy term W remains. This is region II of Fig. 5.21. If the electron can penetrate the barrier, then it will acquire a potential energy $U = eV$ depending upon the potential, V, at the point of space occupied by the electron. For this case $U > W$ and the general solution is

$$\psi = Z(z) = D_1 \epsilon^{-(2\pi/h)\sqrt{2m(U - W)}z} + D_2 \epsilon^{(2\pi/h)\sqrt{2m(U - W)}z} \tag{5.67}$$

This solution applies to regions I and III of Fig. 5.21.

The potential energy, U, of the barrier is much greater than the kinetic energy, W, of the electron. Thus, the coefficients of the exponents in Eq. (5.67) are real, large, and positive. Obviously, the amplitude of the wave function must remain finite in any of these regions. Therefore, in region I the coefficient D_1 must be zero and in region III the coefficient D_2 must be zero. Let region II be the internal volume of the emitter and region III be the surface potential barrier. Region IV represents free space in the vacuum surrounding the emission surface. Within the barrier (region III) the wave function has the value

$$\psi_3 = D_1 \epsilon^{-(2\pi/h)\sqrt{2m(U-W)}z} \tag{5.68}$$

This result is interesting because it states that the electron can penetrate a limited distance into a potential barrier. At the point z_0, where the electron

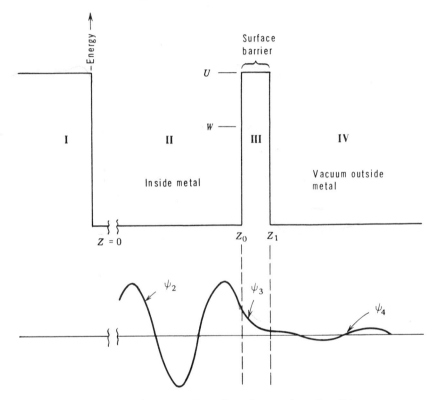

Fig. 5.21. The penetration of an electron through a thin energy barrier of finite height. This is the *tunnel effect*.

enters the barrier, the wave function ψ_2 in region II must join the wave function ψ_3 in region III without any discontinuities. This is shown in Fig. 5.21. If the barrier is not too thick, then the wave function ψ_3 still possesses a small but finite amplitude at z_1 which indicates that there is some probability of a few electrons penetrating the barrier. In Fig. 5.21 the wave function has a finite amplitude, ψ_3', at the point of emergence. In region IV another solution of the form of Eq. (5.66) is applicable and the resulting wave function, ψ_4, expresses the existence of the *emitted electron*.

From theory based upon quantum mechanics, Nordheim and Fowler* were able to derive an expression for the emitted current density caused by high field emission. Their detailed calculations will not be reviewed here. For $T = 0$ they calculated the following equation for the emission current density:

$$J = 1.54 \times 10^{-6} \left(\frac{E^2}{\phi} \right) \epsilon^{-6.83 \times 10^9 \phi^{3/2} f(y)/E} \qquad (5.69)$$

where J is measured in amp/m^2 and E is expressed in v/m. The surface work function in volts is ϕ. The factor $f(y)$ is a dimensionless elliptic function introduced by Nordheim in the inclusion of the effect of the image force at the surface of the emitter. Its approximate value is given by

$$f(y) \approx 1 - 14 \times 10^{-10} \left(\frac{E}{\phi^2} \right) \qquad (5.70)$$

For simplicity, the Fowler-Nordheim equation may be written as

$$J = CE^2 \epsilon^{-D/E} \qquad (5.71)$$

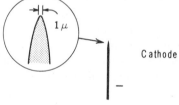

Notice the resemblance in the form of this equation and the Richardson-Dushman equation for thermionic emission. For experimental measurements, it is more convenient to measure total emission current and then calculate emission current density.

$$I = \int_A J \, da \quad \text{amp} \qquad (5.72)$$

Fig. 5.22. Experimental arrangement for investigating high-field emission.

The evaluation of Eq. (5.72) is seldom a simple matter because in order to obtain the very high field strengths (above 10^9 v/m) required for high field emission, it is necessary to employ sharply pointed needle-shaped cathodes. A typical experimental arrangement is shown in Fig. 5.22. The effective area of the point emitter is usually on the order of 10^{-12} m^2 and emission current densities are on the order of 10^6 amp/m^2. Emission currents are then on the order of microamperes.

The reader who contemplates experimental work on high field emission should consult Ref. 9 at the end of this chapter. The problem of computing the effective emission area and the required anode-to-cathode voltage for a required electric field strength is discussed and further references in the literature are given.

* L. Nordheim, "Die Theorie der Elektronemission der Metalle," *Physik. Z.*, **30**, 177–196 (April 1929); R. H. Fowler and L. Nordheim, "Electron Emission in Intense Electric Fields," *Proc. Roy. Soc.* (*London*), **119**, 173–181 (June 1928).

Because the Fowler-Nordheim equation is based upon a temperature of $0°K$, it represents pure high field emission (E-emission). Only electrons that have an energy equal to the Fermi level, W_0, can tunnel through the energy barrier at the surface. At temperatures above absolute zero, a few electrons are to be found with sufficient kinetic energy to permit them to pass over the top of the barrier and thus be emitted thermally. For pure metals and temperatures up to about $1600°K$ and electric field strengths at the cathode of about 10^9 v/m, the emission current is composed of both thermally emitted and high field emitted electrons (TE-emission). At higher temperatures the thermally emitted electrons greatly outnumber those contributed by high field emission and, for all practical purposes, the emission is thermionic (T-emission).

5.11   Emission caused by ion bombardment

The process of electron emission from a metal target under bombardment by positive ions has been recognized for many years. Only recently have the complicating factors been sorted to the extent that generally accepted theories have evolved. Two independent emission processes are possible, and one or both may be present in a particular experiment. The better-understood process utilizes the *potential energy* of the incident ion in releasing two electrons from the metal—one to neutralize the ion and a second "free electron." The second process utilizes the *kinetic energy* of the incident ions in what is believed to result in either localized heating of the target with resultant thermionic emission of one or more electrons, or in inelastic ionizing collisions between the incident ions and the valence electrons in the crystal lattice structure of the target.

In the following discussion, it will be assumed (unless otherwise stipulated) that the target surface has been completely degassed by modern high-vacuum techniques. This is not an easily attained condition, and much of the data reported in the literature prior to the mid-1940's is actually for targets coated with one or more molecular gas layers.

For a completely degassed target, the process of electron emission by virtue of the internal potential energy of the ion proceeds as indicated in Fig. 5.23. The ion approaches the emission surface very closely and in so doing narrows the surface barrier between the Fermi level electrons and the ion. One of these electrons can possibly tunnel through this narrow energy barrier and neutralize the ion with a corresponding release of the potential energy difference between that of the ion, $e\Phi_i$, and that of the electron ($\sim W_0$). This energy difference can be made available to another Fermi level electron by one of two mechanisms.

In the *one-step* (also called the *direct* or *Auger*) mechanism, there is a simultaneous excitation of the second Fermi level electron with the capture of the first electron by the ion. This mechanism appears to be by far the most predominant. In the *two-step* process the ion is first neutralized to an excited state by resonance capture of the first electron. The excited atom or molecule remains in this state for about 10^{-8} seconds and then decays to its ground state by electromagnetic radiation of this energy. It is possible that this radiation may sufficiently excite a second electron in the metal to permit it to escape.

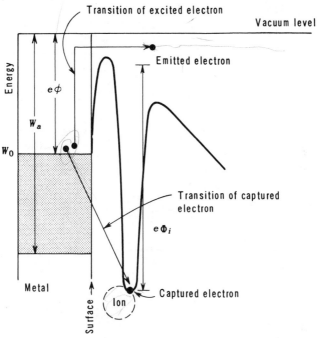

Fig. 5.23. Energy diagram for the emission of an electron from a crystal by virtue of the potential energy of an ion.

With reference to Fig. 5.23, the change in energy accompanying the capture of the first electron by the ion is

$$\Delta W = e\Phi_i - (W_a - W_0) \tag{5.73}$$

Note that the energy of the available electrons in the metal is assumed to be W_0 because all available electrons lie within several kT of W_0.

If electron emission is to occur, then the second electron must acquire a minimum energy of $e\phi$ joules, where ϕ is the surface work function. Set $\Delta W = e\phi$ and recognize that $(W_a - W_0) = e\phi$ also, and the criterion for electron emission from Eq. (5.73) is that

$$\Phi_i > 2\phi \tag{5.74}$$

The presence of a large electron-accelerating field at the target surface lowers the effective work function because of the Schottky effect.

The presence of a *kinetic process*—whether actually operating by virtue of localized heating by the incident ions or by virtue of direct inelastic ionizing collisions with the valence electrons in the lattice bonds of the crystal—should operate basically in about the same manner whether the incident particle is an ion or a neutral atom. High-energy neutral helium atoms have been produced by Berry* and their efficiency at producing electron emission by bombardment of a tungsten target compared with that of helium ions.

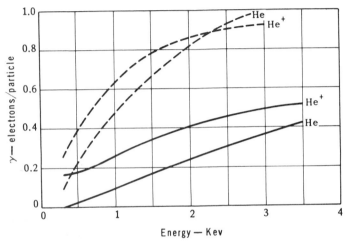

Fig. 5.24. The yield in electrons per incident particle from a tungsten target as a function of incident particle energy. (From H. W. Berry, *J. App. Phys.*, **29**, 1222, 1958.)

In Fig. 5.24, Berry's experimental results are reproduced. The solid curves represent the electron emission coefficient, γ, expressed in electrons per incident particle for a degassed tungsten target. The dotted curves are for a target covered with several molecular layers of gas. In this work the degassed target actually contained a single monolayer of helium.

The solid curves are quite interesting, for with low kinetic energies (below about 300 ev) the ions possess insufficient kinetic energy to liberate electrons, but they do possess their potential energy of ionization which can liberate electrons by the Auger process. The neutral atoms cannot liberate any electrons because they do not possess sufficient potential energy. For kinetic energies above 300 ev, both the neutral atoms and the ions can liberate electrons by transfer of kinetic energy, and the two curves parallel each other as is to be expected.

* H. W. Berry, *J. App. Phys.*, **29**:8, 1219–1225 (August 1958).

5.12   Emission by metastable atoms

The metastable energy levels of the common gases used in electronic devices provide a method of conveying sufficient potential energy to the cathode to excite some of the Fermi level electrons to sufficiently high energy levels to permit them to be emitted. Both positive ions, excited and metastable atoms and molecules gain their energy some distance from the cathode. The excited atoms radiate this energy within 10^{-8} seconds and may or may not contribute to the process of electron emission. If they do, it is because they are in a very high excitation state and when this energy is radiated it releases a photoelectron from the cathode.

Positive ions are accelerated to the cathode by the electric field between anode and cathode. The processes whereby these ions liberate electrons has been covered in the preceding section.

Metastable atoms are able to retain this energy either until they receive additional energy and are raised to an ordinary excitation level or until they make a two-bodied collision with either another free atom or a surface. The average atom remains in a metastable energy state for about 0.1 seconds. Unlike the ion, which is accelerated toward the cathode, the metastable atom arrives there only by diffusion. Only a small percentage of the metastables produced diffuse to the cathode and possess sufficient energy to permit emission. Therefore, the process is inefficient (several per cent).

It is necessary that the metastable atom carry sufficient energy to permit a Fermi level electron to rise above the energy barrier at the surface. For instance, nitrogen gas has metastable energy levels at 2.4, 3.6, and 6.2 electron-volts. If these atoms arrive at a tungsten cathode (surface work function of 4.5 ev), those metastables possessing 6.2 ev of energy can liberate electrons.

In a continuous process it is difficult to distinguish between electron emission by metastable atoms and emission by the release of potential energy from positive ions. However, if time delay techniques are employed, the action of the metastables continues for some milliseconds after the generation of positive ions has been interrupted.

This subject of electron emission by positive ions and metastable atoms will be discussed further in Chap. 7 in conjunction with gas discharge tubes.

PROBLEMS

1. Design a hairpin-type tungsten filament to operate at 2500°K and to furnish a total anode current at saturation of 200 ma. The filament fits within an anode that is 1.30 in. in height. Assume that the effective height of the filament is 1.45 in. What is the wire diameter? What is the required filament heating voltage and current? What is the cathode efficiency?

2. In Prob. 1, if the electric field intensity at the cathode surface is 15,000 v/m, what will be the increase in the saturation current over the zero field value?

3. If the above tube normally operates with an anode current of 40 ma, what is the "employment factor"? What is the emission reserve factor? To what value could the filament temperature be decreased to obtain an employment factor of 0.6? (*Note:* The Richardson-Dushman emission equation is transcendental if temperature is the unknown. To solve for *T*, write

$$I\epsilon^{+e\phi/kT} = SAT^2$$

where S is the effective emission surface area. Plot the numerical values of each side of this equation as a function of various assumed temperatures. An intersection of the two plots yields the correct temperature.)

4. A tungsten and a platinum filament are mounted beside one another in a vacuum system. The platinum filament is placed in operation and then the temperature of the tungsten filament is increased until it appears to be as bright as the platinum filament. The two filaments are viewed through an optical bandpass filter that has a transmission peak at the wavelength of 6500 Angstroms. The resistivity of the tungsten filament is measured and found to be 0.4 micro-ohm meters. What is the true temperature of the platinum filament?

5. Will the temperature of a filament increase or decrease with extensive operating time if the filament power-supply voltage is held constant? Why?

6. What is the minimum energy and corresponding photon wavelength required to release an electron from copper and from cesium?

7. A photomultiplier tube is constructed as shown in the accompanying sketch. The "dynodes" have been silver plated, and after mounting they were induction heated in the presence of an oxygen atmosphere. This

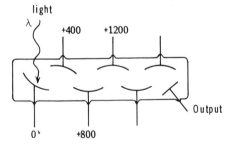

Fig. P5.7

produced a silver and silver oxide surface. The oxygen was pumped out and cesium vapor admitted while the dynodes were heated. The result is a silver-silver oxide-cesium-cesium oxide surface that has a coefficient of secondary emission of about 8 when the energy of the incident electrons is 400 ev. The surface is also a good photoelectron emitter. Light is focused on the first electrode which emits photoelectrons. The geometry of the remaining electrodes is such that the secondary electrons emitted by one dynode are focused on the succeeding dynode.

If the photoemission current is 100 micromicroamperes, how many dynodes are required to obtain an amplified output current of 1 ma?

8. The photoemission surface of Prob. 7 is an *n*-type semiconductor. The donor levels lie about 0.9 ev below the vacuum level and the valence band is about 3.1 ev below the vacuum level. At what colors in the visible spectrum will there be photoemission response peaks?

9. The vacuum tube designed in Chap. 10 is equipped with a Ba-Sr oxide coated cathode of cylindrical construction. The cathode has a radius of 9.77×10^{-4} m and a length of 1.93×10^{-2} m. In normal operation the cathode current might be 6 milliamperes with an emission reserve factor of 49 . Use the mean of the data of Fig. 5.6 to determine the necessary cathode heater current if a heater voltage of 6.3 v is used. What is the cathode employment factor?

10. Design a simple optical pyrometer.

11. A unique electron emitter for use in electron tubes is described by Skellett, Firth, and Mayer (*Proc. I.R.E.*, **47**, 10, 1704–1712 (Oct. 1959)). A nickel cathode base is coated with a layer of magnesium oxide (MgO) that is about 35 microns in thickness. The MgO coating is very porous and it is a semiconductor. An anode-to-cathode (nickel base) voltage of several hundred volts is employed. A means such as photoemission or secondary emission from the MgO is required to start the cathode. This initial electron emission causes the outer surface of the MgO to take on a potential that is about 100 v positive relative to the nickel base. This results in a very high electric field strength throughout the thin MgO coating. It is believed that high field emission establishes electron avalanches through the MgO coating which yields an emission current density,

$$J = J_0 \epsilon^{bV}$$

where J_0 is the initial conduction electron current originating at the nickel base, V is the potential difference across the MgO coating, and b is a constant. The holes created by the formation of other free electrons in the coating move through the MgO semiconductor toward the nickel base where they recombine. The energy released by the recombination process is thought to account for the pale blue glow visible over the cathode during operation.

Sample data taken on an emission surface that was 4×10^{-4} square meters yielded an emission current of 0.5 milliamperes for a film potential of 154 v and an emission current of 0.1 milliamperes for a film potential of 145 v. Compute J_0 and b for the emission current density equation.

12. When emission current densites for the MgO emitter rise above about 1.5 amp per meter square, it has been found that local heating causes the

emission current to rise faster than that predicted by the emission equation presented in Prob. 11. If the Ba-Sr oxide emitter of Prob. 9 were replaced with a MgO emitter, what would be the peak cathode current permissible without noticeable heating of the MgO layer? What would be the voltage drop across the MgO layer if the cathode current is 60 per cent of the above peak cathode current? What will be the per cent change in layer voltage if the cathode current is now increased 5 per cent?

REFERENCES

1. K. R. Spangenberg, *Vacuum Tubes*, McGraw-Hill Book Co., New York, 1948.

2. G. H. Metson, "On the Electrical Life of an Oxide-Cathode Receiving Tube," *Advances in Electronics and Electron Physics*, **8**, 403, Academic Press, New York, 1957.

3. A. S. Eisenstein, "Oxide Coated Cathodes," *Advances in Electronics*, **1**, 1, Academic Press, New York, 1948.

4. A. L. Hughes and L. A. DuBridge, *Photoelectric Phenomena*, McGraw-Hill Book Co., New York, 1932.

5. P. Görlich, "Recent Advances in Photoemission," *Advances in Electronics and Electron Physics*, **11**, 1, Academic Press, New York, 1959.

6. K. G. McKay, "Secondary Electron Emission," *Advances in Electronics*, **1**, 65, Academic Press, New York, 1948.

7. H. Bruning, *Physics and Applications of Secondary Electron Emission*, McGraw-Hill Book Co., New York (or Pergamon Press, London), 1954.

8. O. Hachenberg and W. Brauer, "Secondary Electron Emission from Solids," *Advances in Electronics and Electron Physics*, **11**, 413, Academic Press, New York, 1959.

9. W. P. Dyke and W. W. Dolan, "Field Emission," *Advances in Electronics and Electron Physics*, **8**, 89, Academic Press, New York, 1956.

10. A. van der Ziel, *Solid State Physical Electronics*, Prentice-Hall, Inc., Englewood Cliffs, N.J., 1957.

CHAPTER 6

Semiconductor devices

The applications of solid-state physics are numerous. The field is still in its infancy although research and development proceed at a very rapid pace. Manufacturing facilities that have appeared around the world provide the circuit designer with a wide selection of semiconductor devices.

In general, semiconductor devices are somewhat limited in their applications because of a larger inherent noise level than that found in vacuum tubes. Improvements in fabrication and application in this dynamic field are constantly reducing this limitation.

The large majority of semiconductor items produced at present are individual circuit devices intended for use in conjunction with other circuit elements such as resistors and capacitors to accomplish a specific desired function. An amplifier is a typical example, because here transistors or tunnel diodes are combined with circuit elements to form a complete circuit. There is the possibility that many entire circuits, including the passive elements as well as the active ones, may all be combined in a single multimaterial multi-junction semiconductor. The term *molecular electronics* is applied to this field of growing importance. An amplifier in the true molecular electronic sense would thus appear to the observer as being simply a crystal of semi-conductor material with input, output, and bias leads attached.

6.1 Metal-semiconductor junctions

When two dissimilar materials such as a metal and a semiconductor are brought into intimate contact, valence electrons from the material with the higher Fermi level diffuse over into the material with the lower Fermi level. This process proceeds very rapidly until the Fermi levels are equal. Once

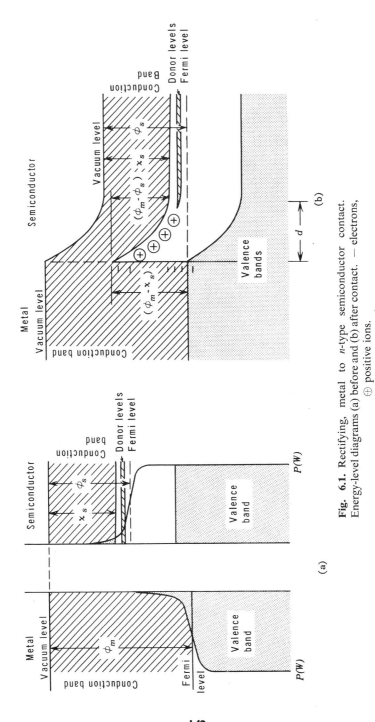

Fig. 6.1. Rectifying, metal to *n*-type semiconductor contact. Energy-level diagrams (a) before and (b) after contact. — electrons, ⊕ positive ions.

142

equilibrium is reached, a slow diffusion of electrons continues and represents a continual balancing of the Fermi levels necessitated by the diffusion of thermally excited electrons from one material to the other. Thus, in equilibrium there are always two equal but opposite currents crossing the junction. The reasons for the Fermi level equalization are given in Chap. 4, Sec. 4.8. In this case, where one of the materials is a semiconductor, it is possible that these equilibrium currents consist in part, or entirely, of either free conduction band electrons or valence electrons lying within several kT of the top of the valence band. The latter charge carriers are called "holes," as was pointed out in Chap. 4.

Figure 6.1(a) is a sketch of the energy diagram of a metal that has a surface work function ϕ_m and an n-type semiconductor with an *effective surface work function* ϕ_s. The concept of effective surface work function is used to emphasize the complexity of the surface of any semiconductor. At any crystalline surface the normal ordered array of the atoms and the co-valent bonds is interrupted. Surface discontinuities and adsorbed impurities give rise to local electrical fields that mask the true surface work function. In this case, it is assumed that $\phi_m > \phi_s$. Upon joining the two materials, a junction is formed and electrons spill from the conduction band of the semiconductor into the metal and leave empty (and therefore ionized) donor sites in the semiconductor in the vicinity of the junction. Because of the large conductivity of the metal, the electrons that have spilled over into the metal are attracted to the metallic surface of the junction by the positive ionized donors in the semiconductor. These donors are distributed throughout the semiconductor and are fixed in position because they are bound into the crystalline structure. As a result, the positive charges due to the ionized donors are distributed over a distance d from the junction and thus give rise to a *space charge layer*.

Within the space charge layer a distribution of free charge will not be found because the electric field set up by the electrons and ionized donors sweeps low-energy electrons, which might diffuse into this space charge layer, back into the semiconductor material. On the other hand, those electrons that have gained sufficient thermal energy to overcome this *junction potential barrier* and pass from the semiconductor to the metal naturally do not linger in the space charge layer. For these reasons, the space charge layer is often called the *depletion layer* because it is devoid of distributed free charge.

Referring to Fig. 6.1(b), a potential barrier is formed between the low-energy conduction electrons in the semiconductor and those in the metal. Consider a conduction electron in the semiconductor whose energy places it at the bottom of the conduction band. For this electron to diffuse over into the conduction band of the metal, it must climb the potential barrier of the space charge layer, which it can do only by increasing its energy by means of thermal agitation. Thus, only high-energy electrons may diffuse across the barrier to the metal. Many of those that do reside on the surface of the metal and contribute to the space charge layer, increasing the barrier potential. Any increase in the barrier potential makes it more difficult for other electrons to cross the barrier into the metal. In this manner, the barrier is self-regulating. Any electron from the metal that possesses sufficient thermal energy to pass over the barrier may enter the semiconductor.

The height of the barrier, as seen from the semiconductor, is readily computed because it is the difference between the bottom of the conduction bands in the two materials, or

$$V_d = (\phi_m - \chi) - (\phi_s - \chi) \qquad (6.1)$$
$$= \phi_m - \phi_s \qquad (6.2)$$

electron-volts. The quantity χ is the energy difference between the vacuum level and the bottom of the conduction band in the semiconductor. The potential difference that exists between the interiors of the metal and the semiconductor is often called the *diffusion potential* because it arises from the net diffusion of electrons. Those high-energy, thermally excited electrons that diffuse from the metal to the semiconductor must climb the somewhat larger potential barrier of $(\phi_m - \chi)$ electron-volts.

The diffusion of electrons across the depletion region depends upon the potential occurring across this region. The potential need not be entirely caused by the diffusion potential, but may also be supplemented by the application of an external bias potential, V, applied between the metal and the semiconductor. In such a case the net voltage across the junction is

$$\psi = V_d + V \quad \text{volts} \qquad (6.3)$$

The effect upon the junction currents of applying the bias voltage V to the junction remains to be investigated. It has been shown that the depletion region width and the junction capacitance each depend upon the sum of the diffusion potential plus any bias voltage. Further, in the absence of any external bias the net junction current is zero. Now, depending upon the polarity of the bias V relative to the metal, two possibilities occur as shown in Figs. 6.2(a) and (b).

In Fig. 6.2(a), negative bias V is applied to the semiconductor material relative to the metal. This raises the energy of any electron in any state in the semiconductor. Thus, the donor states are raised as are the conduction states. The result is that any conduction electron in the semiconductor can pass into the metal more easily owing to the reduced potential barrier $(V_d - V)$. Electrons attempting to pass from the metal into the semiconductor still experience the same potential barrier $(\phi_m - \chi)$ that existed before the bias was applied. There is a relatively large net electron current from the n-type semiconductor to the metal (a conventional current from metal to semiconductor). The junction is said to be *forward biased*.

In general, there is no significant flow of holes across the forward-biased metal to n-type semiconductor junction for surface junction contacts. There may be a significant hole current in the case of point contacts.* The slope of the energy levels in the bulk of the semiconductor is caused by the IR voltage drop.

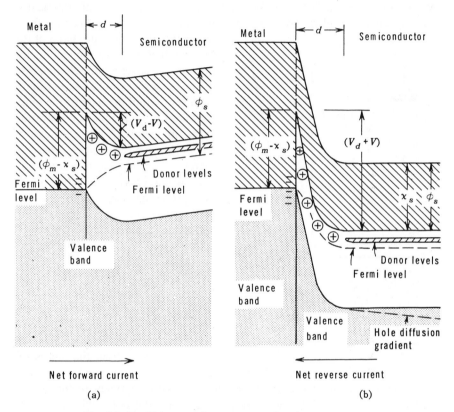

Net forward current

(a)

Net reverse current

(b)

Fig. 6.2. Rectifying metal to n-type semiconductor contact with (a) forward bias and (b) reverse bias.

In Fig. 6.2(b), the bias is such that the semiconductor is positive relative to the metal. This lowers the energy states in the semiconductor with the result that the bottom of the conduction band of the semiconductor is considerably below the bottom of the conduction band in the metal. Electron flow from the semiconductor to the metal is essentially nonexistent. The probability of electron flow from the metal to the semiconductor is still governed by the same potential barrier $(\phi_m - \chi)$. As mentioned previously,

---

* See Lloyd P. Hunter, *Handbook of Semiconductor Electronics*, McGraw-Hill Book Co., New York, 1956, Sec. 3.

this component of current is normally small and constitutes a large portion of the *reverse-bias* current.

The remainder of the reverse-bias current is caused by the diffusion of holes in the semiconductor toward the depletion region. Any hole diffusing into the depletion region is then rapidly accelerated to the metal surface, where it is removed by the capture of an electron from the metal. Physically, valence energy level electrons are passing under the potential barrier from the metal into the valence band of the semiconductor. In the semiconductor the hole possesses a finite *lifetime*. At the metal surface no holes are found; however, within the bulk of the semiconductor a finite hole concentration exists (minority carriers in the case of an *n*-type semiconductor). There is, therefore, a hole concentration gradient existing across the depletion region and extending deeper into the bulk of the semiconductor. This gradient establishes a hole diffusion potential which results in the flow of holes into the depletion region.

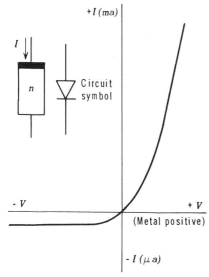

The depth of penetration of the hole concentration gradient back from the depletion region is directly proportional to the lifetime of these minority carriers. The greater the depth of penetration, the less is the magnitude of the hole diffusion potential and the lower is the hole current. For highly reverse-biased junctions the principal component of the reverse current is that caused by the holes passing under the potential barrier and this current is inversely proportional to minority carrier lifetime.

Fig. 6.3. Typical volt-ampere characteristics for a metal to *n*-type semiconductor diode. Note the different current scales.

The volt-ampere characteristics of this metal and *n*-type semiconductor junction are sketched in Fig. 6.3. It is apparent that this device possesses nearly perfect unilateral properties, and therefore the junction or contact is of the *rectifying* type.

An analytical expression for the volt-ampere characteristics of the junction may be obtained by analyzing the "flow" of electrons across the junction when an external potential, V, is applied across the junction in addition to the diffusion potential V_d. The net conventional current density consists of the sum of a component caused by the drift of electrons under the influence of the net junction potential plus a component caused by the *net* diffusion of electrons due to the gradient of electron concentration in the depletion region.

This latter component of current takes into consideration electron diffusion in both directions, which gives rise to a net distribution of charge as evidenced by the appearance of the diffusion potential V_d. The conventional current density in the direction of increasing x is

$$J = (-e)n(-v) + (-e)(-D_n)\left(+\frac{dn}{dx}\right) \quad \text{amp/m}^2 \tag{6.4}$$

The first term is the drift current density and the second term is the diffusion current density. The negative drift velocity $(-v)$ arises from the choice of the direction of increasing x, whereas $(-D_n)$ is the diffusion coefficient and the negative sign indicates that the diffusion is directed away from regions of high carrier concentration. The electron density in the depletion layer is $n(x)$ and is a minimum at the metal surface because only a small number of electrons from the semiconductor can be expected to have sufficient energy to diffuse completely across the depletion layer.

For any electron to diffuse from the n-type semiconductor material to the metal under thermal equilibrium, it must possess a thermal energy equal to that of the potential barrier. In Chap. 2, and in Chap. 3, Sec. 3.4, it was shown that the probability of finding any particle, such as a conduction electron, at a given energy level W is proportional to the Boltzmann factor and

$$P(W) = A\epsilon^{-W/kT} \tag{6.5}$$

If N_d electrons per cubic meter are available in the semiconductor to diffuse across the depletion layer against the diffusion potential, then only

$$n' = N_d\epsilon^{-eV_d/kT} \tag{6.6}$$

electrons possess sufficient energy to overcome the diffusion potential and cross the junction.

Under the conditions of thermal equilibrium and no externally applied potential, the junction must be in equilibrium with $J = 0$. Equation (6.4) becomes

$$eD_n\frac{dn}{dx} = -e\mu_n nE \tag{6.7}$$

where the drift velocity v has been replaced by the product of the mobility μ and the electric field strength E. Let the net potential ψ be used to replace E according to

$$E = -\frac{d\psi}{dx} \tag{6.8}$$

$$eD_n\frac{dn}{dx} = \mu_n en\frac{d\psi}{dx} \tag{6.9}$$

or

$$\frac{dn}{n} = \frac{\mu_n}{D_n}d\psi \tag{6.10}$$

Integrate over the depletion layer from the semiconductor to the metal:

$$\int_{N_d}^{n'} \frac{dn}{n} = \frac{\mu_n}{D_n} \int_{V_d}^{0} d\psi$$

$$n' = N_d \epsilon^{-\mu_n V_d / D_n} \tag{6.11}$$

Compare Eqs. (6.6) and (6.11); it is apparent that

$$D_n = \frac{\mu_n k T}{e} \quad \text{m}^2/\text{sec} \tag{6.12}$$

Equation (6.12) is known as the *Einstein relation.*

With the information just obtained, it is possible to obtain a solution to the diffusion equation (6.4) when an external potential is applied. Substitute Eq. (6.12), multiply by $\epsilon^{-e\psi(x)/kT}$, and integrate across the depletion layer from the metal at $x = 0$ to $x = d$ in the semiconductor and the current density becomes

$$J = e\mu_n N_d \left[\frac{2eN_d(V_d + V)}{\epsilon} \right]^{\frac{1}{2}} \epsilon^{-eV_d/kT} (e^{-eV/kT} - 1) \tag{6.13}$$

amp/m². This equation predicts the volt-ampere characteristic sketched in Fig. 6.3.

In the event that the surface work function of the metal is less than that of the semiconductor ($\phi_m < \phi_s$), electrons initially spill from the metal into the semiconductor to equalize the Fermi levels. As before, because of the high conductivity of the metal, the deficiency of electrons in the metal appears as a surface charge. The electrons that spill over to the semiconductor find themselves in the sparsely occupied conduction band of the semiconductor, and therefore they are able to move about relatively freely with the result that they also form a surface charge. The result is a dipole surface charge as shown in Fig. 6.4. It is impossible to cause any externally applied bias voltage to appear across this surface charge barrier. The barrier potential is $(\phi_s - \chi_s)$ and cannot be externally altered. If $(\phi_s - \chi_s)$ is relatively small, as often is the case, then the flow of charge carriers (both electrons and holes) proceeds with equal facility in both directions. The contact is said to be *ohmic*, which is the type of contact desired when making nonrectifying connections to semiconductors.

If the p-type semiconductor material is used and the surface work function $\phi_m > \phi_s$, electrons from the semiconductor spill over into the metal in order to equalize the Fermi levels. An electron surface charge forms on the metal, while holes collect on the surface of the p-type semiconductor. This latter phenomenon is possible because holes are the majority carrier in the p-type material and any excess is free to collect at such a surface (see Fig. 6.5).

The barrier is due only to a surface dipole charge, and therefore there is no depletion layer and externally applied potentials do not affect the small barrier potential of $(W_v - \phi_s)$ electron-volts. Holes from the semiconductor can diffuse freely and drift across to the metal where they almost immediately recombine with electrons. The energy of recombination is transferred to the metal as thermal energy. Holes thermally produced at the metal surface can freely cross the junction to the semiconductor. The contact is ohmic.

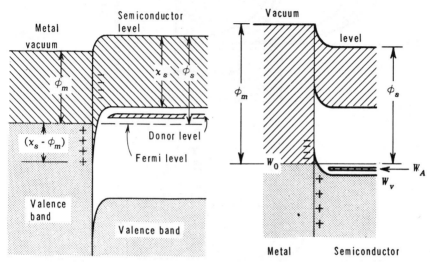

Fig. 6.4. Ohmic metal to *n*-type semi-conductor contact.

Fig. 6.5. Ohmic metal to *p*-type semi-conductor contact.

In the case of a metal-to-*p* type semiconductor junction, where the surface work function of the metal is less than the effective surface work function of the semiconductor ($\phi_m < \phi_s$), a rectifying contact is formed. Figure 6.6 is a sketch of the energy diagram for the three cases: diffusion potential V_d but no external bias, forward bias, and reverse bias. Because the Fermi level of the isolated metal is greater than that of the semiconductor, electrons spill over from the metal into the semiconductor when a junction is formed. These electrons are minority carriers in the *p*-type material and are captured by acceptors in the impurity energy band. The captures take place near the junction and produce a volume charge distribution of negatively ionized acceptors to a depth *d* from the junction. The deficiency of electrons in the metal produces a positive surface charge on the metal junction.

The junction phenomenon is quite similar to that occurring in the case of a metal-to-*n* type semiconductor junction, with the exception that the majority charge carrier is now the hole. With no externally applied bias voltage, the junction is in thermal equilibrium. There are two equal but opposite hole currents crossing the junction and both arise from high-energy holes that possess sufficient energy to cross the barrier to the other material.

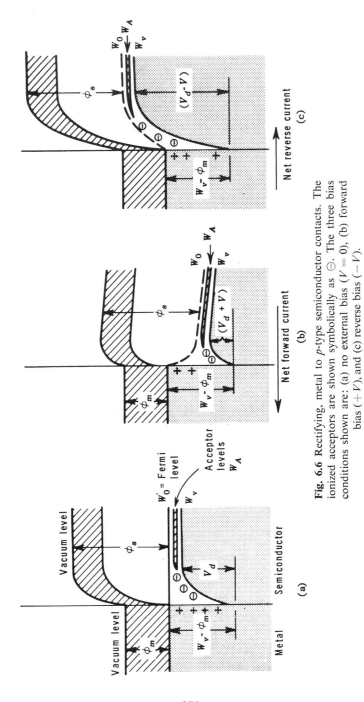

Fig. 6.6 Rectifying, metal to p-type semiconductor contacts. The ionized acceptors are shown symbolically as $\ominus$. The three bias conditions shown are: (a) no external bias ($V = 0$), (b) forward bias ($+V$), and (c) reverse bias ($-V$).

150

The hole current originating in the metal sees a barrier of $(W_v - \phi_m)$ electron-volts, whereas the hole current originating in the p-type semiconductor sees the slightly smaller barrier of $(\phi_s - \phi_m)$ electron-volts.

Regardless of the magnitude (within reason) or polarity of the bias voltage, the metal-to-semiconductor hole current sees a constant barrier height. The semiconductor-to-metal hole current depends upon the magnitude and direction of the bias. If the applied bias makes the semiconductor positive relative to the metal, then the *electron energy levels* in the semiconductor are lowered or the *hole energy levels* are raised. The passage of holes from semiconductor to metal is greatly increased; therefore, this is a forward bias. If the bias is such that the semiconductor is made negative relative to the metal, then the *hole* energies in the semiconductor are lowered and for large *reverse bias* the semiconductor-to-metal hole current is completely cut off. Under this condition, the reverse-bias current is caused by the thermally controlled metal-to-semiconductor hole current.

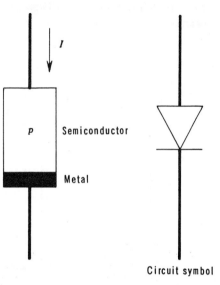

Fig. 6.7. Metal to p-type semiconductor rectifying contact and circuit symbol.

The volt-ampere terminal characteristics of this device are similar to those sketched in Fig. 6.3. The flow of conventional current through the device and the circuit symbol are as shown in Fig. 6.7.

6.2 Formation of *p-n* junction

The basic building block of semiconductor devices is the *p-n* junction. This is the junction between *p*-type and *n*-type semiconductor material. In the discussion that follows, it is helpful to speak of the conditions that exist in each semiconductor material prior to completing the junction contact. It must be emphasized, however, that actual *p-n* junctions cannot be made satisfactorily by completing a physical contact between separate materials. Point-contact devices will not be covered here because their use is comparatively restricted and excellent coverage can be found in the literature.

The *p-n* junction is formed in several ways. The first step in producing any sizable sample of a semiconductor such as germanium or silicon is to grow a large single crystal from a supply of small single crystals in powder form. This may be done by melting the powdered semiconductor in an inert atmosphere. Because of the ease of control, radio-frequency induction heating is used, as indicated in Fig. 6.8. The inert atmosphere prevents oxidation and contamination of the melt.

The reader has probably grown crystals of sugar or various salts, and the basic principle is the same here. A small crystal, termed a *seed crystal*, is oriented so that the axis of easy growth of the crystal is normal to the surface

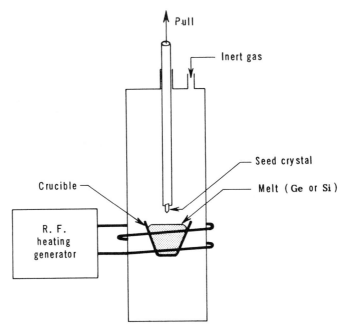

Fig. 6.8. Basic crystal-pulling apparatus for growing semiconductor crystals.

of the melt. The seed crystal is mounted on a pulling rod and lowered until it just touches the surface of the melt. Crystal growth starts immediately and the seed crystal is very slowly withdrawn or *pulled*. Between the solidified crystal and the melt lies the solidification zone. If the rate of crystal pulling is properly adjusted, the atoms in the solidification zone arrange themselves properly to form a nearly perfect single crystal. Too fast or too slow a pulling results in a polycrystalline structure, which is useless. Crystals on the order of 6 in. in length by 1 in. in diameter are readily grown.

The raw semiconductor crystal may be purified by *zone refining*. This process is based upon the relatively high rate of diffusion of impurities in the molten zone of a crystal, compared to the much lower diffusion rate in the zone of solidification. A raw single crystal is passed slowly through a localized radio-frequency heating coil. The crystal is in the molten state within the heating coil and, if the rate of passing the crystal through the coil is not too fast, it resolidifies as a single crystal again. The impurities tend to remain in the molten region and are thereby swept to the end of the crystal. The end containing these impurities may be sawed off and discarded. Repeated zone refining can reduce the impurity concentration to about 10^{17} atoms/m^3.

It is possible to prepare *p-n* junctions by doping the melt with an acceptor such as indium to provide *p*-type material. After a desired length of *p*-type material is grown, the melt can be doped with sufficient donors, such as antimony, to *compensate* for all of the acceptors that remain in the melt plus enough more to yield the desired net donor concentration. The alternate growing of *p*- and *n*-type materials can proceed in this manner to form ten or so junctions. The composite crystal may be sliced into a number of small crystals and nonrectifying electrical contacts added.

An alternative to the above process is to start with a single crystal containing uniformly distributed concentrations of the acceptor indium and the donor antimony. The concentration of antimony is about twice that of the indium. The crystal is zone refined and the velocity of zone refining is great enough so that a reasonable impurity concentration is left behind. The concentration of indium remains about constant with velocity, whereas the concentration of antimony is directly proportional to the velocity of zone refining. Rapid zone refining yields *n*-type material; slow refining produces *p*-type material. In this way, alternate *p*- and *n*-type materials of desired length may be produced. These are known as *rate-grown junctions.*

The most economical junctions are produced by starting with either intrinsic or *p*- or *n*-type material in the single crystal form and slicing the crystal into small wafers of the desired size. Additional impurities are added by various diffusion processes. In any pure crystal at temperatures on the order of 500–600°C, a few of the atoms comprising the crystalline structure can lose their normal position and lodge in the crystal as an *interstitial* atom. If the temperature remains elevated, these displaced atoms may diffuse through the crystal.

In Fig. 6.9, a disk of *n*-type germanium has a solder dot of indium-aluminum alloy placed on top of it and a lead wire of phosphor-bronze held in contact with the solder dot. The entire jig and its components are placed in an inert atmosphere of argon, and the strip heater supporting the crystal is used to flash the temperature to about 500–600°C for several minutes. The solder melts and so does the germanium in the region immediately surrounding the solder. Diffusion in the liquid state distributes a high concentration of indium acceptors throughout the germanium-indium melt. Diffusion in the solid state distributes sufficient acceptors—a mil or more—into the solid germanium, beyond the melt, to produce net *p*-type germanium in this region. When the temperature is lowered, the melt recrystallizes as a single crystal,

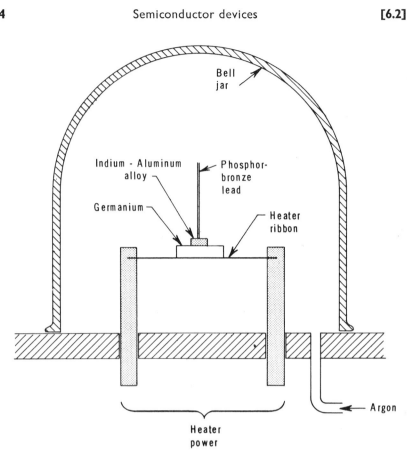

Fig. 6.9. Experimental preparation of an alloy- or fusion-type *p-n* junction.

also of *p*-type germanium (see Fig. 6.10(a)). The aluminum-indium-germanium solder dot solidifies in a polycrystalline form.

In this manner, a *p-n* junction is formed and may be used as a diode. A nonrectifying contact would be soldered to the crystal proper by use of gold solder. A second *p-n* junction can be formed on the reverse side (Fig. 6.10(b)). If the diffusion conditions are carefully controlled, the *n*-type region separating the *p*-type region can be kept quite narrow (1 mil). Such a three-terminal device is a *p-n-p transistor* and will be discussed in detail in Sec. 6.5. By starting with *p*-type crystals and using solder dots of lead alloy containing the donor, antimony, it is possible to produce *n-p-n* transistors in the same manner.

The fabrication of semiconductor devices is an art in itself, and the reader interested in constructing experimental devices should consult the latest literature on this subject.

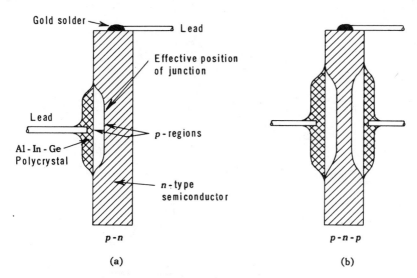

Fig. 6.10. Alloy or fused-junction (a) diode and (b) transistor.

6.3 The *p-n* junction

The *p-n* junction is the basic building block of most semiconductor devices. Several of the more common methods of fabricating the junction were discussed in Sec. 6.2. The physical phenomena occurring at the junction and the resulting electronic characteristics of the junction will be considered at this point.

In Secs. 4.8 and 6.1 it was shown that when two materials are in intimate electrical contact with no externally applied junction voltage, then the Fermi levels of each material must lie at the same level. This requires that electrons spill over from the material that has the higher Fermi level into the other material. This raises the Fermi level of the second material until both are equal. Thus, in Fig. 6.11 conduction band electrons and valence band electrons (holes) from the *n*-type material spill over the junction into the *p*-type material to equalize the Fermi levels.

The result of this initial spilling of electrons into the *p*-type material is that a large number of ionized donors and acceptors are left in the region of the junction. These ionized atoms are locked into the crystal structure and therefore establish a permanent junction barrier potential, V_d.

$$V_d = \frac{W_{cp} - W_{cn}}{e}$$

The bottom of the conduction band found in the *p*-type material is W_{cp} and in the *n*-type material it is W_{cn}. The electronic charge is e. The presence of this barrier tends to discourage further diffusion of electrons from the *n*- to *p*-region and the diffusion of holes from the *p*- to *n*-region. In other

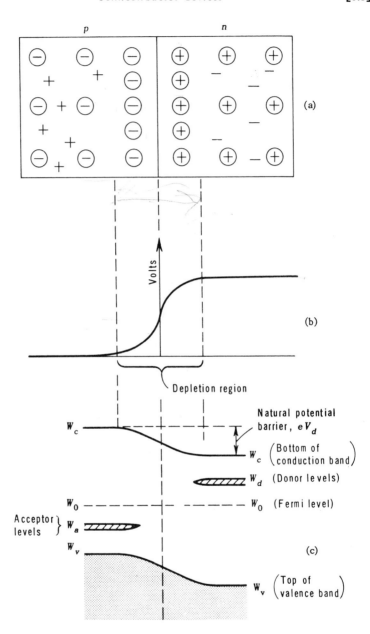

Fig. 6.11. The *p-n* junction showing (a) the free electrons (−) and holes (+) and the ionized donors ⊕ and ionized acceptors ⊖, (b) the potential distribution across the junction, and (c) the composite energy-level diagram.

words, it discourages the diffusion of *minority* charge carriers across the junction.

There are always some minority charge carriers that possess sufficient thermal energy to cross the barrier. The electrons in the n-type material that have sufficient thermal energy to cross the potential barrier into the p-type material are minority charge carriers in this region and eventually they are captured by a *trap* (Sec. 4.6). The now-ionized trap quite likely possesses a good probability for capturing a hole and the trapped hole-electron pair annihilate one another.

Exactly the same life history applies to holes that are able to cross the potential barrier into the n-type material as minority charge carriers where they recombine with free electrons. This continual flow of charge carriers results in a conventional junction current from p- to n-material. Because the current terminates in hole-electron pair annihilation, it is called the *recombination current*, I_R.

$$I_R = I_{Rh} + I_{Re}$$

where I_{Rh} is the recombination hole current and I_{Re} is the recombination electron current. This current is indicated on Fig. 6.12.

The recombination current continually delivers free electrons and valence electrons (holes) to the p-material. This process goes on at room temperature as the semiconductor is held in the hand or stored on a shelf. To establish an equilibrium condition there must also be an equal and opposite current crossing the junction. This is the *thermal current*. It has its origin in both the p- and n-materials where hole-electron pair formation occurs by virtue of thermal excitation. Holes formed in the n-material eventually diffuse into the depletion region where the electric field of the barrier potential accelerates them into the p-material. In the same manner, electrons obtained by hole-electron pair formation in the p-material diffuse into the depletion region where they are accelerated into the n-material. The net *thermal current*, I_T, across the junction can be written as

$$I_T = I_{Th} + I_{Te}$$

An interesting and important feature of the thermal current is its relative independence of the junction potential. The number of charge carriers that are accelerated across the junction depends essentially upon the rate at which these carriers diffuse to the depletion region. Once they arrive at the depletion region they are swept across the junction. Changing the junction potential can affect only the velocity at which the carriers are accelerated across the junction and not the rate at which they arrive. The thermal junction current, therefore, is dependent only upon the rate of formation of hole-electron pairs. This picture must be modified slightly because a second-order dependence of thermal current as a function of junction potential exists because of the slight variation in junction width with junction voltage.

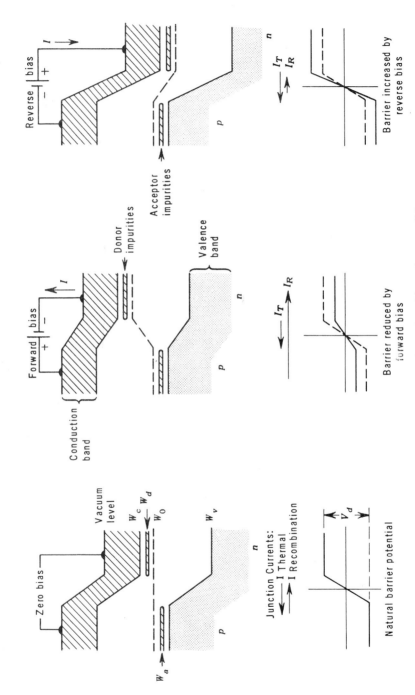

Fig. 6.12. The *p-n* junction under various bias voltage conditions.

In Fig. 6.12(a) the conditions for a natural barrier potential, V_d, are shown. The junction recombination and thermal currents must be equal. In Fig. 6.12(b) an external circuit applies a *forward-bias* voltage V to the junction. The polarity of this bias voltage is such that it tends to reduce the effective barrier height at the junction. This reduction in barrier height results in an increased recombination current, I_R, as more electrons and holes

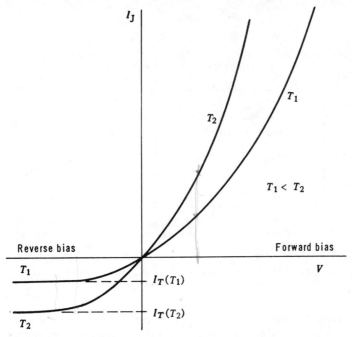

Fig. 6.13. The *p-n* junction volt-ampere characteristic for two operating temperatures.

now possess thermal energy in excess of that of the effective barrier. The thermal current remains unaltered and a net junction current, I_J, is established.

$$I_J = I_R - I_T$$

If the externally applied bias is reversed, then the recombination current is reduced and again the thermal current remains unaltered. This is depicted in Fig. 6.12(c). In the limit, as the *reverse bias* is increased in magnitude, the recombination current approaches zero and the reverse-bias current approaches the thermal current as a limiting value. Figure 6.13 is a sketch of typical junction currents as a function of forward- and reverse-bias voltages for two different operating temperatures.

The volt-ampere characteristics of the *p-n* junction may be determined analytically by use of the diffusion equation and a knowledge of minority charge carrier behavior, as developed in Sec. 4.6. The *continuity equation for minority charge carriers* was shown to be (Eqs. (4.65) and (4.66))

$$\frac{dp}{dt} = -\frac{p - p_n}{\tau_p} - \frac{1}{e}\nabla \cdot \mathbf{J}_p \qquad (6.14a)$$

for holes in *n*-type material and

$$\frac{dn}{dt} = -\frac{n - n_p}{\tau_n} + \frac{1}{e}\nabla \cdot \mathbf{J}_n \qquad (6.14b)$$

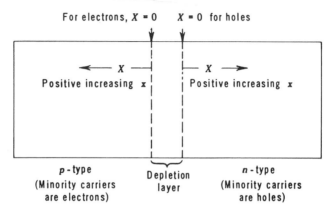

Fig. 6.14. The *p-n* junction discussed in the derivation of its volt-ampere characteristic.

for electrons in *p*-type material. The minority carrier lifetime is τ (see Eq. (4.61)). In each case the net minority charge carrier density consists of the sum of the thermal equilibrium density plus the injected carrier density, or

$$p = p_n + p_m$$

and

$$n = n_p + n_m$$

The injected carriers (p_m and n_m) are those which diffuse across the junction against the electric field of the junction barrier potential. For a steady-state junction current, the terms

$$\frac{dp}{dt} = 0, \qquad \frac{dn}{dt} = 0 \qquad (6.15)$$

are zero. The hole density $p(x, y, z)$ or the electron density $n(x, y, z)$ is greatest near the depletion layer that surrounds the junction and decreases with increasing distance, x, from the junction (see Fig. 6.14). The constant diffusion of the minority carriers across the depletion layer and into the bulk of the semiconductor establishes the junction current density J_p or J_n. It was shown in Sec. 4.6 that the current due to minority carrier motion can be expressed as the sum of two terms. For holes,

$$\mathbf{J}_p = ep\mu_p\mathbf{E} - eD_p\nabla p \tag{6.16a}$$

and for electrons, $\qquad \mathbf{J}_n = en\mu_n\mathbf{E} - eD_n\nabla n \tag{6.16b}$

The mobility of the minority carriers is μ and the electric field caused by the potential drop along the semiconductor is $\mathbf{E}$. The diffusion coefficient is D.

The second term in these equations is caused by the diffusion of the minority carriers; the first term is caused by the drift of the carriers in the applied field, $\mathbf{E}$. The voltage drop along the semiconductor is usually small and therefore the drift terms may be neglected. With this approximation and the combination of Eqs. (6.14), (6.15), and (6.16), a second-order differential equation describing the distribution of minority charge carriers is obtained.

$$\nabla^2 p - \frac{p - p_n}{D_p \tau_p} = 0 \tag{6.17a}$$

and for the electrons, $\qquad \nabla^2 n - \frac{n - n_p}{D_n \tau_n} = 0 \tag{6.17b}$

For a one-dimensional problem where the $+x$-direction is taken as *directed away from the junction*, these equations may be written as

$$\frac{d^2 p}{dx^2} - \frac{p - p_n}{D_p \tau_p} = 0 \tag{6.18a}$$

$$\frac{d^2 n}{dx^2} - \frac{n - n_p}{D_n \tau_n} = 0 \tag{6.18b}$$

The general solution to each of these equations is of the form

$$p(x) = p_n + A_1 \epsilon^{x/\sqrt{D_p \tau_p}} + A_2 \epsilon^{-x/\sqrt{D_p \tau_p}} \tag{6.19a}$$

or $\qquad n(x) = n_p + B_1 \epsilon^{x/\sqrt{D_n \tau_n}} + B_2 \epsilon^{-x/\sqrt{D_n \tau_n}} \tag{6.19b}$

Notice that in the exponent the coefficient $\sqrt{D\tau}$ has the dimension of length. From a knowledge of the exponential function, and because of recombination, the minority carrier density has decreased to 36.8 per cent of its initial value at the junction when

$$x = L = \sqrt{D\tau} \tag{6.20}$$

The term L can be defined as the *diffusion length* of the minority charge carriers.

Appropriate boundary conditions must be applied to the general solution (Eq. (6.19)) to obtain a specific solution. At the end of the depletion region ($x = 0$) the minority charge distribution, p_0 or n_0 is a maximum and its magnitude is the fraction of charge carriers that are able to diffuse over the potential barrier at the junction. The fraction of charge carriers that can surmount a potential barrier is proportional to the Boltzmann factor. For holes,

$$\frac{p_0}{N_p} = \epsilon^{-e(V_d+V)/kT} \tag{6.21a}$$

and for the electrons,

$$\frac{n_0}{N_n} = \epsilon^{-e(V_d+V)/kT} \tag{6.21b}$$

where N_p is the net hole density in the p-material and N_n is the net electron density in the n-material.

As x increases, the minority charge density must decrease. Therefore, the terms with positive exponents must drop out. Set $A_1 = B_1 = 0$. When $x = 0$, for holes

$$p = p_0 = N_p \epsilon^{-e(V_d+V)/kT} = p_n + A_2 \tag{6.22}$$

However, the thermal equilibrium concentration, p_n, is the concentration of minority charge carriers that is present when no external bias is present.

$$p_n = N_p \epsilon^{-eV_d/kT} \tag{6.23}$$

Therefore,
$$p(x) = N_p \epsilon^{-eV_d/kT}[1 + (\epsilon^{-eV/kT} - 1)\epsilon^{-x/L_p}] \tag{6.24a}$$

In a similar manner, the electron minority carrier concentration is

$$n(x) = N_n \epsilon^{-eV_d/kT}[1 + (\epsilon^{-eV/kT} - 1)\epsilon^{-x/L_n}] \tag{6.24b}$$

The total junction current is the flow of minority carriers, holes passing into the n-material and electrons passing into the p-material. From Eq. (6.16) the total junction current density is

$$J = eD_p\frac{dp}{dx} + eD_n\frac{dn}{dx}$$

$$J = e\left[\frac{N_pD_p}{L_p} + \frac{N_nD_n}{L_n}\right]\epsilon^{-eV_d/kT}(\epsilon^{-eV/kT} - 1) \tag{6.25}$$

This equation predicts the volt-ampere characteristic of a p-n junction diode as sketched in Fig. 6.13. For increasing reverse bias, $V > 0$, the term $\exp(-eV/kT)$ soon becomes negligible compared to unity and the junction current density reaches saturation.

$$J_{\text{sat}} = -e\left[\frac{N_pD_p}{L_p} + \frac{N_nD_n}{L_n}\right]\epsilon^{-eV_d/kT} \tag{6.26}$$

The corresponding saturation current (thermal current) is indicated in Fig. 6.13 for two different values of temperature.

6.4 The tunnel diode

This is a *p-n* junction diode whose junction current in normal operation is carried almost entirely by electrons that have tunneled quantum-mechanically at constant energy through the potential barrier at the *p-n* junction instead of climbing over the barrier in the conventional manner. In normal operation the tunnel diode exhibits negative dynamic conductance over a portion of its volt-ampere characteristics. For this reason, circuits may be designed around it that can function as oscillators or amplifiers. Switching

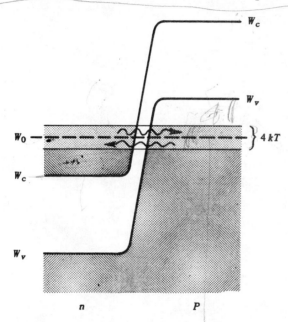

Fig. 6.15. A tunnel diode under equilibrium conditions.

circuits are also feasible. The high-frequency response of the tunnel diode makes it very attractive for applications up to the kilomegacycle frequency range.

L. Esaki* in Japan was studying the behavior of highly doped semiconductors when he discovered the tunnel diode in 1957. In a highly doped *n*-type semiconductor, the Fermi level lies above the bottom of the conduction band and all of the donors are normally ionized. For *p*-type material that is heavily doped, the Fermi level lies below the top of the valence band and all of the acceptors are ionized. A *p-n* junction of such highly doped materials is shown in Fig. 6.15. By careful control of the doping it is possible to produce

* L. Esaki, "New Phenomena in Narrow Germanium P-N Junctions," *Phys. Rev.*, **109**, 603 (1958).

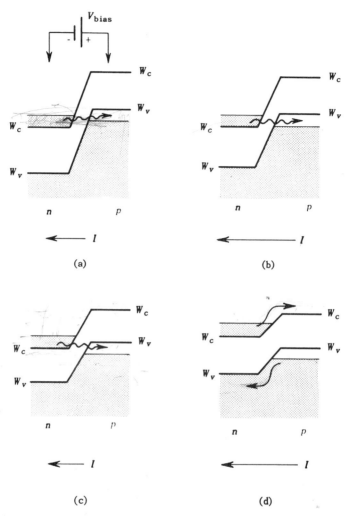

Fig. 6.16. The tunnel diode with (a) low forward bias, (b) forward bias corresponding to peak tunnel current, (c) normal bias, and (d) excessive forward bias with large thermal currents of electrons and holes crossing the barrier.

a junction where the transition from *p*- to *n*-material is very abrupt. The effective width of the junction in a tunnel diode is about 100 Angstroms or about 20 lattice spacings.

The tunnel diode shown in Fig. 6.15 is under equilibrium conditions; therefore, the Fermi levels in each material must be equal. At room temperature the density of electrons about the Fermi level varies according to the Fermi distribution factor. For this reason, there are unoccupied electron energy levels opposite each other in the two materials. The necessary conditions for quantum-mechanical tunneling* thus exist. They are the following: (1) a narrow potential barrier of finite height and (2) empty and permitted energy levels on the opposite side of the barrier. Under equilibrium conditions there will be two equal and opposite junction currents caused by tunneling.

In a tunnel diode the junction currents caused by tunneling are much greater than the junction current caused by thermal excitation of the electrons going over the top of the barrier. This is because of the width and magnitude of the potential barrier.

In circuit operation the tunnel diode is forward biased as shown in Fig. 6.16(a). Most of the conduction band electrons in the *n*-material are opposite empty permitted levels in the *p*-material and a large *n*- to *p*-electron tunneling current exists. The conventional current flow is, of course, from *p* to *n*. A little reflection shows that an initial increase of the bias above zero increases the current because more empty permitted levels in the *p*-material are opposite the conduction band electrons in the *n*-type material which permits an increase in the electrons tunneling from *n* to *p*. On the other hand, the number of electrons tunneling from *p* to *n* must decrease because there are fewer permitted levels opposite those electrons in the *p*-type material. The net junction current for this condition is shown in Fig. 6.17 at point *a*.

Further increases in the bias eventually result in the condition of Fig. 6.16(b), where the maximum tunneling from *n* to *p* can occur while very little tunneling from *p* to *n* is permitted. The junction current now corresponds to point *b* on the volt-ampere characteristics. A further increase in forward bias causes the junction current to start to decrease because some of the conduction band electrons in the *n*-type material are now opposite forbidden levels in the *p*-type material (Fig. 6.16(c)). *This is the region of negative conductance on the volt-ampere characteristics and is the normal region of operation.*

Still further increases in forward bias eventually result in an operation where the conduction band electrons in the *n*-type material and the holes (valence electrons) in the *p*-type material are both opposite forbidden regions. According to the energy diagrams, tunneling should cease and the only junction current should be that caused by thermally excited electrons crossing the barrier (Fig. 6.16(d)). Because of conditions existing at the actual junction, this does not prove to be the case and some tunneling still persists. The minimum current or *excess current* is shown on the volt-ampere diagram.

Higher values of forward bias result in a substantial increase in the thermal current crossing over the barrier. This is the conventional diode current and its extension toward the origin is shown as a dotted line. This extension

---

* The reader should review Sec. 5.10.

would be the volt-ampere characteristic of the diode if tunneling were not present.

The tunnel diode volt-ampere characteristic sketched in Fig. 6.17 is typical of all diodes, because for a given material such as germanium the

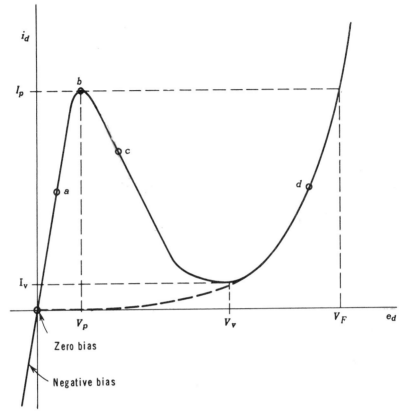

Fig. 6.17. The volt-ampere characteristics of a typical tunnel diode. The points marked are discussed in the text and correspond to Figs. 6.16(a), (b), (c), and (d).

voltages corresponding to the inflection points of the characteristic remain essentially constant. The current scale is relative and changing it does not alter the voltage scale. Let the *peak point current* and corresponding voltage be I_p and V_p and the *valley current* and corresponding *valley voltage* be I_v and V_v. To complete the specification of the shape of the volt-ampere characteristic, define a forward voltage V_F corresponding to a thermal junction current that equals the peak tunneling current.

If negative bias is applied, then tunneling again occurs as shown in Fig. 6.18 and a net electron junction current flows from p- to n-material.

$X_c = \frac{1}{j\omega c}$

$B_c = j\omega c$

The mean characteristic voltages for tunnel diodes made of germanium, silicon, and gallium arsenide are listed in Table 6.1. The peak tunneling current is controlled in the design of the diode and can be held to close tolerances at any preselected value between 100 microamperes and 10 amperes. Typical ratios of peak-to-valley currents run between 5 and 15.

Tunneling is an electromagnetic phenomenon proceeding at near the velocity of light. For this reason, the tunnel diode is not hampered by transit time effects. The junction capacitance is comparatively large and amounts to about 2 μf/cm^2 of effective junction area. A typical small-signal tunnel diode has a junction capacitance of between 10 and 80 $\mu\mu f$. At high frequencies the large susceptance because of this capacitance can be offset by utilizing the large negative conductance possible (a peak current of 10^4 amp/cm^2 is typical). Thus, the tunnel diode, in spite of its large junction capacitance, may be operated into the kmc frequency range. The tunnel diode operation is relatively insensitive to environmental conditions such as temperature and high-energy radiation fields. It is only necessary to derate the dissipation of a typical 50-mw tunnel diode about 0.5 mw/°C at temperatures above

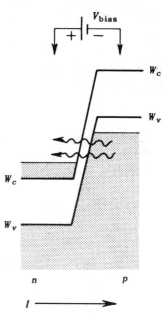

Fig. 6.18. The tunnel diode with reverse bias applied.

25°C. The peak-point current of a germanium tunnel diode probably varies less than 5 per cent for temperature variations between -30 and $+100$°C.

Table 6.1

Characteristic voltages of tunnel diodes

(millivolts)

Material	Germanium	Silicon	Gallium arsenide
Peak-point voltage	55	75	150
Valley-point voltage	350	450	500
Forward voltage	500	750	1200

To represent the tunnel diode as a circuit element, first express the instantaneous diode current as a function of the diode voltage.

$$i_b = f(e_b) \tag{6.27}$$

The differential of this equation is

$$di_b = \frac{\partial i_b}{\partial e_b} de_b \tag{6.28}$$

When operation is biased to the linear portion of the volt-ampere characteristic where the slope is negative, then a *negative dynamic conductance*, g_d, for the diode may be defined.

$$-g_d = \frac{\partial i_b}{\partial e_b} \tag{6.29}$$

The instantaneous diode current, i_b, consists of an average, or quiescent, value, I_{dd}, plus a signal term, i_d.

$$i_b = I_{dd} + i_d \tag{6.30}$$

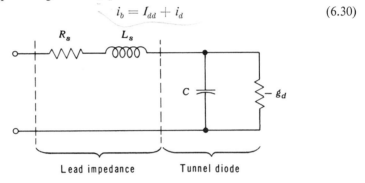

Lead impedance   Tunnel diode

Fig. 6.19. The equivalent circuit of the tunnel diode, including lead impedance and lead-plus-junction capacitance.

In the same manner, the diode voltage may be expressed as

$$e_b = E_{dd} + e_d \tag{6.31}$$

where E_{dd} is the diode bias voltage.

For small signals, the differentials of Eq. (6.28) may be replaced by the signal components of Eqs. (6.30) and (6.31). This yields the dynamic or small-signal equation of the diode alone.

$$i_d = e_d(-g_d) \tag{6.32}$$

The tunnel diode as a circuit element at high frequencies can be represented by means of the equivalent circuit of Fig. 6.19. The diode alone is represented by the negative conductance paralleled by the junction plus lead capacitance, C. The series impedance of the leads is represented by R_s and L_s. The ability of the diode to operate at very high frequencies introduces two problems. First, the limiting factor for high-frequency operation occurs when a simple impedance is connected across the leads. The input impedance of the diode is

$$Z_i = \left[R_s - \frac{r_d}{(1 + \omega^2 r_d^2 C^2)} \right] + j\omega \left[L_s - \frac{r_d^2 C}{1 + \omega^2 r_d^2 C^2} \right] \tag{6.33}$$

where the dynamic resistance of the diode is $r_d = 1/g_d$. From this equation two frequency figures of merit may be defined. One is the frequency at which the real part of the input impedance becomes equal to zero. The diode cannot amplify above this frequency, and therefore it is termed the *resistive cut-off frequency*:

$$f_R = \frac{1}{2\pi} \frac{|g_d|}{C} \sqrt{\frac{1}{R_s |g_d|} - 1} \tag{6.34}$$

The second frequency figure of merit is the *self-resonant frequency* which occurs when the reactive part of the input impedance is equal to zero.

$$f_x = \frac{1}{2\pi} \sqrt{\frac{1}{L_s C} - \left(\frac{|g_d|}{C}\right)^2} \tag{6.35}$$

An imaginary value for f_x indicates a tunnel diode that cannot be stabilized by any selection of shunt-load resistance. Such a diode is useful as a switching element.

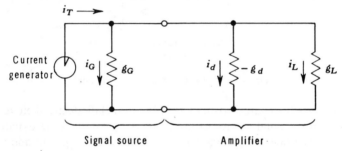

Fig. 6.20. The parallel equivalent circuit of a tunnel-diode amplifier.

A second problem arises because the tunnel diode is operated in the negative conductance region of its characteristics. As a consequence, it is continually trying to break into high-frequency oscillations. Preventing such oscillations is a problem for the designer of low-frequency amplifiers.

Typical values of lead impedance for the equivalent circuit of average small-signal commercial tunnel diodes consist of a lead resistance, R_s, of between 1 and 2 ohms and an associated lead inductance, L_s, of about 5 to 10 millimicrohenrys.

When combined with a signal source or generator that has a conductance g_G and a load conductance g_L, the alternating-current equivalent circuit consists of these three conductances in parallel and excited by a constant current generator. This is sketched in Fig. 6.20. The complete amplifier is sketched in Fig. 6.21 and includes a voltage divider consisting of resistors R_1 and R_2 to provide the low-voltage, low-impedance bias for the tunnel diode. The direct-current conductance of the entire network supplying d-c quiescent current to the diode must be greater than the magnitude of the negative conductance of the diode if the circuit is to be stable. For this reason, the design of the bias supply requires close attention.

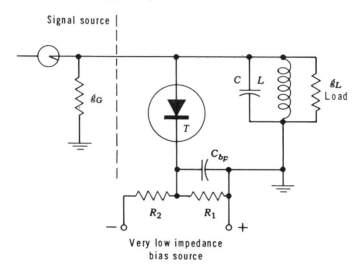

Fig. 6.21. A tuned, tunnel-diode amplifier.

In Fig. 6.22 the characteristics (A) of the tunnel diode are sketched again. The static or d-c conductance of the diode is G_d, whereas the dynamic conductance in the operating range has been defined as $(-g_d)$. In addition, the conductance of the a-c load is also plotted. This is a linear passive conductance and the plot is the straight line B or B' whose slope is g_L. The algebraic sum of the currents flowing in the diode plus the passive branch is plotted as the curve C or C'.

When the magnitude of the load conductance is greater than the diode conductance, $|g_L| > |g_d|$, then the slope and, therefore, the dynamic conductance of the total circuit is always positive as indicated by curve C. When $|g_L| < |g_d|$ (dotted curve C'), then the dynamic conductance of the total circuit is negative over the normal operating range and the circuit may oscillate.

The total conductance is also plotted in Fig. 6.23. The bias voltage is E_{dd} and a signal voltage e_d is superimposed upon it. The corresponding instantaneous currents through each branch are indicated. Each of these currents is expressed as the sum of a quiescent value plus an a-c term. The quiescent values are indicated on the diagram.

It is obvious that, as the diode voltage is varied about the bias point, then the net input current ($I_{in} + i_{in}$) must vary as predicted by the net

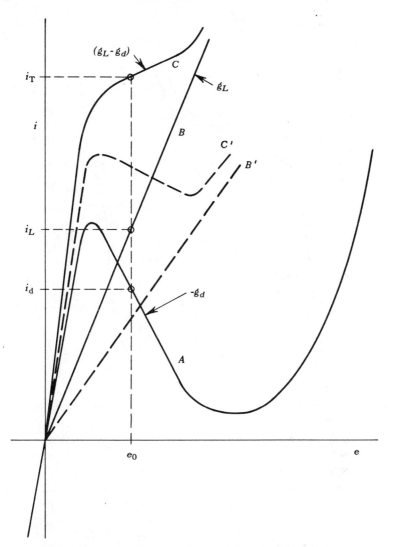

Fig. 6.22. The volt-ampere characteristics of a tunnel diode (A) in parallel with a passive conductance (B or B'). The overall volt-ampere characteristics (C or C') of the parallel circuit is the sum of those of the branches.

conductance characteristic. The total circuit current can be written as a function of the circuit voltage, or

$$(I_{in} + i_{in}) = f(e_b) \tag{6.36}$$

and

$$di_{in} = \frac{\partial i_{in}}{\partial e_b} de_b$$

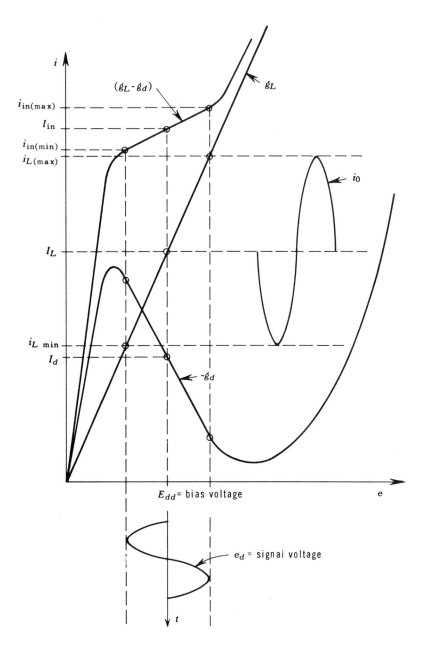

Fig. 6.23. The graphical analysis of a parallel-circuit, tunnel-diode amplifier.

For small signals near the operating point

$$i_{in} = \frac{\Delta i_{in}}{\Delta e_b} \tag{6.37}$$

Upon substitution,

$$
\begin{aligned}
i_{in} &= \left[\frac{e_{b\text{max}}(g_L + G_{d_1}) - e_{b\text{min}}(g_L + G_{d_2})}{e_{b\text{max}} - e_{b\text{min}}} \right] e_d \\
&= \left[g_L + \left(\frac{e_{b\text{max}}G_{d_1} - e_{b\text{min}}G_{d_2}}{e_{b\text{max}} - e_{b\text{min}}} \right) \right] e_d \\
&= (g_L - g_d)e_d \tag{6.38}
\end{aligned}
$$

The input conductance of the amplifier, therefore, is

$$g_{in} = g_L - g_d$$

In Fig. 6.23 the load line g_L has not been selected for maximum current and power gain, but rather to permit emphasizing the graphical constructions involved. Normally, it would be desirable to select g_L to yield a high input impedance

$$Z_{in} = \frac{1}{g_L - g_d} \tag{6.39}$$

To accomplish this, it is necessary to make $(g_L - g_d)$ very small. When $|g_L| = |g_d|$, instability occurs. As both g_L and g_d can be expected to vary somewhat with ambient conditions, it is a problem for the circuit designer to decide how close the conductance of the load may approach that of the diode without risking improper operation.

A typical graphical analysis is shown in Fig. 6.23. The tunnel diode is biased at E_{dd} volts and the quiescent currents are as indicated. The maximum permissible input signal for linear operation is shown. It is apparent that any further increase in input signal would result in distortion and clipping. The output load current can be determined either graphically or analytically. Graphically, the root-mean-square load current for a sinusoidal input signal is

$$\mathbf{I} = \frac{i_{o\text{max}} - i_{o\text{min}}}{2\sqrt{2}} \tag{6.40}$$

Analytically, the *current gain* can be expressed as

$$
\begin{aligned}
A_i &= \frac{i_L}{i_{in}} = \frac{i_L}{i_L + i_d} \\
&= \frac{e_d g_L}{e_d(g_L - g_d)} \\
A_i &= \frac{g_L}{g_L - g_d} \tag{6.41}
\end{aligned}
$$

In a similar manner, the power gain is

$$A_p = \frac{e_d^2 g_L}{e_d^2(g_L - g_d)}$$

$$A_p = \frac{g_L}{g_L - g_d} \tag{6.42}$$

The power gain equals the current gain because the voltage gain is unity. It is possible to devise a series circuit that provides a voltage gain with unity current gain. In general, however, the power gain is the important factor. For additional information refer to Probs. 9 and 16.

6.5   The transistor

If two *p-n* junctions are produced in cascade in germanium or silicon, the result is a three-terminal device consisting of alternate regions of *p-* and *n*-type material. Two arrangements of the acceptor- and donor-type semiconductors are possible. A *p-n-p* transistor is sketched in Fig. 6.24; the alternative construction would be an *n-p-n* transistor. In either case the *p-n* junction (or *n-p* junction) is the basic building block.

In Fig. 6.24 the same symbols are used as in Secs. 6.1 and 6.3. Normal operating bias voltages are shown applied to each junction. The physics of transistor operation is demonstrated by considering the example of the *p-n-p* transistor. The junction between the *emitter* and *base* regions is externally biased in the *forward* direction. In other words, the external bias, V, is opposed to the natural barrier diffusion potential, V_d. The result is a large current of minority charge carriers (holes in this case) crossing into the base region. There is also a current of minority charge carriers moving from base to emitter; however, the impurity concentration in the base region is small and therefore this current is correspondingly small.

The impurity concentration in the base region is also kept small to lessen the probability of carrier recombination in this region, and, to further reduce the probability of carrier recombination, the base is made very thin in comparison to the diffusion length of the minority carrier (L_p in this case). In commercial junction transistors, between 1 and 5 per cent of the minority carriers injected into the base recombine there. The largest portion of this injected current traverses the base and enters the *collector*.

All minority charge carriers moving from emitter to base must possess thermal energy in excess of the net potential barrier at this junction. This is because the electric field within the depletion region of the emitter-base junction is directed in such a manner as to be decelerating for minority charge carriers. Now as these same minority charge carriers approach the second (base-to-collector) junction, the electric field in this depletion region is

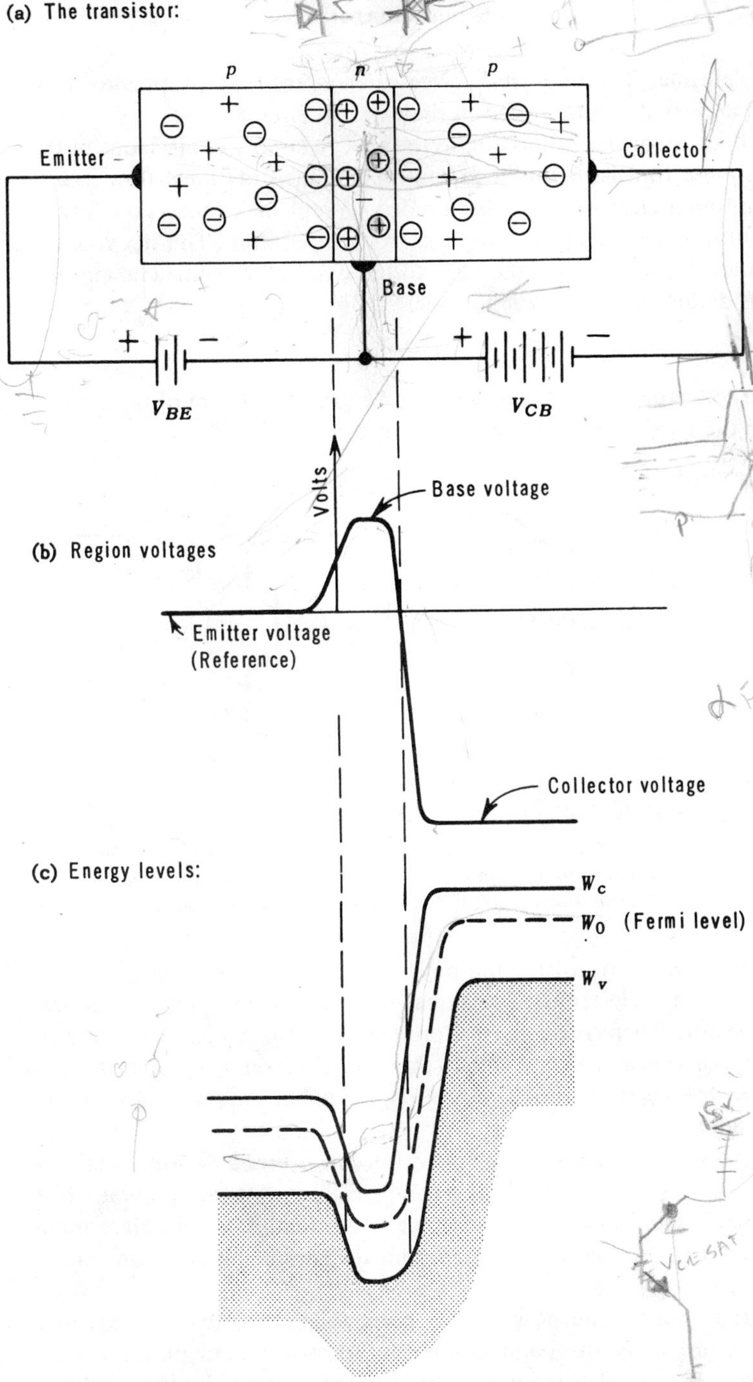

(a) The transistor:

Emitter

Collector

Base

V_{BE}

V_{CB}

Volts

Base voltage

(b) Region voltages

Emitter voltage
(Reference)

Collector voltage

(c) Energy levels:

W_c

W_0 (Fermi level)

W_v

Fig. 6.24. The junction transistor with forward emitter bias and reverse collector bias supplied.

175

accelerating. The minority charge carriers are thus swept into the collector and a current is established in the external circuit.

Because of recombination in the base, a supply of electrons in the case of this *p-n-p* transistor (holes for an *n-p-n* transistor) must flow into the base. Additional electrons are also needed to replenish those that form the very small minority electron flow from base to emitter. The net result is a conventional current from the base to the external circuit. The emitter current thus divides into two components.

$$i_E = i_B + i_C \qquad (6.43)$$

The collector current, i_C, is between 95 and 99 per cent of the emitter current and the base current, i_B, is the balance.

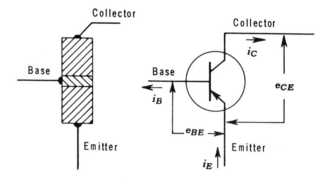

Fig. 6.25. The junction transistor and circuit symbol. If the arrow on the emitter is interpreted to show the flow of conventional current, then a *p-n-p* transistor is shown.

In an *n-p-n* transistor the minority charge carriers that are injected into the base are electrons. The same basic reasoning applies to either type of transistor. There is no general preference in the choice between a *p-n-p* and an *n-p-n* transistor except that the manufacturer may prefer one over the other, for a certain application, when manufacturing problems are taken into consideration.

As a circuit element, the transistor constitutes a two-terminal pair device that can be used in three basic configurations depending upon which region is made the common (or grounded) terminal. The circuit symbol of the transistor is shown in Fig. 6.25, and the three configurations are shown in Table 6.2.

It is not the purpose of this book to go into detailed circuit analysis. Therefore, only the common-emitter transistor configuration will be considered because it is the one generally used. It provides the maximum power gain along with values of input and output resistance suited to the demands of the circuit designer (see Table 6.2). The common-emitter transistor configuration and the grounded-cathode, vacuum-tube configuration are analogous.

The transistor is a two-terminal-pair device; therefore, two voltages and two currents are required to completely specify its operation. Refer to Fig. 6.25 and let the instantaneous values of these variables be e_{BE} for the base-to-emitter voltage, i_B for the base current, i_C for the collector current, and e_{CE} for the collector-to-emitter voltage.

Table 6.2

Transistor configurations

Common base	Common emitter	Common collector
$R_i \approx 10^2$ ohms	$R_i \approx 10^3$ ohms	$R_i \approx 10^4$ ohms
$R_o \approx 10^5$ ohms	$R_o \approx 10^4$ ohms	$R_o \approx 10^3$ ohms
$A_i \approx -0.95$	$A_i \approx 10$ to 100	$A_i \approx -10$
$A_v \approx 10^3$	$A_v \approx -10$ to 10^3	$A_v \approx 0.95$
$A_p \approx -10^3$	$A_p \approx -10^4$	$A_p \approx -10$

Typical values of transistor input and output resistance and current, voltage, and power gain are listed. These values are typical for small-signal transistors. The values of A_i and A_p are for the transistor alone and do not include any losses in the input network.

Of these four variables, the base current and the collector-to-emitter voltage may be chosen as the independent variables. By use of function notation, the collector current may be written as

$$i_C = f_C(i_B, e_{CE}) \tag{6.44}$$

The base-to-emitter voltage may be written as

$$e_{BE} = f_B(i_B, e_{CE}) \tag{6.45}$$

These four variables can be represented by the family of collector characteristics and the input characteristic shown in Fig. 6.27 for a typical junction transistor. The input characteristics are actually a set of coincident curves for various e_{CE}.

The common-emitter circuit is sketched in Fig. 6.26. The collector-emitter loop contains two linear resistors, the coupling resistor, R_C, and the emitter stabilization resistor, R_e. The transistor and these two resistors plus the collector supply voltage E_{CC} complete the *d-c collector circuit*. Such a series circuit can only be solved graphically because of the nonlinear characteristics of the transistor. Apply Kirchhoff's laws to this loop.

$$E_{CC} = I_C R_C + I_E R_e + V_{CE} \qquad (6.46)$$

but

$$I_E = I_C + I_B \qquad (6.47)$$

where the currents and voltages are the d-c components of the respective instantaneous values. That is,

$$i_C = I_C + i_c \qquad (6.48)$$

$$e_{CE} = E_{CE} + e_{ce} \qquad (6.49)$$

$$i_B = I_B + i_b \qquad (6.50)$$

$$e_{BE} = E_{BE} + e_{be} \qquad (6.51)$$

where i_c, e_{ce}, i_b, and e_{be} are the signal components of the corresponding instantaneous voltages and currents.

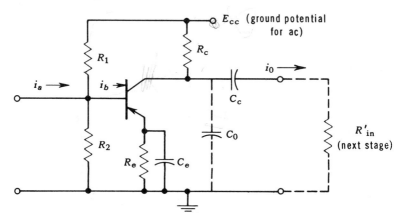

Fig. 6.26. A common emitter transistor amplifier. Component values for the transistor and operating condition are: $R_1 = 16,700\Omega$; $R_2 = 5800$; $R_e = 1140$; $R_c = 1430$; and $R'_{in} = 4000$ (assumed).

Return to Eq. (6.46) and solve for the voltage drop across the transistor.

$$E_{CE} = E_{CC} - I_C(R_C + R_e) - I_B R_e \qquad (6.52)$$

The term $I_B R_e$ is very small compared to the other terms and may be neglected. Equation (6.52) can be solved graphically by plotting the d-c load line ($R_C + R_e$) on the collector characteristics, as shown in Fig. 6.27. If a constant average base current, I_B, is supplied to the transistor, this will *bias* the transistor at the intersection of the collector characteristic, corresponding to $i_B = I_B$ and the d-c load line.

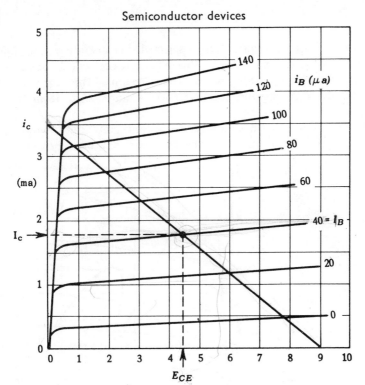

Collector characteristics

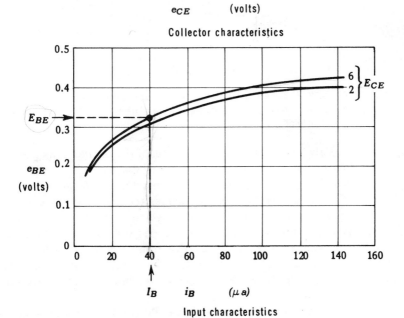

Input characteristics

Fig. 6.27. Common emitter junction transistor characteristics.

Once the base bias current I_B is selected, the operating point and the corresponding quiescent (average) value of collector current, I_C, and collector-to-emitter voltage, E_{CE}, are known. The selection of the base bias current also permits obtaining the base-to-emitter voltage, E_{BE}, from the input characteristic.

The d-c operation must always be solved graphically; however, the solution of the a-c operation of the amplifier may be approached either

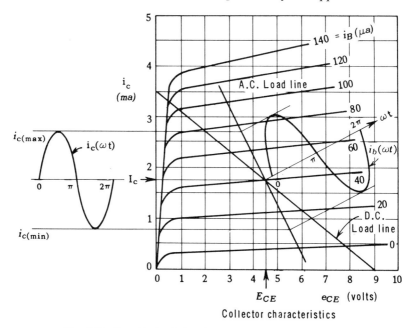

Collector characteristics

Fig. 6.28. Graphical solution for the collector current from a common emitter transistor amplifier. An arbitrary input signal current is assumed.

graphically or analytically. The a-c load consists of the parallel combination of the coupling resistor, R_e, and the net input resistance, R'_{in}, of the next stage, provided the signal frequencies are within the *mid-frequency range*. In this frequency range the voltage drop across the coupling capacitor C_c is negligible, as is the current through the stray shunt capacitance, C_o. The resistor, R_e, is assumed to be completely bypassed for a-c signals, and therefore it does not enter into the a-c load. This resistor is usually selected to provide a d-c voltage drop of 20 to 30 per cent of E_{CC}. This tends to stabilize the transistor against drift caused by temperature variations and variations in individual transistors.

For a graphical solution, the a-c load line is plotted through the operating point determined by the d-c load line. The family of collector characteristic curves divides the a-c load line into a current scale. If a signal current, i_b, is superimposed upon base bias current, I_B, then the instantaneous operating point swings up and down the a-c load line. The collector current may be obtained by means of graphical construction, as indicated in Fig. 6.28. Graphical construction of this type must be used when the signal swing is large, because the current scale along the a-c load line is nonlinear over a wide range.

If the signal swing is small, then the current scale along the a-c load line in the vicinity of the operating point may be assumed to be linear. This assumption permits treating the transistor as a linear, small-signal amplifier and an equivalent circuit may be constructed to represent the transistor.

6.6   The transistor equivalent circuit

As a small-signal amplifier operating in the vicinity of the d-c operating point, the transistor may be represented by a linear equivalent circuit. According to Eqs. (6.44) and (6.45), the base-to-emitter voltage and the instantaneous collector current can be written in function notation as

$$e_{BE} = f_B(i_B, e_{CE})$$
$$i_C = f_C(i_B, e_{CE})$$

The differentials of these equations are

$$de_{BE} = \frac{\partial e_{BE}}{\partial i_B} di_B + \frac{\partial e_{BE}}{\partial e_{CE}} de_{CE} \tag{6.53}$$

$$di_C = \frac{\partial i_C}{\partial i_B} di_B + \frac{\partial i_C}{\partial e_{CE}} de_{CE} \tag{6.54}$$

By means of Eqs. (6.48), (6.49), (6.50), and (6.51) the d-c terms may be dropped from Eqs. (6.53) and (6.54). Also, for small signals there is not any difference between the signal and its derivative. With these substitutions, Eqs. (6.53) and (6.54) become

$$e_{be} = h_{ie} i_b + h_{re} e_{ce} \tag{6.55}$$
$$i_c = h_{fe} i_b + h_{oe} e_{ce} \tag{6.56}$$

where the common-emitter parameters are

$$h_{ie} = \frac{\partial e_{BE}}{\partial i_B} = \text{input resistance} \tag{6.57}$$

$$h_{re} = \frac{\partial e_{BE}}{\partial e_{CE}} = \text{reverse voltage ratio} \tag{6.58}$$

$$h_{fe} = \frac{\partial i_C}{\partial i_B} = \text{forward current ratio} \tag{6.59}$$

$$h_{oe} = \frac{\partial i_C}{\partial e_{CE}} = \text{output admittance} \tag{6.60}$$

Equations (6.55) and (6.56) are interesting in that the parameters are of mixed dimensions. Usually electric network equations are written in a manner so that the parameters have the dimensions of ohms or mhos. These two equations employ *hybrid parameters.*

The parameters may be determined directly from the curves of Fig. 6.27. The indicated derivatives are evaluated at the operating point. For the operating point on Fig. 6.27, the numerical values of the hydrid parameters are

$$h_{ie} = 2200 \text{ ohms}, \qquad h_{fe} = 31 \text{ amp/amp}$$
$$h_{re} = 0.0041 \text{ v/v}, \qquad h_{oe} = 37 \times 10^{-6} \text{ mhos}$$

where h_{re} has been determined by a graphical solution that simultaneously uses both sets of curves.

$$h_{re} = \frac{\Delta e_{BE}}{\Delta e_{CE}} \tag{6.61}$$

To sketch an equivalent circuit to represent Eqs. (6.55) and (6.56), first note that in Eq. (6.55) the first term is a voltage drop whereas the second term is a generated voltage. This suggests a series circuit for the input. The output is represented by Eq. (6.56) and consists of a conductance, h_{oe}, in parallel with a current generator $h_{fe}i_b$. The result is the transistor equivalent circuit shown in Fig. 6.29. Also shown is the a-c path R_B caused by the bias network. The net a-c load includes the coupling resistor R_C, the bias network of the next stage, R'_B, and the input resitance, R'_i, of the next transistor.

There are several ways to obtain the desired base-to-emitter voltage and to provide the proper base bias current, I_B. For the method shown in Fig. 6.26, the resistors R_1 and R_2 form a d-c voltage divider to establish the desired e_{BE}; however, as far as the signal current i_s is concerned, each of these resistors provides an impedance to ground. (The collector voltage supply, E_{CC}, is at ground potential for a-c.) Thus, the effective impedance of the bias network is

$$R_B = \frac{R_1 R_2}{R_1 + R_2} \tag{6.62}$$

For sinusoidal signal analysis, replace the instantaneous values of voltage and current in Eqs. (6.55) and (6.56) with the phasor values:

$$\mathbf{E}_1 = h_{ie}\mathbf{I}_1 + h_{re}\mathbf{E}_2 \tag{6.63}$$
$$\mathbf{I}_2 = h_{fe}\mathbf{I}_1 + h_{oe}\mathbf{E}_2 \tag{6.64}$$

where the currents and voltages have the polarities and directions indicated in Fig. 6.29. The load resistance is

$$R_L = \frac{R_C R'_B R'_i}{R_C R'_B + R_C R'_i + R'_B R'_i}$$
$$= -\frac{\mathbf{E}_2}{\mathbf{I}_2} \tag{6.65}$$

where R'_B is the effective resistance of the bias network of the next transistor and R'_i is the input resistance of the next transistor succeeding or following the transistor stage. With the load in place, the input resistance, R_i, seen by looking into the transistor itself, is

$$R_i = \frac{E_1}{I_1} = \frac{h_{ie}(1 + h_{oe}R_L) - h_{re}h_{fe}R_L}{1 + h_{oe}R_L} \qquad (6.66)$$

For the a-c load, $R_L = 1080$ ohms; in the example (see Fig. 6.26) $R_i = 2070$ ohms.

In a similar manner, the output resistance R_o of the transistor alone is determined by connecting the signal source resistance, R_S, to the input of the transistor and looking into the output terminals.

$$R_o = \frac{E_2}{I_2} = \frac{R_S + h_{ie}}{h_{oe}(R_S + h_{ie}) - h_{re}h_{fe}} \qquad (6.67)$$

If there is a stage preceding this one, then the source resistance is the parallel combination of the R_o and the load R_L of the preceding stage. The output

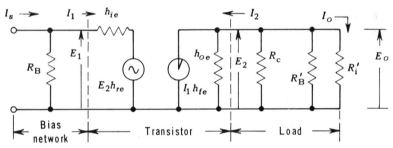

Fig. 6.29. An *R-C*-coupled common emitter transistor amplifier.

resistance, R_o, is used in determining the required size of the coupling capacitor for a desired low-frequency response. See Prob. 5.

Return to Eqs. (6.63) and (6.64) and solve for the ratio I_2/I_1. This is the *current gain* of the transistor.

$$A_i = \frac{I_2}{I_1} = \frac{h_{fe}}{1 + h_{oe}R_L} \qquad (6.68)$$

In the example,
$$A_i = 29.8$$

Unfortunately, the *net current gain* of the amplifier is not I_2/I_1 because only a fraction of the signal current, I_S reaches the transistor input. The rest of the signal current branches to ground through the bias network. This loss in signal current is

$$a = \frac{I_1}{I_S} = \frac{R_B}{R_B + R_i} \qquad (6.69)$$

The net current gain of the stage is

$$A_{i\,net} = aA_i \qquad (6.70)$$

For the example, the net current gain is

$$\mathbf{A}_{i_{net}} = (0.672)(29.8) = 20.0$$

Once the current gain is known, the *voltage gain*

$$\mathbf{A}_{v_{net}} = \mathbf{A}_v = \frac{I_2 R_L}{I_S R_{in}} = \mathbf{a}\mathbf{A}_i \frac{R_L}{R_{in}} = \mathbf{A}_i \frac{R_L}{R_i} \tag{6.71}$$

is readily calculated. The net input resistance is R_{in}

$$R_{in} = \frac{R_B R_i}{R_B + R_i} \tag{6.72}$$

Again, with reference to the example

$$R_{in} = 1410$$

and the voltage gain is

$$\mathbf{A}_v = 15.4$$

The over-all *power gain* is

$$A_{p_{net}} = A_{i_{net}}^2 \frac{R_L}{R_{in}} = A_{i_{net}} A_v \tag{6.73}$$

For the example, the power gain is

$$A_p = 310$$

The power gain of the transistor alone is

$$A_p = A_i^2 \frac{R_L}{R_i} = 462$$

PROBLEMS

1. *The photojunction cell.* If a *p-n* junction is fabricated so that the junction lies very near a surface of the semiconductor, then illumination of the surface with visible or ultraviolet light results in electron-hole pair formation by photoionization. These charge carriers lie in and near the depletion region and those lying near the depletion region can enter it by diffusion. If the junction is reverse biased similar to the collector junction of a transistor, then these charge carriers will form a junction current. The volt-ampere characteristics of this *photojunction cell* will be similar to the collector characteristics of a transistor.

The volt-ampere characteristics will depend upon the wavelengths of the light. For white light, typical photojunction cell characteristics are shown below. In the absence of any light there will be a *dark current*.

(a) Use this photojunction cell in circuit (a) and determine the output sensitivity in volts per lumen.

(b) In circuit (b) the transistor is the same as that shown in Fig. 6.27. The pull-in current of the relay is 3 ma. What illumination is required to cause the relay to pull in?

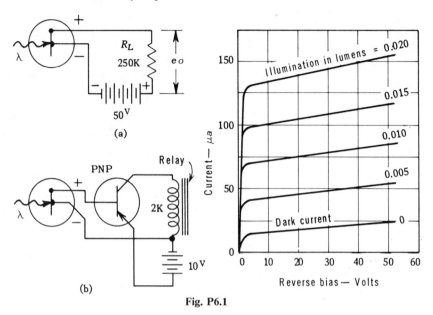

Fig. P6.1

2. *The Zener diode.* If a large reverse-bias voltage is applied to a *p-n* junction, two types of electrical breakdown may occur. Each may be nondestructive to the crystal, provided that excessive heating is prevented by limiting the junction current. If the depletion region is relatively thin, then electron tunneling may occur and provide the breakdown current. This is known as *Zener breakdown*. When the junction width is on the order of, or greater than, the mean diffusion length of the charge carriers, then an *avalanche breakdown* occurs. In the avalanche breakdown the electrons make ionizing collisions with the lattice, thus producing additional electrons which in turn are accelerated and free additional electrons by further ionizing collisions.

Experimentally, these two processes are difficult to distinguish between. The term *Zener breakdown* is often loosely applied to all junction breakdowns although the prevalent process is the avalanche breakdown. The *Zener diode* is a *p-n* junction that has been designed so that its volt-ampere characteristic displays a very abrupt *avalanche breakdown*. The Zener breakdown potential is usually measured at a specified junction test current, I_{ZT}. The manufacturer will also supply the maximum d-c Zener current (limited by power dissipation).

The constant voltage characteristic of the Zener diode permits its use as a reference voltage device or directly as a voltage regulator. Use a Zener diode with the characteristics given below and design a voltage regulator to supply 20 ma at 60 nominal volts with a possible load variation of ± 5 ma. The power supply possesses an internal impedance of 300 ohms and a no-load voltage of 75 v.

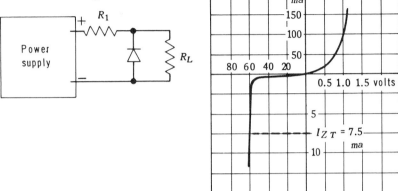

Fig. P6.2

3. *The tunnel diode.* An amplifier employing a gallium arsenide tunnel diode is designed so that the d-c conductance of the bias circuit is 56 millimhos and the a-c signal conductance of the load is 50 millimhos. Plot the d-c and a-c load lines. Determine the signal current gain of the amplifier analytically and graphically. Use the tunnel diode characteristics given. The supply voltage for the bias circuit is 0.35 v.

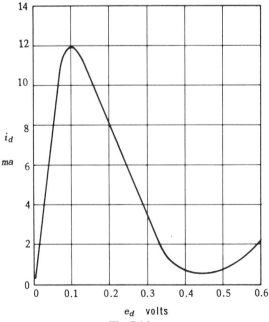

Fig. P6.3

4. Compute the total current, voltage, and power gain of the following transistor amplifier. Use the transistor characteristics of Fig. 6.27 for each stage.

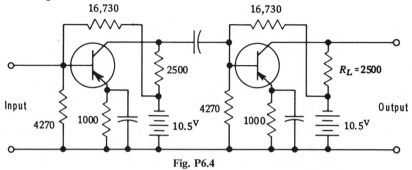

Fig. P6.4

5. Show that the magnitude of the current gain, A, for the first stage of the amplifier of Prob. 4 will be down by the factor $1/\sqrt{2}$ when the signal frequency has dropped to the point where the reactance of the coupling capacitor

$$\frac{1}{2\pi f_1 C} = \frac{R_o R_C}{R_o + R_C} + \frac{R'_B R'_i}{R'_B + R'_i}$$

The frequency f_1 is called the *lower half-power frequency*.

6. By definition, the current gain expressed in decibels is

$$db = 20 \log_{10} I_{out}/I_{in}$$

Show that the gain is -3 db when the signal frequency is equal to the lower half-power frequency.

7. What must be the size of the coupling capacitor in Prob. 4 if the lower half-power frequency is 20 cps?

8. Many manufacturers publish typical values for the hybrid parameters for their transistors. They may give the grounded-emitter or the grounded-base hybrid parameters. If the latter is given, then the designer must compute the grounded-emitter parameters from the grounded-base values. The conversion equations are not difficult to derive. They may be reduced to

$$h_{ie} \approx \frac{h_{ib}}{1 + h_{fb}}, \qquad h_{fe} \approx -\frac{h_{fb}}{1 + h_{fb}}$$

$$h_{re} \approx \frac{\Delta^h - h_{rb}}{1 + h_{fb}}, \qquad h_{oe} \approx \frac{h_{ob}}{1 + h_{fb}}$$

where $\Delta^h = h_{ib}h_{ob} - h_{rb}h_{fb}$. The term $(-h_{fb})$ is often called α and has a value of about 0.95.

In addition to this information, the manufacturer usually specifies the frequency, f_α, at which the transistor current gain has fallen off by $1/\sqrt{2}$ because of collector capacitance and possibly charge carrier drift time effects. This information is usually presented by specifying f_α in the following equation for current gain at high frequencies in terms of the mid-frequency gain:

$$(h_{fb})_{\text{high}} = h_{fb} \frac{1}{(1 + jf/f_\alpha)}$$

Show that the common-emitter forward current gain will have dropped by $1/\sqrt{2}$ when the signal frequency has the specific value f_β, which is given by

$$f_\beta = f_\alpha(1 + h_{fb})$$

9. Equation (6.42) expresses the actual power gain of the tunnel diode; Eq. (6.73) expresses the actual power gain of a transistor. It is important to note that in each case an explicit value of power gain does not answer the question of efficiency. In order to indicate how efficiently the power source is being utilized, circuit designers have defined the concepts *available gain*, *transducer gain*, and *insertion gain*. The appropriate definition of each power gain is as follows:

(a) Power gain

$$A_p = \frac{\text{power in load}}{\text{power delivered by generator}}$$

(b) Available gain

$$A_{pa} = \frac{\text{power available from output}}{\text{power available from generator}}$$

(c) Transducer gain

$$A_{pt} = \frac{\text{power in load}}{\text{power available from generator}}$$

(d) Insertion gain

$$A_{pi} = \frac{\text{power in load with transducer inserted}}{\text{power in load because of generator alone}}$$

In each case the term *available power* indicates that source and load are to be assumed to be matched.

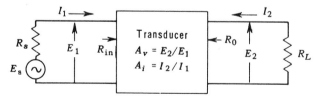

Fig. P6.9

With reference to the general two-terminal pair network shown in the accompanying sketch, show that the different definitions of power gain are:

(a)
$$A_p = \left(\frac{E_2}{E_1}\right)^2 \frac{R_{\text{in}}}{R_L} = A_v^2 \frac{R_{\text{in}}}{R_L} = A_i^2 \frac{R_L}{R_{\text{in}}}$$

(b)
$$A_{pa} = \left(\frac{V_{oc}}{E_s}\right)^2 \frac{R_s}{R_{\text{out}}}$$

where V_{oc} is the output open circuit voltage ($R_L = \infty$).

(c) $$A_{pt} = \left(\frac{E_2}{E_s}\right)^2 \frac{4R_s}{R_L} = A_v^2 \frac{4R_s R_{in}^2}{R_L(R_s + R_{in})^2}$$

$$= A_i^2 \frac{4R_s R_L}{(R_s + R_{in})^2}$$

(d) $$A_{pi} = A_v^2 \frac{R_{in}^2(R_L + R_s)^2}{R_L^2(R_s + R_{in})^2}$$

Let R_{in} be the input impedance and R_{out} be the output impedance of the transducer.

10. Compute the transducer and available power gains for the generalized equivalent circuit of the transistor shown in the sketch.

$$\textit{Ans. } A_{pt} = \frac{4R_s R_L h_{21}^2}{(R_s + h_{22}R_L R_s + h_{11} + h_{11}h_{22}R_L - h_{12}h_{21}R_L)^2}$$

$$A_{pa} = \frac{(h_{21})^2 R_s}{(\Delta^h + R_s h_{22})(R_s + h_{11})} \quad \text{where } \Delta^h = h_{11}h_{22} - h_{12}h_{21}$$

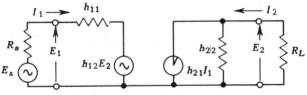

Fig. P6.10

11. Two transistors of the same type are employed in the two-stage amplifier shown in the accompanying sketch. The battery voltages and biasing conditions are such that the operating point of each transistor is identical and the common-base, small-signal parameters are

$$h_{ib} = 50 \text{ ohms}, \qquad h_{fb} = -0.97 \text{ amp/amp}$$
$$h_{rb} = 5 \times 10^{-3} \text{ v/v}, \qquad h_{ob} = 10^{-5} \text{ mhos}$$

Compute the over-all current, voltage, and power gain.

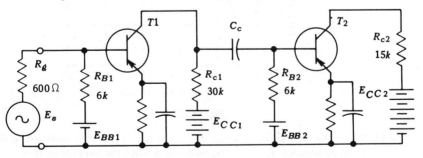

Fig. P6.11

12. A power transistor has the characteristics shown in the accompanying sketches. Design a Class A power amplifier to develop maximum output power.

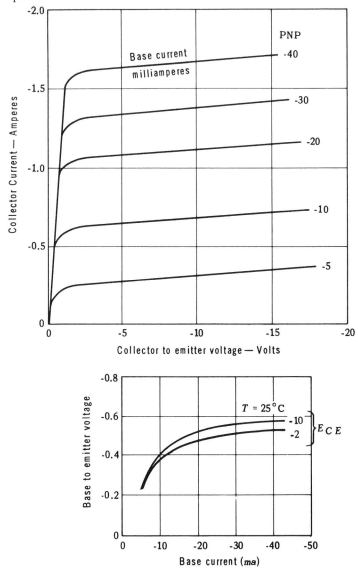

Fig. P6.12

13. When the internal impedance, R_s, of the signal source is matched to the input impedance, R_i, of the transistor and when the load impedance R_L is matched to the output impedance R_o of the transistor, then the maximum available power gain (M.A.G.) is realized. Under these conditions the transducer, available, and actual power gains are all equal to the M.A.G. Show that the M.A.G. of any transistor is given by

$$\text{M.A.G.} = \frac{h_{21}^2}{[(\Delta^h)^{1/2} + (h_{11}h_{22})^{1/2}]^2}$$

This gain depends only upon the parameters of the transistor, and therefore it is a "factor of merit" for comparing various transistors.

14. Data from two commercial tunnel diodes are tabulated below. Ascertain which diode is suitable for low-level switching as well as small-signal amplification and which diode is suited only for switching applications.

	$-g$ (mho)	C ($\mu\mu f$)	L_s (henry)	R_s (ohms)
Diode A	-0.125	25	6×10^{-9}	2.0
Diode B	0.01	7	6×10^{-9}	1.0

15. Show that the transducer power gain for the tunnel diode is

$$A_{pt} = \frac{4R_g R_L r_d^2}{[R_g R_L - r_d(R_g + R_L)]^2}$$

16. A tuned, tunnel-diode amplifier is to be designed to operate at 30 megacycles with a bandwidth of 2.5 megacycles. The characteristics of the tunnel diode are

$$-r_d = -25 \text{ ohms}, \qquad L_s = 0.5 \times 10^{-9} \text{ henry}$$
$$C = 130 \ \mu\mu f, \qquad R_s = 1.2 \text{ ohms}$$

Follow the steps outlined below in the design:

(a) Check the resistive cut-off frequency of the diode alone to ascertain whether this diode can be operated at 30 megacycles.

(b) The diode can only be operated as an amplifier within the conditions established by the expressions for f_R and f_x. From these two expressions, show that the conditions for amplifier operation may be written as

$$\frac{L_s |g_d|}{C} < R_s < \frac{1}{|g_d|}$$

Will this tunnel diode be satisfactory?

(c) Compute the series input impedance of the diode alone. Convert this series input impedance to its equivalent parallel impedance.

(d) The reactive component of the parallel equivalent of the input impedance of the diode is capacitive. Determine the magnitude of the inductor required to form a parallel circuit that is series resonant at 30 megacycles.

(e) The bandwidth of any resonant circuit is given by $B = f_0/Q_0$, where Q_0 is the factor of merit of the circuit. For a series circuit $Q_0 = \omega_0 L/R_s$, and for a parallel circuit $Q_0 = R_p/\omega_0 L$. This is the case of a parallel circuit because the resistance of the load and generator must also be included. Show that

$$B = \frac{1}{2\pi R_p C}$$

where

$$R_p = \frac{-r_d R_g R_L}{-r_d R_g - r_d R_L + R_g R_L}$$

(f) Compute the proper value of the total equivalent parallel resistance, R_p, for the desired bandwidth of 2.5 megacycles. From this, compute the required parallel combination of R_g and R_L. If $R_g = R_L$, what are their values? *Ans.* 47.5 ohms

(g) What is the transducer gain?

REFERENCES

1. H. C. Torrey and C. A. Whitmer, *Crystal Rectifiers*, McGraw-Hill Book Co., New York, 1948.

2. A. van der Ziel, *Solid State Physical Electronics*, Prentice-Hall, Inc., Englewood Cliffs, N.J., 1957.

3. T. L. Martin, Jr., *Physical Basis for Electrical Engineering*, Prentice-Hall, Inc., Englewood Cliffs, N.J., 1957.

4. R. L. Sproull, *Modern Physics*, John Wiley & Sons, New York, 1956.

5. R. L. Riddle and M. P. Ristenbatt, *Transistor Physics and Circuits*, Prentice-Hall, Inc., Englewood Cliffs, N.J., 1958.

CHAPTER 7

Conduction in vacuum

and gas

In this chapter we will consider electrical conduction by small densities of charge carriers moving in a gas or vacuum. (Chapter 8 deals with conduction by means of very large densities of both electrons and ions moving simultaneously in a *plasma*.) The motion of free electrons and ions in a gaseous medium is the basis of electron tube operation. If the gas pressure is on the order of 10^{-6} mm Hg or less, the device is commonly referred to as a *high-vacuum tube*. This is in contrast to *gas tubes*, where the operating pressure may lie between 10^{-3} mm Hg for voltage regulator tubes and 120 atm for high-pressure illumination tubes.

It is not always possible to place a certain device in one of these two categories from a knowledge of the operating pressure alone. For instance, an operating pressure of 10^{-6} mm Hg may be sufficient for a standard high-vacuum receiving tube but may be considered as gaseous for an electrometer tube. The physicist studying surface phenomena might consider any pressure above 10^{-9} mm Hg as gaseous, whereas the ultra high-vacuum research worker strives for pressures on the order of 10^{-13} mm Hg.

The decision as to whether a specific problem may be treated as a high-vacuum device or whether gaseous electronics must be considered is largely dependent upon two factors:

1. the critical interelectrode dimensions compared to the mean free path (mfp) of the electrons and gas ions at the operating pressure;
2. the percentage of electrode current that may be permitted to arise from gas ionization.

The first condition will be developed theoretically in this chapter. From it, it becomes apparent that the spacing of electrodes can have as much influence on the electronic behavior as does the pressure. The second condition involves the use to which the device is to be put. Large interelectrode currents can be obtained by utilizing the charge carriers obtained from ionization of the gas in a tube. Gas tubes are intentionally filled with selected gases at various pressures to obtain desired operating volt-ampere characteristics. On the other hand, interelectrode currents arising from gas ionization are erratic. That is, they contain a significant noise spectrum. Low-noise tubes must be pumped to the highest practical vacuums to minimize this effect.

In view of the basic importance of a knowledge of the processes of conduction in gases, this subject will be considered first. Conduction in a vacuum will be treated as a special case of gaseous electronics. The careful investigator should bear in mind that "gas" in any evacuated device may arise in part from solid surfaces such as metals that possess a vapor pressure near or above that of the ambient pressure in the vessel.

7.1   Ionization

Ionization is the process by which one or more electrons are either added to or removed from initially neutral gas atoms or molecules, thereby rendering them electrically charged. This is accomplished in two ways:

1. The molecule (including single atoms) picks up one or more electrons by *attachment*. This process provides *negative ions* by removal of *free electrons* from the gas.
2. The molecule receives sufficient energy to raise one or more of its valence electrons to the vacuum level (see Chap. 3). By this process of *electron removal* an ion pair is formed, a *free electron* and the *positive ion*.

Attachment. Molecules of certain gases possess less potential energy when an excess electron is attached to them than when they are in their normal ground state. As a result, these gases display an affinity for attaching one or more electrons. In Chap. 2, the collision frequency for a neutral particle having an effective collision diameter, d_1, in a gas possessing an effective collision diameter, d_2, was shown to be

$$\zeta = \sqrt{2}\,\frac{\pi}{4}(d_1 + d_2)^2 n v_a \quad \text{collisions/sec} \tag{7.1}$$

for a real gas. The number of gas molecules per cubic meter is n, and v_a is their average thermal velocity. For an electron moving in oxygen (O_2) with an ambient thermal energy only and at standard conditions ($0°C$ and a pressure of 760 mm Hg), the collision frequency is 2×10^{11} collisions/sec.

This result of kinetic theory does not agree with the experimental value of 4×10^4. The large discrepancy arises from the affinity of oxygen for electrons. Singly, doubly, and triply ionized negative oxygen ions are readily formed.

The average observed number of collisions an electron makes in a gas before attachment occurs is termed the *coefficient of attachment, a.* Under standard conditions $a = 4 \times 10^4$ for oxygen. The ratio of the attachment coefficient to the kinetic theory collision frequency yields the *mean time preceding attachment,*

$$t_a = \frac{a}{\zeta} \quad \text{sec} \tag{7.2}$$

For oxygen, this is 2×10^{-7} seconds. In other words, on the average, an electron in oxygen can remain free only 0.2 microseconds—in contrast to electrons in gases such as nitrogen, hydrogen, and the noble gases, which possess an attachment coefficient that is infinite (no attachment).

At standard conditions, *water vapor* (H_2O) possesses the same attachment coefficient as oxygen, whereas chlorine gas (Cl_2) has a coefficient of 2×10^3.[*] Small traces of any of these gases in a gas discharge can materially affect the electrical characteristics of the discharge.

The attachment coefficient depends upon the probability of attachment which varies inversely with temperature. For this reason, very few negative ions are found in arcs. From a set of experimental data it appears at first glance that the probability of attachment varies inversely with pressure. Actually, the decrease in formation of negative ions is because of the increased mean free path and associated increased loss of electrons to the walls of the tube.

Electron removal. The formation of positive ions can be illustrated by applying the Bohr atomic theory to the hydrogen atom. In Chap. 3 it was shown that the energy required to move an electron from an orbit, n_1, to another orbit, n_2, corresponding to a higher energy level, is (Eq. (3.12))

$$\Delta W = + RchZ^2 \left(\frac{1}{n_1^2} - \frac{1}{n_2^2} \right) \quad \text{joules} \tag{7.3}$$

where R is the *Rydberg constant* (10,967,758 cycles/m), c is the velocity of light (2.998×10^8 m/sec), h is Planck's constant (6.624×10^{-34} joule-seconds), and Z is the atomic number.

The ground (lowest) energy level of hydrogen corresponds to $n_1 = 1$. The electron becomes free of the coulomb force holding it to the nucleus when $n_2 = \infty$. With these substitutions, Eq. (7.3) yields 13.60 electron-volts as the energy required to ionize the hydrogen atom. This result is in excellent agreement with experimental measurements. This energy may be supplied by any one of three basic mechanisms.

* K. T. Compton and I. Langmuir, *Rev. Modern Phys.*, **2**, 193 (1930).

1. Kinetic energy may be transferred to the atom as the result of an inelastic collision with an electron, ion, or high-energy neutral atom. The probability of occurrence of the latter process (Saha process*) is very small except at the very high temperatures found in electric arcs and stellar atmospheres.

Collisions between electrons and neutral gas molecules do not necessarily lead to ionization. First of all, the electron must possess a kinetic energy ($\frac{1}{2}mv^2$) in excess of the ionization energy of the molecule and, secondly, it must make an inelastic collision with the gas molecule. In Eq. (2.72) we found that the mean free path of a neutral particle of collision diameter d_1 in a gas of molecules of collision diameter d_2 was

$$\lambda = \frac{4kT}{\sqrt{2}\,\pi(d_1 + d_2)^2 P} \quad \text{meters} \tag{7.4}$$

If the incident particle is an electron (or proton), then $d_1 \approx 0$.

These particles often possess velocities considerably greater than the thermal velocities of the neutral gas molecules. As a result, the gas molecules may be considered as being at rest relative to the electron. The factor $\sqrt{2}$ drops out under this condition (see Eqs. (2.68) and (2.69)). The mean free path of the electron is then

$$\lambda_e = \frac{4kT}{\pi d_2^2 P} \tag{7.5}$$

and the ratio of the mean free path of the electron to that of the gas molecules in a gas of their own type ($d_1 = d_2$) is

$$\frac{\lambda_e}{\lambda} = \frac{\sqrt{2}\,(2d_2)^2}{d_2^2} = 5.66 \tag{7.6}$$

Following Eq. (2.67), Eq. (7.6) may be written as

$$\lambda_e = 5.66\lambda = \frac{4}{\pi d^2 n} \tag{7.7}$$

$$\lambda_e = \frac{1}{\pi \sigma_e^2 n} \tag{7.8}$$

where the *effective collision radius* of the gas molecules for electrons is σ_e. The electron that possesses a kinetic energy of even a few electron-volts does not satisfy the kinetic theory of gases, and therefore such an electron does not satisfy thermal equilibrium conditions. For this reason, Eq. (7.4) cannot properly be applied to such electrons. The general form of the equation can be expected to apply, however, and the mfp may be written as

$$\lambda_e = \frac{1}{\pi \sigma_e^2 n} = \frac{1}{\varphi n_1 P} \tag{7.9}$$

* M. N. Saha, *Phil. Mag.*, **40**, 472 (1920).

where $(\pi\sigma_e^2) = \varphi(v)$, the *collision cross-section* of the gas molecules for an electron. The collision cross-section is a function of the velocity of the incident electron. The number of molecules per unit volume at a pressure of 1 mm Hg is n_1 and the pressure is P mm Hg.

The fraction of electrons that have not yet experienced a collision by virtue of their x-component of motion is (see Sec. 2.8)

$$f_x = \frac{n_e}{n_{e0}} = \epsilon^{-\varphi n_1 P x} \tag{7.10}$$

where n is the number of electrons out of an initial number, n_0, that have not collided with molecules.

By experimental measurements of n and n_0 over a known distance x and at a certain pressure, P, the collision cross-section, φ, may be determined. The experimental data is usually presented graphically in several ways. From Eq. (7.9) the collision cross-section is

$$\varphi(v) = \frac{1}{\lambda_e} = P_c \tag{7.11}$$

where P_c is the *collision probability*. From the equation it is apparent that the dependent variable may be φ in m^2/m^3 or $1/\lambda_e$ in $1/m$ or P_c in $1/m$. The independent variable is electron velocity, which is proportional to $\sqrt{V}$ where V is the potential difference through which the electron has been accelerated. That is, for an electron moving under the force eE because of an electric field E and traveling from an initial point x_0, the kinetic energy is found by integration.

$$\text{K.E. of electron} = \int_{v_0}^{v} v\, m\, dv = \int_{x_0}^{x} -eE\, dx$$

$$\frac{1}{2}\, m(v^2 - v_0^2) = eV \tag{7.12}$$

The initial velocity may be assumed as zero, which permits the velocity of the electron to be expressed in terms of the potential difference through which it has traveled.

$$v = \sqrt{\frac{2eV}{m}} \tag{7.13}$$

Figure 7.1 is a plot of the collision probability of helium (He), neon (Ne), argon (Ar), krypton (Kr), and xenon (Xe).* The characteristic maxima of the curves are caused by those electrons which possess velocities in this range and are especially effective in exciting or ionizing the gas molecules. These characteristic maxima are called the *Ramsauer effect*.

* Most of this data is from C. Ramsauer.

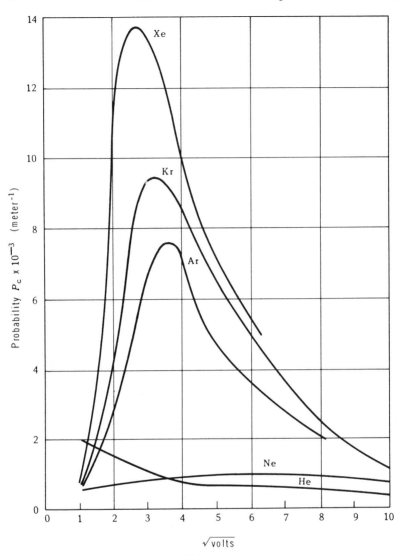

Fig. 7.1. Electron-gas collision probability at 0°C and 1 mm Hg for the noble gases as a function of electron velocity expressed in √volts. (Data from Ramsauer and other sources.)

     2. Potential energy may be transferred to the atom from another atom. The most important process involves an energy exchange between an atom in a metastable state and another species of atom whose ionization potential is below that of the metastable state of the first atom. Such encounters are called *collisions of the second kind.* An example of such an ionizing exchange is that between a neon atom, Ne*, in the first metastable state (16.53 ev) and an argon atom in the ground state. The first ionization potential of argon is 15.69 ev. The energy exchange may be written as follows:

$$\text{Ne*} + \text{Ar} \rightarrow \text{Ne} + \text{Ar}^+ + e + \text{energy} \qquad (7.14)$$

where the result is a normal neon atom plus an *ion pair* consisting of the positive argon ion and a free electron. The difference in energy (16.53 − 15.69 = 0.84 ev) may appear as increased thermal velocity of the atoms, or it may be radiated as a photon.

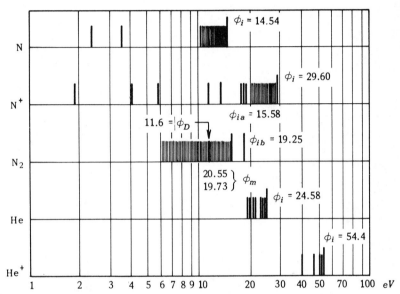

Fig. 7.2. Excitation and ionization energies for nitrogen and helium. The ionization potential is ϕ_i and the metastable potentials are ϕ_m. The dissociation energy of molecular nitrogen is ϕ_D.

3. Ion pairs may also be formed by transferring energy in the form of electromagnetic radiation to the neutral atoms in sufficient amounts of energy to ionize the atoms. This process is called *photoionization* and plays an important role in gas discharges. The effective cross-section of a gas molecule for intercepting the photon is generally small. Experimental evidence indicates that the cross-section is a maximum when the energy content of the photon (*hf*) is just slightly greater than the ionization potential of the molecule.

It is possible to remove more than one electron from a molecule, thereby producing doubly and triply ionized molecules. Higher degrees of ionization are possible but seldom encountered. A neutral atom possesses a definite spectrum of excitation levels such as shown for atomic nitrogen (N) in Fig. 7.2.

Molecular nitrogen (N_2) possesses a somewhat different spectrum, and singly ionized atomic nitrogen has still a third spectrum. Note the dissociation energy of molecular nitrogen. The spectrum of helium (He) and singly

Table 7.1

Properties of some of the more important gaseous conductors

Element	Z	Metastable potentials	Ionization potentials first, second, third
H	1		13.53
He	2	19.73 20.55	24.58 54.4
Li	3		5.37 75.3 121.9
N	7		14.54 29.60 47.4
O	8		13.55 34.9 54.9
Ne	10	16.53 16.62	21.47 40.9 63.2
A	18	11.49 11.66	15.69 27.8 36.8
Kr	36	9.86 10.51	13.94 26.4 31.2
Xe	54	8.28 9.4	12.08 21.1 28.5
Cs	55		3.87 23.4
Hg	80	4.64 5.44	10.38 18.7 41

ionized He^+ is also shown. Note the metastable levels of helium. The data of Fig. 7.2 includes only the more prominent spectral lines. For detailed information on a specific element the reader should consult the literature.[*] Table 7.1 lists the electronic properties of some of the more commonly used gases.

[*] C. Moore, "Atomic Energy Levels," *Nat. Bur. Stdards* (*U.S.*), *Circ.* 467, Vols. I, II, III, and IV.

7.2   Mobility and drift velocity

Any charged particle in a region containing an electric field, E, experiences a force

$$\mathbf{f} = q\mathbf{E} \quad \text{newtons} \tag{7.15}$$

where q is the charge in coulombs. Let the mass of the particle be m; then the electrical force is opposed by the mechanical force of acceleration, or

$$q\mathbf{E} = \frac{d}{dt}\, m\mathbf{v}$$

For energies below about 50,000 ev, relativity effects are negligible and any change in mass may be neglected.

$$q\mathbf{E} = m\frac{d\mathbf{v}}{dt} = m\mathbf{a} \tag{7.16}$$

According to Eq. (7.16), as long as an electric field is present, the charged particle continues to accelerate, provided that nothing interferes with its trajectory. Consider an electric field established between two plane-parallel plates by applying an emf of V volts between the plates (Fig. 7.3). The sketch is for an electron moving in a gas; however, the same basic concepts apply to an ion. According to Eq. (7.15) the force on an electron is directed opposite to the direction of the electric field, E, because $q = -e$. The electric field is, by definition, directed opposite to the gradient of the electric potential.

$$\mathbf{E} = -\nabla V \tag{7.17}$$

Assume that an electron starts with negligible thermal or other initial velocity at the negative electrode. Its energy is a function of the potential at the point in space occupied by the electron (Eq. (7.13)). The *average electron* travels a mean free path $1/\varphi n_1 P$ meters, according to Eq. (7.9), before colliding with a gas molecule.

If the collision is elastic, the scattering of the electrons is entirely random in fashion. Any component of backscattering (in the same direction as the electric field) results in electron deceleration. When the mfp is relatively small compared to the electrode and wall spacings, there are many elastic collisions. As a result of the random scattering, the average electron only attains a mean energy, W. This energy can be expressed in terms of an apparent electron temperature, T_e, according to

$$W = \tfrac{3}{2}kT_e$$

This is not the equilibrium temperature of the gas. It only provides an alternative method of referring to the mean energy of the electrons.

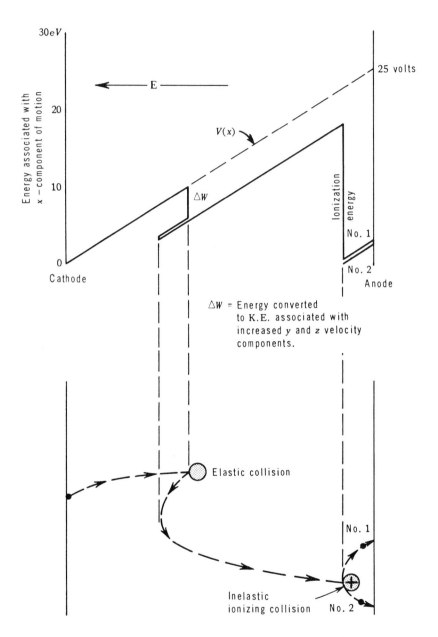

Fig. 7.3. An elastic collision between an electron and a molecule resulting in random scattering of the electron followed by an inelastic collision resulting in ionization.

Those electrons that make inelastic collisions often lose almost all of their energy and start essentially from rest after the collision. The result of these collisions is a delayed motion of the electron through the gas. If a measurement of the current density is made, it is found that the electrons travel with an average drift velocity that is proportional to the electric field strength.

$$v_d = \mu_e E \tag{7.18}$$

The proportionality factor, μ_e, is called the *mobility* of the electron in the specific gas. The same equation applies to ions when their mobility, μ_i, is employed.

According to Eq. (4.23), the current density because of the drift of electrons along the x-axis is

$$J = -e \int v_x f'(v) \, dv \tag{7.19}$$

where $f'(v)$ expresses the number of electrons per cubic meter possessing velocities between v and $v + dv$. By following the development employed in Chap. 4, Eq. (7.19) may be written as

$$J = -\frac{4\pi}{3} \frac{e^2 E_x}{m} \int_0^\infty \lambda_e \frac{\partial f_0'}{\partial v} v^2 \, dv \tag{7.20}$$

where λ_e is the electron mfp and

$$f'(v) = \frac{\lambda}{v} \left[\frac{\partial f_0'}{\partial x} - \frac{eE_x}{mv_x} \frac{\partial f_0'}{\partial v_x} \right]$$

according to Eq. (4.31). The first term in the brackets can exist only if there is a significant thermal gradient. Except in arcs and stellar atmospheres this term is negligible.

The current density may also be written as

$$J = nev_d$$

where n is the electron density. Therefore, the drift velocity is

$$v_d = -\frac{4\pi}{3} \frac{eE_x}{mn} \int_0^\infty \lambda_e \frac{\partial f_0'}{\partial v} v^2 \, dv \tag{7.21}$$

Often it is more convenient to deal with electrical conductivity, σ, instead of drift velocity. Because

$$\sigma_x = \frac{J_x}{E_x}$$

then

$$\sigma = -\frac{4\pi}{3} \frac{e^2}{m} \int_0^\infty \lambda \frac{\partial f_0'}{\partial v} v^2 \, dv \quad \text{mhos/m} \tag{7.22}$$

Equation (7.21) may also be applied to ions if their relatively large mass is taken into account. Let M be the mass of the ambient gas and m the mass of the ion. It can be shown that Eq. (7.21) may be written as

$$v_d = -\frac{4\pi}{3}\frac{eE_x}{n}\frac{M+m}{Mm}\int_0^\infty \lambda \frac{\partial f_0'}{\partial v} v^2 \, dv \qquad (7.23)$$

7.3 Ion mobility

Expressions for the mobility of ions and electrons have been derived by many investigators. A very comprehensive discussion of this subject is given by Loeb* and the reader contemplating work along these lines should review this material. In the following discussion, expressions for the mobility of the ion and the electron will be derived, based upon a very simplified theory. These results are of value only in discussing the major factors affecting mobility. For actual computations, the generally accepted equations of Langevin and Compton will be introduced.

The derivations of the simple expressions for ion and electron mobility are approached in a similar manner, based upon the expression derived in Sec. 2.8 for the fraction of particles that have not yet experienced a collision because of an x-component of motion. According to Eq. (2.76) the fraction is

$$f_x = \epsilon^{-x/\lambda} \qquad (7.24)$$

where λ is the corresponding mfp of the ion or the electron moving in a certain ambient gas at prescribed pressure and temperature.

Two simplifying assumptions are common to both derivations:

1. Neither the ions nor electrons exert forces on neutral particles.
2. The ion or electron concentration is everywhere uniform so that there are no diffusion currents caused by concentration gradients.

At this point the derivations diverge in general character. *The ions are assumed to make only elastic collisions with the gas.* Also, the average drift velocity of the ion is assumed to be on the same order of magnitude, or less than, the average thermal velocity (*agitation velocity*) of the gas. Experimental data show that the mobility remains constant under this condition. The electrons, on the other hand, give up very little energy to the gas molecules in any elastic collision because of the large difference in the mass of each of these particles. The elastic collisions only serve to scatter the electrons. As a result, the electrons' energy increases and inelastic collisions occur—which are, in fact, the only collisions of interest. *The electrons are assumed to make inelastic collisions and thus start each free path from rest.*

* L. B. Loeb, *Fundamental Processes of Electrical Discharge in Gases*, John Wiley & Sons, New York, 1939, and *Basic Processes of Gaseous Electronics*, University of California Press, Berkeley, 1955.

For *ions*, the fraction of free paths that lie within x and $x + dx$ and that have not terminated in an elastic collision is

$$\frac{1}{\lambda} f_x \, dx$$

The average distance traveled by an ion in the direction of the electric field may be expressed statistically as

$$L_{avg} = \int_0^\infty L \frac{1}{\lambda} f_x \, dx \tag{7.25}$$

The position of a specific ion is given by

$$L = \int \int a \, dt \, dt + \int v_0 \, dt + x_0$$

The acceleration is $a = f/m$ where f is the force on the ion and m is its mass. For a singly ionized molecule the acceleration is eE/m where e is the electronic charge and E is the electric field strength. Let the ion initially start at rest at $x_0 = 0$. Then $L = eEt^2/2m$. The time of transit, t, of a specific ion is dependent upon the path length. However, the average velocity of the ions is a constant and the x-component of motion of a specific ion is $x = v_a t$. With these substitutions the average path length in the presence of an external electric field, E, may be expressed by

$$L_{avg} = \frac{eE}{2m\lambda v_a^2} \int_0^\infty x^2 \epsilon^{-x/\lambda} \, dx$$

$$= \frac{eE\lambda^2}{mv_a^2} \tag{7.26}$$

If the *drift velocity* is taken as the average distance traveled in the direction of the electric field divided by the average time between collisions, then

$$v_d = \frac{L_{avg}}{\lambda/v_a} = \frac{eE\lambda}{mv_a} \tag{7.27}$$

The mobility of the ion is then

$$\mu = \frac{v_d}{E} = \frac{e\lambda}{mv_a} \tag{7.28a}$$

Compton* suggests a more accurate equation for the mobility:

$$\mu = \frac{8}{3\pi} \frac{e}{m} \frac{\lambda}{v_a} \left(\frac{m + M}{M} \right)^{\frac{1}{2}} \tag{7.28b}$$

where m is the mass of the ion and M is the mass of the ambient gas molecules.

From Eq. (7.27) the drift velocity may be written in function notation as

$$v_d = f\left(\frac{E}{P}\right) \tag{7.29}$$

* K. T. Compton and I. Langmuir, *Rev. Modern Phys.*, **2**, 123 (April 1930).

because the mfp, λ, is inversely proportional to pressure P. For this reason, experimental data on drift velocity are usually plotted using E/P as the independent variable. The pressure is usually expressed in mm Hg. A very interesting, typical plot of this type by Varney* is shown in Fig. 7.4. This is a plot of v_d for nitrogen ions in nitrogen gas. (It is always necessary to identify the species of ion as well as the type of ambient gas—for example, experiments may be done with nitrogen ions in argon gas, etc.)

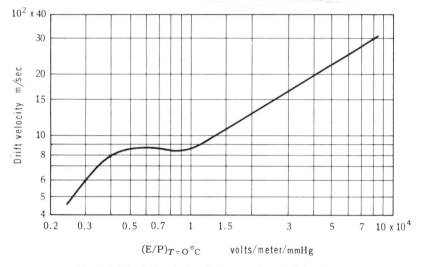

Fig. 7.4. The drift velocity of nitrogen ions (N_2^+) in nitrogen gas as a function of E/P. (From R. N. Varney, *Phys. Rev.*, **89**, 709, 1953.)

For values of E/P (volts/meter $\times$ mm Hg) greater than 10^4 the drift velocity is a linear function of E/P. The mobility varies little in this range. Remember that mobility is defined as the *ratio* of v_d/E and *not* the derivative. This linear portion of the curve is caused by N_2^+ ions acting as the predominant charge carrier. At low values of E/P, Varney suggests that the predominant charge carrier is N_4^+, which is formed according to the reversible reaction

$$N_2^+ + N_2 \longrightarrow N_4^+ \tag{7.30}$$

$$N_4^+ + N_2 \longrightarrow N_2^+ + 2N_2 \tag{7.31}$$

For $3700 < (E/P) < 9000$, a transition region exists. For low (E/P) the attachment reaction (Eq. (7.30)) applies. For high values of (E/P), attachment is much less probable and any large ions so formed are quickly broken by collision according to Eq. (7.31). In the transition region, both

* R. N. Varney, *Phys. Rev.*, **89**, 708 (1953).

reactions are in operation and of the same order of magnitude. Figure 7.5 is a plot of the *reduced mobility*,

$$\mu_0 = \frac{v_d}{E}\left[\frac{P}{760}\right]\left[\frac{273}{T}\right] \tag{7.32}$$

taken from the data of Fig. 7.4. The factor of $P/760$ expresses the actual pressure P as a fraction of atmospheric pressure. The factor $273/T$ corrects for changes in mobility because of variations in gas density caused by varying temperature. It does not correct for the small variations of mobility with temperature under conditions of constant density. Thus, the mobility is obtained by taking the ratio $v_d/(E/P)$ from Fig. 7.4 and dividing by 760.

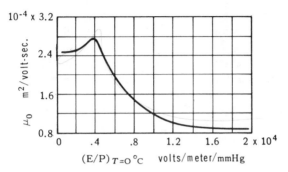

Fig. 7.5. The mobility of N_2^+ in N_2 at 0°C and 760 mm Hg as a function of E/P. (From R. N. Varney, *Phys. Rev.*, **89**, 710, 1953.)

Table 7.2 lists the reduced mobility of several species of ions in a gas of their own type.

Table 7.2

Reduced ion mobilities* at standard conditions
and $E/P = 6000$ v/m × mm Hg

Ion	Gas	Mobility (m²/volt-sec)
He$^+$	He	8.1 × 10^{-4}
Ne$^+$	Ne	2.4 × 10^{-4}
A$^+$	A	1.29 × 10^{-4}
Kr$^+$	Kr	0.77 × 10^{-4}
Xe$^+$	Xe	0.45 × 10^{-4}
H$^+$	H$_2$	18.3 × 10^{-4}
H$_2^+$	H$_2$	13.9 × 10^{-4}
N$_2^+$	N$_2$	1.86 × 10^{-4}

* The data used in these computations are from the papers of E. A. Mason and J. T. Vanderslice, *Phys. Rev.*, **114**, 499 (1959); J. A. Hornbeck, *Phys. Rev.*, **80**, 297 (1950); **83**, 374 (1951); **84**, 615 and 1072 (1951); R. N. Varney, *Phys. Rev.*, **88**, 362 (1952); **89**, 708 (1953); L. A. Chanin and M. A. Biondi, *Phys. Rev.*, **94**, 910 (1954).

In view of Eq. (7.32), the mobility under other than standard pressure can be written in terms of the reduced mobility, μ_0, at standard conditions because

$$\mu = \mu_0 \left[\frac{760}{P}\right]\left[\frac{T}{273}\right] \tag{7.33}$$

or, in terms of gas density, ρ,

$$\mu = \mu_0 \frac{\rho_0}{\rho} \tag{7.34}$$

It is difficult to obtain absolute values of ion mobility for several basic reasons. First, it must be possible for the average ion to make a reasonable number of collisions in crossing the drift space in the experimental measuring apparatus. This is not possible if the dimensions for the drift space are on the same order of magnitude as the mfp of the ion. For this reason, very low pressures are usually out of the question. Second, the number of collisions per second per unit volume is quite high and can easily be ten to a thousand times the impurity concentration. This means that a noticeable number of ions collide with foreign molecules each second, and thereby modify the measured value of mobility. Third, many gases that form multi-charged molecules or molecular clusters cannot maintain themselves very long because of splitting and charge transfer caused by collision. This is known as the *Kallmann-Rosen effect**

These effects yield one value of mobility if the measurement is made in a very short time. If sufficient time is permitted to elapse before or during the measurement, the history of the ions becomes very complex. Their character changes as a result of many collisions. Modern measurement techniques are directed at overcoming these problems.

The mobility of an ion is relatively insensitive to temperature changes provided the density is held constant. The data available indicates about a ten per cent increase in mobility as the temperature is raised from $100°K$ to $500°K$ at constant density.

Several equations are available which permit calculating the mobility of ions of a given species in a gas. These expressions are based upon a theory that assumes that the energy of the ion is on the same order of magnitude as the thermal energy of the neutral gas molecules. The two most successful derivations are those of Langevin[†] and Hassé and Cook.[‡] The result of each of these approaches is nearly the same. Therefore, only the Langevin equation will be considered. In the cgs system of units,

$$\mu = \frac{3}{16 Y} \frac{0.462\sqrt{(M + m)/m}}{(\rho/\rho_0)\sqrt{(D_0 - 1)M_0}} \quad \text{cm}^2/\text{volt-second} \tag{7.35}$$

* See L. B. Loeb, *Atomic Structure*, John Wiley & Sons, New York, 1938, pp. 287, 324.
† P. Langevin, *Ann. Chim. et Phys.*, **8**, 238 (1905).
‡ H. R. Hassé and W. R. Cook, *Phil. Mag.*, **12**, 554 (1931).

where M_0 is the molecular weight, the mass of the gas molecule is M, and that of the ions is m. The relative dielectric constant of the gas at standard conditions is D_0 and the gas density is ρ. The gas density at standard conditions is ρ_0. The variable $3/16Y$ is a function of the variable

$$\lambda = \frac{e}{2\sigma^2} \sqrt{\frac{D_0 - 1}{2\pi P_0}} \qquad (7.36)$$

where e is the electronic charge and P_0 is the pressure at standard conditions expressed in dynes/cm². The dielectric constant can be obtained from tables.

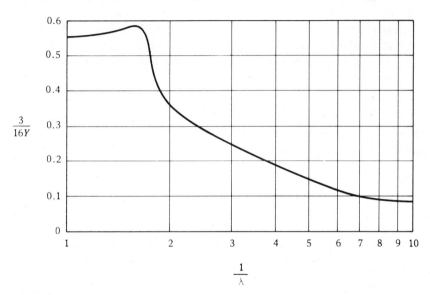

Fig. 7.6. Langevin's functional dependence between $\frac{3}{16} Y$ and λ.

The term σ is the distance between centers of mass of the ion and the molecule. It can be assumed to be equal to the average collision radii of the ion and molecule.

$$\sigma = \frac{1}{2}(\sigma_m + \sigma_M) \qquad (7.37)$$

The correct values to use for σ_m and σ_M are in doubt. Values determined by viscosity measurements are not usually satisfactory.

Langevin evaluated the functional dependence between $3/16Y$ and λ. A plot of this relationship appears in Fig. 7.6. To convert Eq. (7.35) to the mks system, multiply the mobility by 10^{-4}. The units will then be m²/volt-second.

7.4   Electron mobility

The derivation of the basic expression for *electron mobility* begins in the same manner as that used for computing the mobility of the ion. Again, the fraction of electron free paths that lie within x and dx, and that have not terminated in an *inelastic* collision, is

$$\frac{1}{\lambda_e} f(x)\, dx = \frac{1}{\lambda_e} \epsilon^{-x/\lambda_e}\, dx \tag{7.38}$$

Each electron is assumed to start its free path from rest after making a prior inelastic collision. The electron, therefore, only possesses a component of velocity parallel to the applied electric field. This is different from the ion which was scattered at random at its last collision and possesses considerable velocity in directions perpendicular to the applied electric field. The energy of an electron is

$$\frac{mv^2}{2} = eEx \tag{7.39}$$

where v is the velocity of the electron at a position x meters from the last collision. From Eq. (7.39)

$$x = \frac{mv^2}{2eE} \tag{7.40}$$

and

$$dx = \frac{mv}{eE}\, dv \tag{7.41}$$

If Eqs. (7.40) and (7.41) are used to replace x and dx, then the number of electrons that possess terminal velocities between v and $v + dv$ is

$$f(v)\, dv = \frac{mv}{\lambda_e eE} \epsilon^{-mv^2/2eE\lambda_e}\, dv \tag{7.42}$$

Statistically, the average drift velocity is

$$v_d = \int_0^\infty v f(v)\, dv$$

provided that $f(v)$ is normalized.

$$v_d = \frac{m}{\lambda_e eE} \int_0^\infty v^2 \epsilon^{-mv^2/2eE\lambda_e}\, dv$$

$$= \sqrt{\frac{\pi \lambda_e eE}{2m}} \tag{7.43}$$

The electron mobility is

$$\mu_e = \frac{v_d}{E} = \sqrt{\frac{\pi \lambda_e e}{2mE}} \quad \text{m}^2/\text{volt-second} \tag{7.44}$$

Compton[*] and others have applied more rigorous analysis to the problem with the result that *if the electron energy distribution is or can be assumed to be Maxwellian*, then

$$\mu_e = 0.775\left(\frac{e\lambda}{mE}\right)^{\frac{1}{2}}(f)^{\frac{1}{4}} \quad \text{m}^2/\text{volt-second} \tag{7.45}$$

where f is the fraction of energy that an electron loses to a gas particle upon making an *elastic* collision.

$$f = 2.66 \frac{mM}{(m+M)^2}\left(1 - \frac{Mv_m^2}{mv_{em}^2}\right) \tag{7.46}$$

where v_m and v_{em} are the rms velocities of the gas molecule and of the electron, respectively.

Loeb[†] points out that in many applied calculations the results obtained for electron mobility by use of Eq. (7.45) are quite satisfactory, even if the electron energy distribution is not Maxwellian.

7.5   Deionization

In an ionized gas the free electrons and positive ions usually possess energies greater than the thermal energies of the ambient neutral gas molecules. Thus, if an electron is to combine with a positive ion to form a neutral molecule, all kinetic energy of these two particles in excess of normal thermal kinetic energy must be transferred to some third body. It is asking a great deal to expect an electron and a positive ion to unite and simultaneously find a third body to which to release their excess kinetic energy. It is much more probable that one or the other of these charged particles will encounter the third body *before* they unite. Because the electron is considerably more mobile than the positive ion, it is the particle most likely to encounter the third body first.

Two third bodies are readily available to the electron. The walls of the vessel are one. The electrons diffuse to the walls where they give up their kinetic energy as heat. Positive ions also diffuse to the walls where they also give up the greater part of their kinetic energy and unite with an electron to form a neutral molecule. After some microseconds the neutral gas molecule is released from the wall (see Fig. 7.7).

The second type of third body that is available is one of the neutral gas molecules. By the attachment process discussed in Sec. 7.1, a free electron may attach itself to certain types of gases. The negative ion formed may collide with a positive ion (see Fig. 7.8). When the electron attached itself to

[*] Compton and Langmuir, *Rev. Modern Phys.*, **2**, 219 (1930).
[†] L. B. Loeb, *Basic Processes of Gaseous Electronics*, University of California Press, Berkeley, 1955, p. 226.

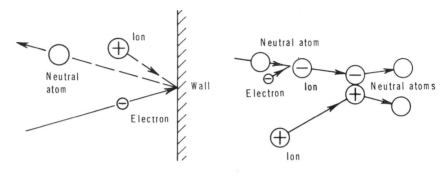

Fig. 7.7. Surface deionization where the wall serves as the third body.

Fig. 7.8. Volume deionization where a negative ion is formed and acts as the third body.

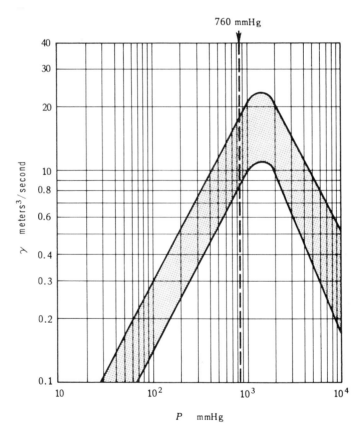

Fig. 7.9. The variation in the recombination coefficient as a function of pressure for common gases.

the neutral molecule, it transferred its kinetic energy to the negative ion that was formed. Now, when these two ions collide, a charge exchange may take place and, at the same time, the two neutral molecules formed may redistribute their kinetic energies in the collision.

The time rate of electron (or negative ion) and positive ion recombination is proportional to the concentration of negative ions, n^-, and positive ions, n^+, that is,

$$rn^-n^+$$

where r is the recombination coefficient. This is similar to the recombination of electrons and holes in semiconductors (see Sec. 4.6).

In many cases it suffices to assume that the concentrations of negative and positive ions are equal. In such cases $n^- = n^+$ and the time rate of change of ion concentration is

$$\frac{dn}{dt} = -rn^2 \tag{7.47}$$

where the minus sign accounts for the time decrease in concentration. The solution to Eq. (7.47) is

$$n = \frac{n_0}{1 + rn_0 t} \tag{7.48}$$

where n_0 is the concentration of ion pairs (one negative and one positive ion form a pair) at time $t = 0$. The recombination coefficient is a function of pressure. The recombination coefficients for many of the commonly encountered gases fall within the shaded region of Fig. 7.9.

7.6 Space charge

The presence of any concentration of charge carriers has a pronounced effect upon the potential distribution throughout any high-vacuum or gaseous electron device. Neglecting the effect of *space charge* upon the potential distribution can result in conclusions that are completely erroneous. Figure 7.10 is a plot of the potential distribution, $V(x)$, between a plane-parallel cathode or anode under different conditions of electron or ion flow. The pressure is assumed to be sufficiently low so that the mfp of the charge carriers is much greater than the interelectrode spacing.

Curve (a) of Fig. 7.10 is the usual straight-line linear relationship between potential and position that is expected for this type of electrode configuration when there is a negligible space charge present. It is easy to demonstrate that this is the proper relationship by applying Poisson's equation to the problem. (The reader may wish to refer to Chap. 9 to review the derivation of this equation.)

$$\nabla^2 V = -\frac{\rho}{\epsilon_0} \tag{7.49}$$

If there is no charge density in the region between the plates, then $\rho = 0$ and Poisson's equation reduces to Laplace's equation

$$\nabla^2 V = 0 \qquad (7.50)$$

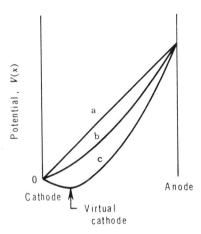

Because the plates are plane and parallel, there is only a variation of potential in the direction normal to the plates (x-direction). Equation (7.50) may be written as

$$\frac{d^2V}{dx^2} = 0 \qquad (7.51)$$

Integration yields

$$V(x) = C_1 x + C_2 \qquad (7.52)$$

where C_1 and C_2 are integration constants. If the cathode is taken as the reference for measuring potential, $x = 0$, then $C_2 = 0$. The voltage is therefore a linear function of the distance x.

Fig. 7.10. The potential distribution in a plane-parallel plate diode. Curve (a) is for no space charge, curve (b) is for space charge but no emission velocity, and curve (c) is for space charge when the electron-emission velocity is noticeable.

Suppose that electrons are emitted by the cathode with zero initial velocity. The region between the cathode and anode now contains an electric charge distribution and Poisson's equation must apply.

$$\frac{d^2V}{dx^2} = -\frac{\rho}{\epsilon_0} \qquad (7.53)$$

Let the electron current density be

$$J = -\rho v \qquad (7.54)$$

The energy of the electron is

$$\frac{mv^2}{2} = eV \qquad (7.55)$$

Solve Eqs. (7.54) and (7.55) for the charge density, ρ.

$$\rho = -\frac{J}{v} = -J\left(\frac{m}{2eV}\right)^{\frac{1}{2}} \qquad (7.56)$$

If this value for charge density is substituted into Eq. (7.53), then

$$\frac{d^2V}{dx^2} = \frac{J}{\epsilon_0}\left(\frac{m}{2eV}\right)^{\frac{1}{2}} \qquad (7.57)$$

Multiply both sides of this equation by $2\ dV/dx$ and integrate.

$$2\left(\frac{dV}{dx}\right)\left(\frac{d^2V}{dx^2}\right) = \frac{J}{\epsilon_0}\left(\frac{m}{2e}\right)^{1/2} 2V^{-1/2}\frac{dV}{dx}$$

$$\left(\frac{dV}{dx}\right)^2 = \frac{4J}{\epsilon_0}\left(\frac{m}{2e}\right)^{1/2} V^{1/2} + C_1 \qquad (7.58)$$

The gradient, $-dV/dx$, is always zero when the potential, V, is zero. Thus, $C_1 = 0$.

A second integration yields

$$\frac{4V^{3/4}}{3} = \left(\frac{4J}{\epsilon_0}\right)^{1/2}\left(\frac{m}{2e}\right)^{1/4} x + C_2 \qquad (7.59)$$

The cathode may be taken as reference potential and the origin, $x = 0$. For this reason $C_2 = 0$. The current density is

$$J = \frac{4\epsilon_0}{9\left(\frac{m}{2e}\right)^{1/2}} \frac{V^{3/2}(x)}{x^2} \quad \text{amp/m}^2 \qquad (7.60)$$

Equation (7.60) may be applied to ions or electrons (but not to a mixture). Evaluate the constants of Eq. (7.60) for the case of the electron:

$$J = \frac{2.335 \times 10^{-6} V^{3/2}(x)}{x^2} \quad \text{amp/m}^2 \qquad (7.61)$$

where the potential $V(x)$ corresponds to the position x, between cathode and anode. Normally only the potential, $V(d)$ at the anode $(x = d)$, is known and used in these equations.

This three-halves power variation of current density with voltage is caused by the *space charge* of the electrons as they move from cathode to anode. This is shown in curve (b) of Fig. 7.10. Equation (7.61) is often called *Child's law* or the *Child-Langmuir law* and written as

$$J = KV^a \qquad (7.62)$$

where $a \approx \frac{3}{2}$. This relationship closely fits actual diode vacuum tubes. The exponent, a, commonly varies between 1.35 and 1.65. Both the exponent a and the coefficient K are readily obtained by plotting $\log J$ as a function of $\log V$.

$$\log J = \log K + a \log V \qquad (7.63)$$

This is the equation of a straight line on log-log paper *provided the origin for the independent variable, log V, is at log 1.* The slope yields a and the intercept, on the ordinate axis, yields $\log K$.

Should the average electron possess a noticeable emission velocity, then the potential distribution between cathode and anode assumes the form of

curve (c), Fig. 7.10. The point where the electric field is zero is called the
virtual cathode. All electrons that reach the anode may be assumed to have
been emitted by a _virtual cathode_ located at this point.

On the other hand, if the region between the cathode and anode is at
a sufficiently _high pressure_ so that the mfp of the electrons emitted by the
cathode is small compared to the interelectrode spacing, then the electrons
drift from cathode to anode according to

$$v_d = \mu E \tag{7.64}$$

This is in contrast to the high-vacuum case where the instantaneous velocity
of the electrons is

$$v = \left(\frac{2eV}{m}\right)^{\frac{1}{2}}$$

The current density in the high-pressure case is

$$J = -nev_d = -\rho\mu E_x = -\rho\mu\frac{dV}{dx} \tag{7.65}$$

where it is assumed that the electric field is low enough so that the mobility,
μ, remains constant and ionization of the gas by electron collision does not
occur. Substitute the value for ρ from Eq. (7.65) into Poisson's equation:

$$\frac{d^2V}{dx^2} = \frac{J}{\epsilon_0}\frac{1}{\mu}\left(\frac{dV}{dx}\right)^{-1} \tag{7.66}$$

Multiply Eq. (7.66) by $2(dV/dx)$ and integrate with respect to dx.

$$2\left(\frac{dV}{dx}\right)\frac{d^2V}{dx^2} = \frac{2J}{\epsilon_0\mu}$$

$$\left(\frac{dV}{dx}\right)^2 = \frac{2J}{\epsilon_0\mu}x + D_1 \tag{7.67}$$

If it assumed that there is a sufficient number of electrons emitted when the
electric field at the cathode is zero, then the constant of integration, D_1, may
be set equal to zero.

$$\frac{dV}{dx} = \left(\frac{2J}{\epsilon_0\mu}\right)^{\frac{1}{2}}x^{\frac{1}{2}}$$

A second integration yields

$$V = \frac{2}{3}\left(\frac{2J}{\epsilon_0\mu}\right)^{\frac{1}{2}}x^{\frac{3}{2}} \tag{7.68}$$

The cathode has been taken as the origin for measuring potential; therefore,
the integration constant is zero.

It is interesting to note that the current density in this case depends upon
the square of the voltage,

$$J = \frac{9}{8}\frac{\epsilon_0\mu V^2(x)}{x^3} \tag{7.69}$$

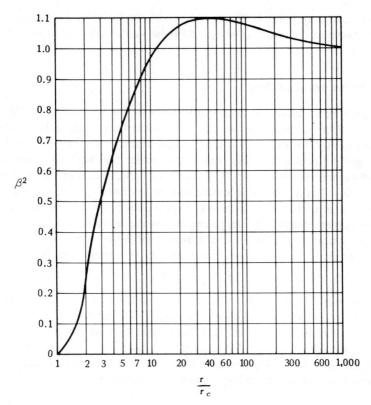

Fig. 7.11. The Langmuir-Compton function, β^2, for cylindrical electrode structures.

instead of $V^{3/2}$ as in the high-vacuum case. Also, the mass of the charge carriers does not enter into Eq. (7.69). This equation may be applied to ions as well as electrons (no mixtures).

If the constants are evaluated ($\epsilon_0 = 8.85 \times 10^{-12}$), then

$$J = \frac{9.94 \times 10^{-12} \mu V^2(x)}{x^3} \quad \text{amp/m}^2 \tag{7.70}$$

Many practical electron devices are designed around a coaxial cylindrical structure. For the case of a *high vacuum* and an anode coaxial with and surrounding the cathode, an expression for the *current per unit length* has been determined by Langmuir and Compton.*

$$\frac{I}{l} = 14.66 \times 10^{-6} \frac{V^{3/2}(r)}{r\beta^2} \quad \text{amp/unit length} \tag{7.71}$$

where the factor β^2 is plotted in Fig. 7.11 as a function of the ratio of the radial

* I. Langmuir and K. T. Compton, *Rev. Modern Phys.*, **3**, 247 (1931).

position, r, of any point to the radius, r_c, of the cathode. Normally, $V(r)$ is only known at the anode $(r = r_a)$ and these values are used in evaluating Eq. (7.71).

7.7   Electron and ion diffusion

In addition to moving with a drift velocity in the presence of an electric field, both electrons and ions move by diffusion as long as any concentration gradients exist. This diffusion is identical in character to that displayed by neutral gas molecules. For this reason, the reader may wish to review Sec. 2.10 before proceeding further. The concept of charge carrier diffusion was first introduced in Sec. 4.6 and should also be reviewed.

If a charge carrier concentration, n, possesses a spatial gradient ∇n, a material current density of charge carriers *moves away* from the region of *increased* concentration or *toward* a region of *lesser* concentration. This diffusion of charge carriers gives rise to an electric current density,

$$\mathbf{J}_D = -eD\nabla n \tag{7.72}$$

where the minus sign indicates that the diffusion is away from a region of increased concentration. The electronic charge is e and the diffusion coefficient is D. The diffusion coefficient has a unique value for the particular species of ion (or the electron) in a particular gas.

According to Eq. (2.90), the diffusion coefficient for a gas of type 1 and concentration n_1 into a gas of type 2 and concentration n_2 is

$$D = \frac{8}{\pi} \frac{\zeta_1 \lambda_1^2 n_2 + \zeta_2 \lambda_2^2 n_1}{n_1 + n_2} \quad \text{m}^2/\text{sec} \tag{7.73}$$

where ζ is the collision frequency of each gas and λ is the mean free path. The factor $8/\pi$ has been used to replace $\frac{1}{3}$ according to Maxwell-Boltzmann statistics. The collision frequency may be expressed in terms of the average velocity, v_a, of the gas.

$$\zeta = \frac{v_a}{\lambda}$$

With this substitution,

$$D = \frac{8}{\pi} \frac{v_{a1} \lambda_1 n_2 + v_{a2} \lambda_2 n_1}{n_1 + n_2} \tag{7.74}$$

The total concentration is $n = n_1 + n_2$.

In Sec. 6.1 the diffusion of charge carriers across metal-to-semiconductor junctions was discussed. It was shown that the diffusion coefficient can be expressed in terms of the mobility. The relationship (Eq. (6.12)) is

$$D = \frac{\mu k T}{e} \tag{7.75}$$

and is known as the *Einstein relation*. This equation makes it possible to determine the diffusion coefficient from a measurement of the mobility. The Einstein relation was developed for the case where no externally applied electric field is used; therefore, a value of μ corresponding to a very small (E/P) should be used.

For instance, from Fig. 7.5 the low field value of reduced mobility for N_2^+ ions in N_2 gas is about 2.5×10^{-4} m²/volt-second. This is the mobility at 273°K and a pressure of 760 mm Hg. The corresponding reduced diffusion coefficient is

$$D_0 = \mu_0 \frac{kT}{e} \tag{7.76}$$

The term $kT/e = 0.0235$ for $T = 273°K$. Therefore, Eq. (7.76) may be written as

$$D_0 = 0.0235\mu_0$$

The reduced coefficient for N_2^+ is 0.059×10^{-4} m²/sec. The diffusion coefficient, D, for any temperature and pressure is found by determining the mobility, μ, under these conditions and substituting into Eq. (7.75). Table 7.3 lists the reduced diffusion coefficients for some of the common gases.

Table 7.3

Reduced diffusion coefficients at standard conditions*

Ion	Gas	Diffusion coefficient (m²/sec)
He$^+$	He	0.247×10^{-4}
Ne$^+$	Ne	0.093×10^{-4}
A$^+$	A	0.031×10^{-4}
Kr$^+$	Kr	0.020×10^{-4}
Xe$^+$	Xe	0.012×10^{-4}
H$^+$	H	0.430×10^{-4}
N$_2^+$	N$_2$	0.054×10^{-4}

* Data taken from references listed in Table 7.2. The lowest available values of E/P were used.

The net current density, J, that arises from one species of charge carrier in any region of space consists of the sum of two components. One is the current density, J_d, because of carrier drift velocity in the presence of an externally applied electric field. The other is the diffusion current density, J_D, which is caused by the diffusion of charge carriers in regions where their concentration is not uniform. For positive ions,

$$\mathbf{J}^+ = \mathbf{J}_d^+ + \mathbf{J}_D^+$$
$$= en^+\mathbf{v}_d^+ - eD^+\nabla n^+$$
$$= en\mu^+\mathbf{E} - eD^+\nabla n^+ \tag{7.77}$$

For negative ions or electrons

$$J^- = -en\mu^-\mathbf{E} - eD^-\nabla n^- \tag{7.78}$$

From Eqs. (7.77) and (7.78), the net velocities of the positive and negative ions are, respectively,

$$\mathbf{v}^+ = \mu^+\mathbf{E} - \frac{D^+}{n^+}\nabla n^+ \tag{7.79}$$

and

$$\mathbf{v}^- = -\mu^-\mathbf{E} - \frac{D^-}{n^-}\nabla n^- \tag{7.80}$$

If a homogeneous mixture of positive and negative ions exists and $n^+ = n^- = n$, then $\nabla n^+ = \nabla n^- = \nabla n$. Further, *if the net velocities of the two charge carriers can be assumed equal*, then $\mathbf{v}^+ = \mathbf{v}^- = \mathbf{v}$. Under these special conditions a simultaneous solution of Eqs. (7.79) and (7.80) yields a net velocity for either charge carrier of

$$\mathbf{v} = -\frac{D^+\mu^- + D^-\mu^+}{n(\mu^+ + \mu^-)}\nabla n \tag{7.81}$$

From this equation an *average* or *ambipolar diffusion coefficient* for mixed ions may be defined.

$$D_a = \frac{D^+\mu^- + D^-\mu^+}{\mu^+ + \mu^-} \tag{7.82}$$

7.8 Diffusion currents

The general principles of ion diffusion can be illustrated by means of the experimental arrangement shown in Fig. 7.12. An ion cloud is produced in the immediate region of the origin at time $t = 0$. Let the ion distribution vary only in the x-direction.* The ion concentration also varies with time, so write $n(x, t)$ for the concentration. Let the two electrodes be connected by a low-impedance ammeter which fixes both electrodes at the same potential. This eliminates any external electric fields and any movement of the ions is by diffusion alone.

The incremental ion current density to electrode B, located a distance b from the origin, is

$$dJ_B(x, t) = \frac{v_D}{b}dQ(x, t) \tag{7.83}$$

The ratio b/v_D is the average diffusion transient time for ions. The differential charge, in an incremental volume of thickness dx and unit cross-sectional area, is $dQ(x, t)$.

$$dQ(x, t) = en(x, t)\,dx \tag{7.84}$$

* In practice the lateral diffusion in the y- and z-directions cannot always be neglected.

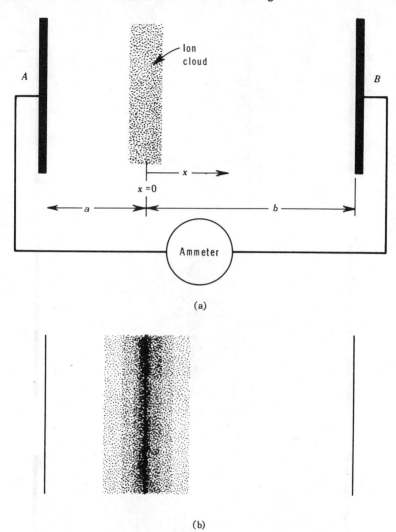

(a)

(b)

Fig. 7.12. The diffusion of an ion cloud. (a) Initial position and (b) position after an elapsed time.

The diffusion velocity is

$$v_D = - \frac{D}{n(x, t)} \frac{dn(x, t)}{dx} \qquad (7.85)$$

Substitute Eqs. (7.84) and (7.85) in Eq. (7.83) to obtain

$$dJ_B(x, t) = - \frac{eD}{b} dn(x, t) \qquad (7.86)$$

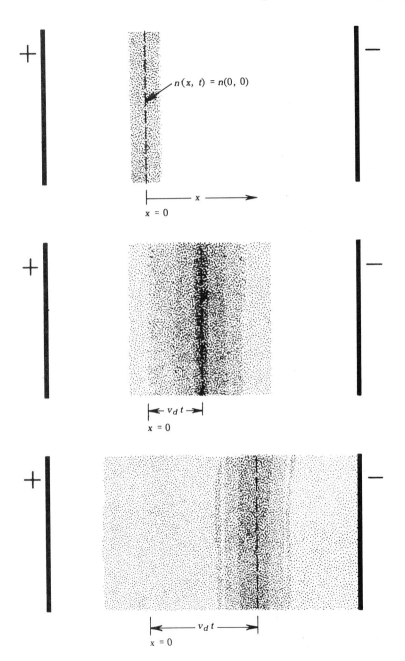

Fig. 7.13. Combined drift motion and diffusion of an ion cloud.

The total ion current density to electrode B is found by integrating over the interelectrode region from $x = 0$ to $x = b$.*

$$J_B(t) = -\frac{eD}{b}\int_{n_0}^{n_B} dn(t)$$

$$J_B(t) = \frac{eD}{b}[n_0(t) - n_B(t)] \tag{7.87}$$

The instantaneous current density to electrode B, therefore, is dependent only upon the difference in instantaneous ion densities at the two points. Because these two ion densities change with time, the magnitude of the current density also changes.

In a similar manner, the current density caused by ions diffusing to electrode A is

$$J_A(t) = -\frac{eD}{a}[n_0(t) - n_A(t)]$$

The net current in the external circuit is

$$J_{net}(t) = J_B(t) - J_A(t)$$

$$= eD\left[\left(\frac{1}{b} - \frac{1}{a}\right)n_0(t) + \left(\frac{n_A(t)}{a} - \frac{n_B(t)}{b}\right)\right] \tag{7.88}$$

If the electrodes are located equal distances apart ($a = b$), the first term vanishes. If the system is symmetrical, then $n_A = n_B$ and the net current density is zero.

The ions in this example could be positive or negative ions or electrons. If an externally applied electric field is present, then a component of velocity because of drift will be added to the motion of diffusion as shown in Fig. 7.13.

7.9   The general problem

Many problems involving the diffusion of charge carriers are quite complex and beyond the scope of this text. An insight into the general problem may be obtained by considering the case of two plane, parallel electrodes whose spacing is small compared to their cross-sectional dimensions. If this is the case, the lateral diffusion of charge carriers out of the *sensitive volume* between the electrodes is negligible.

Suppose that an ionizing source is present and produces N_0 *ion pairs per cubic meter per second*. Also, a small amount of recombination occurs in the gas within the sensitive volume at a rate of rn^-n^+ ion pairs/m^3/sec.

---

* The ion density is zero at each electrode but rises quickly to the interelectrode density $n(x)$ a very short distance from each electrode. The proper values of n_A and n_B to use would be those measured just beyond these transition regions.

The divergence of the current density at any point in space in the sensitive volume is equal to the *net production or loss* of ion pairs at the point.

$$\nabla \cdot \mathbf{J}^+ = \nabla \cdot \mathbf{J}^- = eN_0 - ern^-n^+ \qquad (7.89)$$

In this example, this may be written as

$$\frac{dJ}{dx} = eN_0 - ern^-n^+$$

Upon integration

$$J = \int eN_0 \, dx - \int ern^-n^+ \, dx + a \qquad (7.90)$$

where $N_0 \neq f(x)$ and a is the constant of integration.

An accurate evaluation of the recombination term requires an advance knowledge of the carrier concentrations, $n^-(x)$ and $n^+(x)$. Ion loss by volume recombination in a gas is usually small and this term is often neglected. Under this assumption,

$$J^+ = e \int_0^x N_0 \, dx + a^+ = eN_0x + a^+ = en^+v_d^+ - eD^+ \frac{dn^+}{dx} \qquad (7.91)$$

In a similar manner

$$J^- = eN_0x + a^- = -en^-v_d^- - eD^- \frac{dn^-}{dx} \qquad (7.92)$$

These two differential equations are of the form

$$D \frac{dn}{dx} - nv_d = -N_0x - \frac{a}{e} \qquad (7.93)$$

These equations may be solved for $n^+(x)$ and $n^-(x)$ (see Prob. 2 at the end of this chapter).

The electrode current is determined by the net rate at which carriers of the opposite sign arrive at a given electrode. The net rate of arrival of carriers is equal to the rate of creation of ion pairs in the sensitive volume, less the rate of diffusion of carriers of the same sign to this electrode, and less the diffusion of carriers of the opposite sign to the other electrode. Suppose the electrode in question is negative; then, its current is

$$I = e \int_K N_0 \, dK - \int_{S^-} \mathbf{J}^- \cdot d\mathbf{S}^- - \int_{S^+} \mathbf{J}^+ \cdot d\mathbf{S}^+ \qquad (7.94)$$

where dK is an increment of sensitive volume and is to be integrated over the entire sensitive volume. An increment of electrode surface area is $d\mathbf{S}$.

Equations (7.91) and (7.92) are to be substituted into Eq. (7.94) after applying the following electrode surface boundary conditions to these equations:

$$n^+ = n^- = 0, \qquad \mathbf{v}_d \cdot d\mathbf{S} = 0$$

With these substitutions the electrode current is

$$I = e \int_K N_0 \, dK + e \int_{S^-} D^-(\nabla n^-) \cdot dS^- + e \int_{S^+} D^+(\nabla n^+) \cdot dS^+ \quad (7.95)$$

The first term on the right-hand side of this equation represents the *saturation current* and is independent of any voltage applied between the two electrodes. The second and third terms will be negative after integration and thus reduce the electrode current. These two terms are voltage-dependent inasmuch as $n(x)$ varies with drift velocity (see Prob. 2).

If the indicated integration is carried out, the negative electrode current can be obtained (see Prob. 3). The current to the positive electrode is obtained in a similar manner. There are only two electrodes involved in this problem; therefore, the current in the external circuit is the sum of each electrode current.

PROBLEMS

1. Two plane-parallel electrodes are separated a distance b and a concentration gradient of positive ions is established in the sensitive volume between the electrodes. The concentration $n(x)$ varies only with spacing and is a maximum at one of the two electrodes. Let $n(x) = n_0 \epsilon^{-x/a}$. What is the current density to the other electrode?

2. For the example of Sec. 7.9, show that the solution to Eq. (7.93) for positive ions is

$$n^+(x) = \frac{N_0}{v_d^+}\left[x - b\,\frac{1 - \epsilon^{v_d^+ x/D^+}}{1 - \epsilon^{v_d^+ b/D^+}}\right]$$

where the constants of integration have been evaluated by use of the boundary conditions that require that the carrier density $n(x)$ be zero at the electrodes ($x = 0$ and $x = b$).

3. Use the result of Prob. 2 and show that the current collected by the negative electrode is

$$I = eN_0 K - \frac{eS^- D^- N_0}{v_d^-}\left[1 - b\,\frac{v_d^-}{D^-}\,\frac{1}{1 - \epsilon^{-v_d^- b/D^-}}\right]$$
$$- \frac{eS^+ D^+ N_0}{v_d^+}\left[1 + b\,\frac{v_d^+}{D^+}\,\frac{1}{1 - \epsilon^{v_d^+ b/D^+}}\right]$$

4. In the high-vacuum diode with planar electrodes, show that the voltage distribution between the electrodes may be written as

$$V(x) = V_a\left(\frac{x}{d}\right)^{4/3}$$

where V_a is the cathode-to-anode voltage and d is the interelectrode spacing. To do this, eliminate J between Eqs. (7.59) and (7.60).

5. Determine the expression for electron transit time in the high-vacuum diode. Neglect any initial electron velocity so that

$$\frac{dx}{dt} = \sqrt{\frac{2eV(x)}{m}}$$

Use the result of Prob. 4 to evaluate $V(x)$. *Ans.* $t_1 = 3d\left(\frac{2eV_a}{m}\right)^{-\frac{1}{2}}$

6. An argon-filled tube consists of two plane-parallel electrodes separated 7 cm. The pressure in the tube is 3×10^{-3} mm Hg and the velocity of the electron is essentially constant and equivalent to $5\sqrt{\text{volts}}$. At what distance from the cathode will half of those electrons that originate near the cathode have experienced a collision?

7. Compute by means of Eq. (7.27) the average velocity between collisions of a nitrogen ion (N_2^+) in nitrogen gas at a pressure of 10^{-2} mm Hg and 0°C. The experimental tube is equipped with plane-parallel electrodes spaced 5 cm, and a potential difference of 15 v is established between these electrodes. The proper value of drift velocity from Fig. 7.4 is 16 m/sec. What is the mobility of these ions under the above conditions?

8. Under the conditions of the preceding problem, compute the drift velocity and mobility of an electron in nitrogen gas.

9. Experimental data on three common types of diode high-vacuum rectifier tubes are presented in the following table. Plot the volt-ampere character-istics of each on rectilinear graph paper and also on log-log paper. For the log-log plot, be sure to start the abscissa axis at one volt because log 1 = 0 and therefore any straight-line plot can be interpreted as being of the form

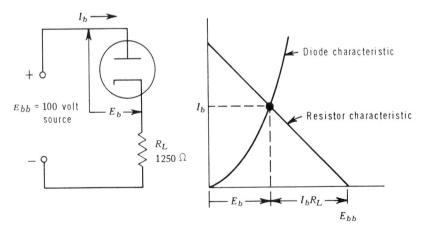

Fig. P7.9.

$y = b + ax$. From the log-log plot, evaluate the coefficients K and a in the Child-Langmuir equation.

e_b (volts)	Diode A i_b (ma)	Diode B i_b (ma)	Diode C i_b (ma)
0	0	0	0
5	22	11.5	4
10	68	26	9
15	127	42	16
20	200	65	25
25		95	34
30		124	44

10. Use the results of Prob. 9 to determine what anode current will flow in each tube when the anode-to-cathode voltage is 18 v. Obtain these answers graphically and analytically. A series circuit, as shown in the accompanying sketch, consists of one of these diodes, a 1250-ohm resistance, and a 100-v potential source. For each diode, determine graphically the anode current by plotting the volt-ampere characteristic of the resistor on the same graph (rectilinear plot) used for the tube characteristics. (*Hint:* See the sketch.)

11. A high-vacuum diode consists of a cathode and an anode that may be treated as plane-parallel electrodes, each 4 cm² in area. The cathode-to-anode spacing is 7 mm. Plot the volt-ampere characteristics of this tube. Determine the coefficients in the Child-Langmuir equation for this tube.

At approximately what pressure of neon gas would the tube in the preceding example begin to exhibit gas-tube characteristics? For operation at this pressure, plot the volt-ampere characteristics for anode-to-cathode voltages less than the first ionization potential of neon.

12. A vacuum tube of cylindrical symmetry is designed in Sec. 10.7. This tube consists of a cylindrical cathode that has a radius of 9.77×10^{-4} m and a concentric anode with a radius of 3.13×10^{-3} m. The effective length of the tube is 1.93×10^{-2} m. There is also a third electrode (grid) located between the cathode and anode. Neglect the presence of this electrode and plot the diode volt-ampere characteristics of this tube.

REFERENCES

1. L. B. Loeb, *Fundamental Processes of Electrical Discharges in Gases*, John Wiley & Sons, New York, 1939.

2. L. B. Loeb, *Basic Processes of Gaseous Electronics*, University of California Press, Berkeley, 1955.

3. J. D. Cobine, *Gaseous Conductors*, Dover Publications, Inc., New York, 1941 and 1958.

4. F. Llewellyn-Jones, *Ionization and Breakdown in Gases*, John Wiley & Sons, New York, 1956.

CHAPTER 8

Plasma and breakdown

It has been over 200 years since William Watson, in his London laboratory, studied the passage of electricity through gases at low pressures. It remained for J. S. Townsend and his co-workers, between 1900 and 1920, to introduce the first form of the general theory of electrical breakdown and the resulting conduction of electricity in gases.* In the following years L. B. Loeb and his associates have improved and extended Townsend's theories.†

Gas-filled electron tubes are used primarily for current rectification and voltage regulation. Also, in the field of illumination large numbers of gas tubes are used for indoor and street lighting as well as for advertising signs. Special-purpose gaseous electronic devices include transmit-receive switches for radar systems and Geiger tubes for radioactivity detectors. Basically, the operation of all of these devices is similar, and for this reason the subject of the electrical breakdown of gases and conduction of electricity in the resulting plasma will be treated in a general manner.

8.1 Plasma

Consider the case where the gas pressure is sufficiently high so that the mfp of the ions or electrons is small compared to the interelectrode spacing; also, the electric field strength is great enough so that ionizing collisions occur

* J. S. Townsend, *Electricity in Gases*, Oxford University Press, Fair Lawn, N.J., 1915.

† L. B. Loeb, *Fundamental Processes of Electrical Discharge in Gases*, John Wiley & Sons, New York, 1939. (The reader planning any extensive research on this subject should start with Loeb's recent treatise, *Basic Processes of Gaseous Electronics* University of California Press, Berkeley, 1955.)

in the gas. Under these conditions ion pairs (electron plus positive gas ion) fill most of the region between the cathode and anode. Any negative ions formed have a very short lifetime under these conditions because they collide with positive ions in a recombination process. This region is, therefore, filled with an essentially heterogeneous mixture of electrons and positive ions which is called a *plasma*.

In the plasma the electrons and positive ions both move about with random motion and, at the same time, each exhibits a drift velocity because of the applied electric field. The electrons drift opposite to the direction of the field and the positive ions drift with the field. The net current density caused by charge carrier drift is

$$J = (n^-e\mu^- + n^+e\mu^+)E \tag{8.1}$$

The electrons possess a mobility that is much greater than that of the positive ions. Also, the electron can lose very little energy in making an elastic collision with the ambient gas molecules because of its relatively small mass compared to the molecules'. For these reasons, the electrons constantly gain energy until they make inelastic collisions with the gas molecules. The net result is that the electrons perform the function of maintaining the plasma by creating new ion pairs to replace those that have recombined. Some photoionization is also present in a plasma and aids in supplying ion pairs.

In the preceding chapter it was pointed out that the probability of volume recombination in a gas is small, as is the probability of electron attachment. For these reasons, the loss of ion pairs from the plasma is caused primarily by electrons and ions diffusing to the walls and recombining there.

If the applied electric field is small, the electrons, positive ions, and neutral gas atoms may be in thermal equilibrium. In general, the *equivalent electron temperature* defined by

$$\tfrac{1}{2}mv_{em}^2 = \tfrac{3}{2}kT_e \tag{8.2}$$

is much greater than the temperature of the neutral gas. In Eq. (8.2) the rms electron velocity is v_{em} and the electron temperature is T_e. Actually, the electrons do not possess any thermal equilibrium temperature. The temperature, T_e, is merely a way of expressing the energy of the electrons.

The positive ions, on the other hand, possess a relatively low mobility and exchange a large proportion of their energy with neutral gas molecules at each elastic collision. For this reason, the *equivalent positive ion temperature*, T_i, is usually almost equal to the temperature of the neutral gas. This exchange of energy from the positive ions to the neutral gas raises the temperature of the gas.

Should the electric field be removed, the electrons, positive ions, and neutral molecules all reach a thermal equilibrium according to

$$\frac{mv_m^2}{2} = \frac{3}{2}kT$$

where v_m is the rms velocity of the particle in question. If an electric field is present, this thermal equilibrium is immediately destroyed and the kinetic energy of any of these three particles is given by

$$\frac{mv_m^2}{2} = \epsilon\left(\frac{3}{2}kT\right) \tag{8.3}$$

where the appropriate value of ϵ is to be used. For instance, for the electron a comparison of Eqs. (8.2) and (8.3) yields a relationship between the electron temperature and the gas temperature.

$$T_e = \epsilon^- T \tag{8.4}$$

The coefficient ϵ is determined by an equilibrium condition between the energy supplied by the external electric field to the electrons or ions and the energy lost by these charge carriers through collisions with the neutral gas. For positive ions, we may write

$$T_i = \epsilon^+ T \tag{8.5}$$

The coefficient is very nearly unity for positive ions unless the electric field is very large. Figure 8.1 displays the general range of ϵ^- for the common gases of the atmosphere. The coefficient is sometimes called the *Townsend factor*, or more commonly the *agitation energy coefficient*.

The presence of large concentrations of negative ions, with the attendant large rate of volume recombination in the gas, modifies the rate of elastic collisions in the ion-gas mixture to the extent that velocity distribution laws such as Maxwell's cannot easily be applied. For this reason, and because large negative ion concentrations are not commonly encountered, this condition will not be treated. In each case, a true plasma is assumed wherein the number of positive ions and the number of electrons present are equal. The assumption that a Maxwellian velocity distribution holds for a plasma is usually valid, because the drift velocity of the electrons and ions is usually small compared to the random thermal velocity of the charge carriers and neutral gas molecules.

The electronic conditions in a plasma are quite similar to those in a metallic conductor. The ions move relatively slowly compared to the fast, random motion of the electrons. As a result, a high-temperature electron gas moves under near-Maxwellian conditions through a space containing a uniform distribution of positive ions. The electron temperatures may reach $15,000°K$. Under d-c or low-frequency conditions, the drift motion of the positive ions must be considered. At high frequencies or under rapid transient conditions, the positive ions may be considered to be at rest compared to the drift velocities of the electrons.

Because of the equal and uniform concentration of the electrons and positive ions in a plasma, it is impossible for any space charges to occur. The result is a low voltage drop across the plasma even when large current densities are present. Electric field strengths on the order of 100 v/m are sufficient to maintain a plasma.

In the preceding chapter we mentioned the subject of the loss of electrons and ions from a sensitive volume. If the sensitive volume contains ion pairs at

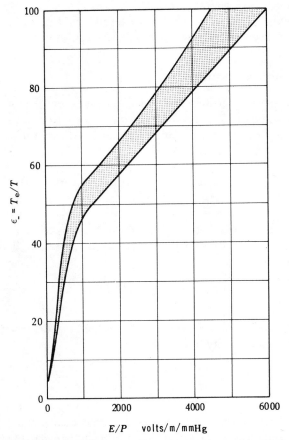

Fig. 8.1. The ratio of electron to neutral gas temperatures. (Data from J. S. Townsend and V. A. Bailey, *Phil. Mag.*, **42**, 873, 1921. Also R. H. Healey and J. W. Reed, p. 79, *Amalgamated Wireless, Ltd.*, Sidney, 1941.)

densities on the order of 10^{14} to 10^{17} pairs per cubic meter, then a true plasma exists. Any loss of ions can have a pronounced effect upon the operation of the electronic device. Ion loss by pair recombination in the volume is quite small and amounts to $rn^{+}n^{-}$ pairs per unit volume per second. The major loss of ions will occur because of lateral diffusion out of the plasma to the walls of the chamber where surface recombination will occur. The net current loss by these two mechanisms can be expressed as

$$I_{loss} = \int_{S'} \mathbf{J} \cdot d\mathbf{S}' + \int_{K} ern^{+}n^{-} \, dK \tag{8.6}$$

where S' is the effective lateral surface of the sensitive volume and dK is an increment of sensitive volume. These two terms could be included in the example given in Sec. 7.9 to correct for ion and electron losses.

8.2   Drift velocities in a plasma

In a plasma the ions possess drift velocities that may be represented by modified forms of Eqs. (7.27) and (7.43). If the ions are from the same gas as the neutral molecules of the ambient gas, the drift velocity for positive ions near thermal equilibrium is given by

$$v_d^{+} = \frac{4e\lambda_i E}{3\pi} \left(\frac{\pi}{2kT} \frac{M+m}{Mm} \right)^{1/2} \text{ m/sec} \tag{8.7}$$

where M is the mass of the ambient gas and m is the mass of the electron. In a similar manner, the drift velocity for electrons, as obtained from Eqs. (7.45) and (7.46), is

$$v_d^{-} = 4.16 \times 10^{5}(E\lambda_e)^{1/2}\left(\frac{m_e}{M}\right)^{1/4} \text{ m/sec} \tag{8.8}$$

In each case the results are satisfactory for estimating drift velocity in a plasma. The d-c conductivity of a plasma is

$$\sigma = \frac{ne}{E}(v_d^{+} + v_d^{-})$$

where $n = n^{-} = n^{+}$.

It was mentioned earlier that if $\mathbf{E}$ varies with time, then at high frequencies the ions in a plasma are essentially at a standstill compared to the rapid drift of the electrons. The electrons are, therefore, a gas drifting through a space containing fixed positive charges at regular intervals. The situation is very similar to the conditions in a metallic conductor. The electron gas possesses a Maxwell-Boltzmann distribution and the radiofrequency conductivity of the plasma is given by*

$$\sigma = -\frac{4\pi}{3}\frac{e^2}{m}\int_{0}^{\infty}\frac{1}{v+j\omega}\frac{\partial f_0'}{\partial v}v^3 \, dv \tag{8.9}$$

---

* H. Margenau, *Phys. Rev.*, **109**, 6–9 (Jan. 1958).

A comparison of Eqs. (8.9) and (7.20) indicates that the mean free path of the electron in Eq. (7.20) has been replaced by

$$\lambda_e = \frac{v}{\zeta}$$

The complex collision frequency is ζ and is equal to

$$\zeta = v + j\omega$$

The radian frequency of the electromagnetic wave is ω. All other terms are defined and discussed in detail in Secs. 7.2 and 4.5.

Equation (8.9) reduces to*

$$\sigma = \frac{ne^2}{m(v + j\omega)} \tag{8.10}$$

for plasmas in air at pressures of 10^3 to 10^{-1} mm Hg and neutral gas temperatures between 3000–12,000°K.

8.3 Pre-spark volt-ampere characteristics

Gaseous electron tubes all possess the same basic volt-ampere characteristic although the design and normal use of a given device may obscure the over-all characteristics. As an example, consider a gas-filled tube at a pressure of several microns (1 micron $= 10^{-3}$ mm Hg). If the anode-to-cathode voltage is increased from zero, a volt-ampere characteristic similar to that sketched in Fig. 8.2 is obtained. (The current scale is arbitrary and is included to give the reader an estimate of the order of magnitude of current that is typically encountered.)

At very low voltages the only ions present in the gas come from external sources of ionization such as photons from light, x-rays, β and γ rays, and radiofrequency generators. The current is *space-charge limited*, as indicated by the portion of the volt-ampere characteristic between O and A. At point A all the available charge carriers are being utilized and the device is *current limited* from point A to point B.

At point B the current begins to increase because the electrons present attain sufficient energy from the applied electric field to permit inelastic ionizing collisions to occur in the gas. This is sometimes called Townsend's α-process. The additional electron-ion pairs thus formed permit the current to rise. This α-process continues for all higher voltages.

At point C several other ionization processes begin to provide additional ion pairs. The first is termed the β-process and represents the formation of ion pairs by positive ions making inelastic collisions in the gas. The probability of this process' occurring is very small. A far more important process

* M. P. Bachyuski, T. W. Johnston, and I. P. Shkarofsky, *Proc. I.R.E.*, **48**:4, 347 (March 1960).

is the emission of electrons from the cathode. This is termed the γ-*process*, which arises from three basic emission processes:*

1. γ_i—electron emission because of positive ion impact on the cathode,
2. γ_p—electron emission because of photons incident upon the cathode,
3. γ_m—electron emission because of the action of neutral atoms in a metastable energy level that have diffused to the cathode.

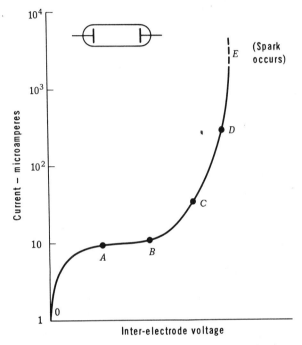

Fig. 8.2. Pre-spark volt-ampere characteristics of a gas tube. The regions identified by the letters are discussed in the text.

Electron emission is also occurring at the anode. In fact, the emission of secondary electrons may be quite high. However, all of the electrons emitted at the anode are immediately recaptured by the anode before they can participate in any ionization process.

As the electric field is further increased, many of the inelastic collisions between electrons and neutral gas molecules result in very high energy excitations. When the excited molecule returns to the ground state, this energy is radiated as a photon which may, in turn, be able to release a photoelectron at the cathode (θ-*process*) or it may raise another excited atom in the gas to the first ionization level (ξ-*process*). The probability of photoionization

* Electronic emission by various processes is treated in detail in Chap. 5.

of the gas is ξ. These processes are believed to be responsible for the final steep rise in current from point D to point E.

At point E, electron-ion pairs are being formed very rapidly, and the additional electrons thus obtained are in turn acquiring energy from the electric field and producing still more charge-carrier pairs. The result is an avalanche of electron-ion pairs termed a *spark* that terminates in a true plasma in the sensitive volume between the two electrodes. The plasma will not support a large voltage drop; therefore, the anode-to-cathode voltage must fall to a lower value. For instance, a typical $\frac{1}{4}$-w miniature neon lamp requires 79 v to reach the breakdown point (E). Immediately following breakdown, the lamp voltage falls to about 60 v. This corresponds to rated operating conditions.

8.4 Pre-spark phenomena

Photons of light, as well as β and γ rays arising from the natural radioactivity in the earth's surface, are the principal sources of ionization for the initial production of small numbers of ion pairs in any gaseous electronic device. Satisfactory estimates for the number of ion pairs produced per cubic centimeter per second in air at atmospheric pressure are 1 for β rays and 3 for γ rays. These estimates apply to any enclosed chamber containing dust-free air. The presence of dust and large molecular clusters in the atmosphere gives rise to very high concentrations of large charged particles, commonly called *Langevin ions*. Their concentration is a maximum in industrial areas and falls to about 200 ions/cm³ over the oceans.

The small ion pairs, which are formed at approximately 4 pairs/cm³/sec, represent the minimum net number of charge carriers present when establishing the current shown between O and A in Fig. 8.2. This estimate of available ion pairs because of radioactive ionizers is quite low and is only found in chambers that have been very well cleaned and shielded from all light. The effect of light in supplying additional charge carriers is very pronounced and arises from photoelectric emission from the walls and electrodes of the gas tube.*

As the electrode voltage is increased, the current increases and is space-charge limited. Eventually, a saturation region is reached where almost all of the ion pairs present are contributing to the conduction of electric current through the gas. This is the region from A to B.

1. *Townsend's first coefficient.* As point B is reached, some of the electrons from the ion pairs produced by external energy sources begin to acquire

---

* Several interesting and inexpensive experiments can be performed using an ordinary $\frac{1}{4}$-w neon bulb of the type without any added series resistor. By exercising care to avoid instrument damage, the curves of Figs. 8.2 and 8.6 may be produced. The low cost of the neon bulb makes it feasible to carry the operation into the destructive arc region. The effects of incident ultraviolet light upon the spark potential (point E) can also be observed.

energies on the order of the first ionization potential of the gas (see Table 7.1). These electrons become efficient at making inelastic ionizing collisions and charge-carrier amplification results.

To compute the degree of amplification in the gas, assume that σ_0 electrons per second per unit area in the immediate vicinity of the cathode are accelerated toward the anode. Let x be the displacement toward the anode. Then the number of ion pairs formed per second by electrons making ionizing collisions with gas molecules in a volume of unit cross-section and depth dx is

$$d\sigma = \sigma \alpha \, dx \tag{8.11}$$

where α is a coefficient of proportionality and has the dimensions of electrons/meter/primary electron. This is often called the *Townsend coefficient*.*

Assume steady-state conditions with a constant source, σ_0, of electrons near the cathode. The total number of electrons per square meter to be found at any point between the cathode and the anode is obtained by solving Eq. (8.11).

$$\sigma(x) = \sigma_0 \epsilon^{\alpha x} \tag{8.12}$$

Equation (8.12) predicts an *avalanche* of electrons whose density starts near the cathode and increases exponentially to the anode. It must be emphasized that we are discussing a steady-state situation. If Eq. (8.12) is multiplied by the charge on the electron, then the current density at any point x is

$$J(x) = e\sigma_0 \epsilon^{\alpha x} = J_0 \epsilon^{\alpha x} \tag{8.13}$$

because σ is the density per square meter of charge carriers appearing at a point x each second. The anode current density is

$$J_a = J_0 \epsilon^{\alpha d} \tag{8.14}$$

where d is the cathode-to-anode spacing. The initial current density at the cathode is J_0 and is often referred to as the *saturation photoelectric current density* because the easiest method of establishing this current density is by use of a photocathode. It is apparent from Eq. (8.13) that *gas amplification* of the initial current density is taking place in the gas.

If a strong ionizing source such as x-rays were to irradiate the gas, then N_0 ion pairs per unit volume per second would be generated throughout the sensitive volume of gas instead of only near the cathode and Eq. (8.11) must be modified. The increase in the electron density is now caused by electron multiplication $\alpha\sigma \, dx$ in an incremental distance plus a number $N_0 \, dx$ produced by photoionization in the gas

$$d\sigma = (\alpha\sigma + N_0) \, dx$$

* Townsend originally assumed that negative ions were responsible for the ionization in the gas; however, this has long since been disproved.

Integrate and set the electron density equal to zero at the cathode.

$$\alpha\sigma + N_0 = A\epsilon^{\alpha x}$$

When $x = 0$, $\sigma = 0$, and $A = N_0$. Therefore, the steady-state electron concentration at any point is

$$\sigma(x) = \frac{N_0}{\alpha}(\epsilon^{\alpha x} - 1)$$

The corresponding current density is

$$J(x) = \frac{eN_0}{\alpha}(\epsilon^{\alpha x} - 1) \tag{8.15}$$

The Townsend coefficient α varies directly with pressure because the electron-molecule collision frequency is directly proportional to pressure. The coefficient is also a direct function of the average energy acquired by the electron while traversing each mean free path. This energy is directly proportional to the electric field strength, E, and the mean free path, λ. The mfp, however, is inversely proportional to the pressure. With these factors in mind, the Townsend coefficient may be written as

$$\alpha = Pf(E/P) \tag{8.16}$$

Figure 8.3 is a plot of the experimental values of α/P as a function of E/P.

2. *Townsend's second coefficient.* Further increases in the electric field strength in the sensitive volume result in a second important process' participating in the supply of additional electrons. This is the emission of electrons from the cathode and is known as the γ-*process*, which was discussed earlier. Experimentally, it is very difficult to separate the various cathode emission processes occurring in the operation of a discharge tube. For this reason, only the net effect will be considered.

When only the α-process is active, the density of electrons available per second in the immediate vicinity of the cathode is σ_0. With the γ-process providing a considerable number of electrons emitted from the cathode each second, the electron density is now σ_0'. The difference between σ_0' and σ_0 is the rate at which electrons are supplied by the γ-process, and it is proportional to the total number of positive ions formed in a sensitive volume of unit cross-sectional area. The density of positive ions at any point is equal to the density of electrons. From Eq. (8.12)

$$\sigma^+ = \sigma = \sigma_0'\epsilon^{\alpha x}$$

The total number of positive ions produced over a sensitive volume of unit cross-sectional area is

$$\int_0^d \alpha\sigma_0'\epsilon^{\alpha x}\,dx = \sigma_0'(\epsilon^{\alpha d} - 1)$$

The number of electrons supplied by the γ-process is proportional to the total number of positive ions found in the sensitive volume per second and to

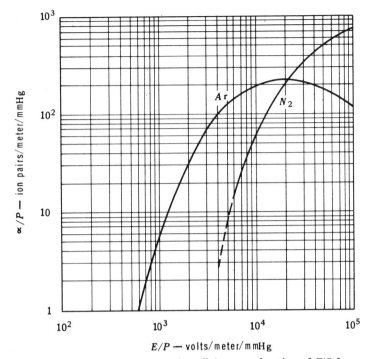

Fig. 8.3. The Townsend coefficient as a function of E/P for pure nitrogen and pure argon. (No traces of mercury present.) Data on N_2 from W. E. Bowls, *Phys. Rev.*, **53**, 293, 1938. Data on A from A. A. Kruithoff, *Physica*, **7**, 519, 1940.

the probability, γ, that a fraction of these positive ions will contribute to electron emission at the cathode. It is also proportional to the probability χ that a fraction of those electrons emitted at the cathode will not diffuse back to the cathode. With these factors taken into account, the *effective number* of electrons emitted per unit area at the cathode is

$$\gamma\chi\sigma_0'(\epsilon^{\alpha d} - 1) = \sigma_0' - \sigma_0 \tag{8.17}$$

The surface density of electrons available at the cathode is

$$\sigma_0' = \frac{\sigma_0}{1 - \gamma\chi(\epsilon^{\alpha d} - 1)} \tag{8.18}$$

and, therefore, the current density at any point, according to Eq. (8.13), is

$$J(x) = e\sigma_0'\epsilon^{\alpha x}$$
$$= \frac{e\sigma_0\epsilon^{\alpha x}}{1 - \gamma\chi(\epsilon^{\alpha d} - 1)}$$
$$J(x) = \frac{J_0\epsilon^{\alpha x}}{1 - \gamma\chi(\epsilon^{\alpha d} - 1)} \tag{8.19}$$

The current density at the anode, J_b, is found by setting $x = d$ in Eq. (8.19). The loss of electrons by back diffusion is usually small, and as a result χ is often assumed to be unity.

Data on γ is available to a limited extent. The data for the specific cathode material and gas composition must be obtained. Typical values of γ are 0.06 for nitrogen and argon gases with cathode metals such as copper and nickel.

The contribution of photoionization in the gas remains to be considered. Loeb discusses this phenomenon in detail.* The effect is not very pronounced in steady-state conduction in the Townsend discharge region and can usually be neglected. For this reason, it will not be considered here.

8.5 Spark breakdown

Equation (8.19) can be used to predict the conditions for breakdown in the gas. A spark occurs when the current density in the sensitive volume rises very sharply (point E, Fig. 8.2). A sharp rise in current density occurs when the denominator of Eq. (8.19) approaches zero. Thus,

$$\gamma\chi(\epsilon^{\alpha_b d} - 1) = 1$$

where α_b is the particular value of α that satisfies this condition for a spark breakdown. Let $\chi = 1$, and note that $\epsilon^{\alpha_b d} \gg 1$. Then, the condition for a spark breakdown of the gas is

$$\frac{1}{\gamma} = \epsilon^{\alpha_b d} \tag{8.20}$$

For a uniform electric field, the spark breakdown potential corresponding to α_b is V_b. Because

$$\alpha = Pf\left(\frac{E}{P}\right)$$

according to Eq. (8.16), the Townsend coefficient for breakdown may be written as

$$\alpha_b = Pf\left(\frac{V_b}{Pd}\right) \tag{8.21}$$

The conditions for breakdown therefore vary directly with V_b and inversely with pressure and interelectrode spacing for plane-parallel electrodes. The sparking potential, V_b, is thus a function of Pd. This is known as *Paschen's law*, after its discoverer. A plot of V_b as a function of Pd is shown for air in Fig. 8.4.

* L. B. Loeb, *Basic Processes of Gaseous Electronics*, University of California Press, Berkeley, 1955, pp. 801–807.

With reference to Fig. 8.4, the sparking potential varies directly with spacing or with pressure for values of $Pd > 5.7$ (mm Hg $\times$ mm). For lower values of Pd, the sparking potential increases rapidly, which indicates that the mean free path of the electron is now on the same order of magnitude as the gap spacing. This condition lessens the probability of an electron avalanche's forming except at greatly increased gap voltages.

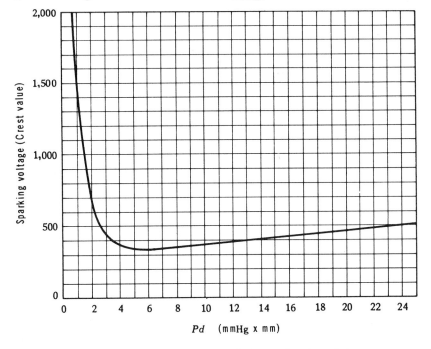

Fig. 8.4. The sparking potential of air as a function of the product of the pressure and the spacing for plane-parallel electrodes.

8.6 The spark

If a voltage somewhat greater than the required sparking voltage is applied between the electrodes of a gas tube, an interesting sequence of events occurs in the gas. With reference to Fig. 8.5, the few free electrons present start an avalanche (Fig. 8.5(a)). During the growth of the avalanche the more mobile electrons drift quickly to the head of the avalanche (Fig. 8.5(b)), leaving a positive ion streamer.

The positive ions *drift* relatively slowly toward the cathode and they *diffuse* both laterally and across the gap. Because of diffusion, the head of the positive ion cloud is essentially spherical with a conical tail trailing off toward

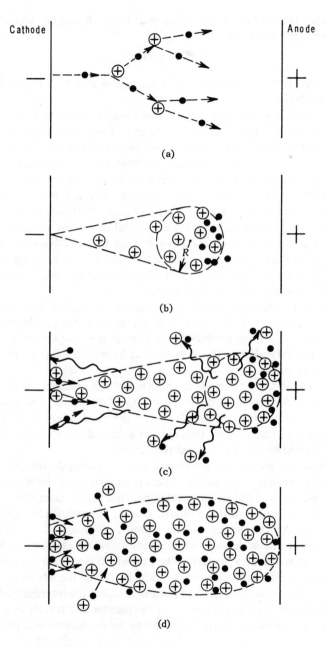

Fig. 8.5. The mechanism of the electric spark. The sequence
of events is discussed in the text. Positive ion ⊕; electron ●.

the cathode. The average radial diffusion distance, R, can be calculated from the Raether-Jaffé equation,

$$R = \sqrt{4Dt}$$

where t is the time of advance of the avalanche and D is the positive ion diffusion coefficient.

Loeb has shown that spark breakdowns may occur in less time than the electrons would require to drift across the gap. This implies that some ionization process must be forming electron-ion pairs in *advance* of the avalanche. In addition to the ionization of many molecules in the avalanche, there are up to ten times as many molecules that have their atoms raised to very high excitation levels. A fraction of the photons liberated when these highly excited atoms revert to their ground state produce photoionization in the gas (ξ-process). Its effect is to permit the original avalanche to advance more rapidly. In addition, electron-ion pairs formed well in advance of the avalanche may establish additional avalanches that aid in bridging the interelectrode gap in a relatively short time. Photoelectrons are also produced by these photons at the cathode (θ-process).

The photoelectrons produced in the gas are attracted into the positive ion streamer, where they begin to form a plasma at the anode head of the streamer. Photoelectrons produced several mean free paths from the streamer initiate small avalanches to the streamer but have little effect on the over-all sparking mechanism.

The acceleration of electrons to the head of the streamer results in additional ion-pair formation at the cathode end of this head. The electrons so produced are drawn into the anode end of the head where they add to the growing plasma. The positive ions remain a part of the streamer and cause the *cathode head* to advance toward the cathode.

The positive ion streamer advances toward the cathode, leaving a plasma behind it that reaches to the anode. There is comparatively little voltage drop across the plasma and its low electrical impedance results in an effective movement of the anode toward the cathode. That is, the cathode head becomes a *virtual anode*. As this virtual anode progresses toward the cathode, the gradient between cathode and virtual anode increases rapidly (see Fig. 8.6).

As the virtual anode approaches the cathode, the positive ion and photon bombardment of the cathode increases rapidly. When the advancing cathode head reaches the cathode, there is a plasma bridging the interelectrode space, and a surge of cathode electrons enters the plasma and travels as a pulse to the anode. This electron pulse forms many more electron-ion pairs in the plasma.

The final voltage distribution across the gap is shown in Fig. 8.6(f). There is a small voltage drop in the immediate vicinity of the anode. The *anode drop* is at least somewhat greater than the first ionization potential of the gas. Positive ions are repulsed by the anode, which leaves a net electronic charge. The emission of photoelectrons and secondary electrons by the anode possibly serves to intensify the density of electrons in this region, and the result is an increase in electric field strength which accounts for the *anode drop*. This region is about one electron mean free path in thickness.

In the immediate vicinity of the cathode there is a large potential drop between the cathode and the positive ions in the cathode head of the plasma. This potential drop is on the order of the minimum sparking potential, in accordance with Paschen's law. The high electric field in this region accelerates positive ions from the cathode head of the plasma to the cathode where they cause electron emission.

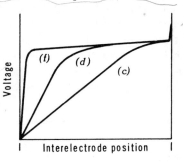

Fig. 8.6. The voltage distribution between cathode and anode during the formative stages—(c) and (d)—and the spark breakdown (f) of a gas. The curves (c) and (d) correspond to identically labeled conditions in the preceding figure.

The remaining voltage drop in the gas is found in the plasma or *positive column*. The electric gradient may be on the order of 1 to 10 v/cm in this region. It is interesting to note that if the interelectrode spacing is shortened a small amount only, the length of the positive column will be changed. This experiment can be carried to the point where the positive column completely disappears. During the experiment the required anode-to-cathode voltage has decreased according to the required gradient in the column and the reduction in the length of the positive column. Further decreases in interelectrode spacing result in an increase in the required anode-to-cathode voltage to compensate for the inefficient length of the tube.

8.7 The glow discharge

Once the spark has occurred, it is possible to maintain a sustained discharge in the gas at a relatively high current level. The necessary electron supply required to make the discharge self-sustaining is obtained from the cathode. The anode-to-cathode voltage required to maintain the discharge is usually 20 per cent or so less than the sparking voltage. Electron emission by positive ion bombardment of the cathode is probably the principal source of electrons.

The breakdown criterion

$$\frac{1}{\gamma} = \epsilon^{\alpha_b d}$$

must be satisfied. If nonplanar electrodes are employed, then this criterion must be written as

$$\left(1 + \frac{1}{\gamma}\right) = \epsilon^{\int_0^d \alpha dx} \tag{8.22}$$

If the pressure in the tube is between 5 and 5×10^{-2} mm Hg, visible light emanates from the discharge. In particular, a bright glow appears on part of the cathode surface. Slight increases in tube voltage result in large increases in tube current. Further increases in tube current eventually result in a *cathode glow* that covers the cathode. Any further increases in tube current require a significant increase in tube voltage (see Fig. 8.7).

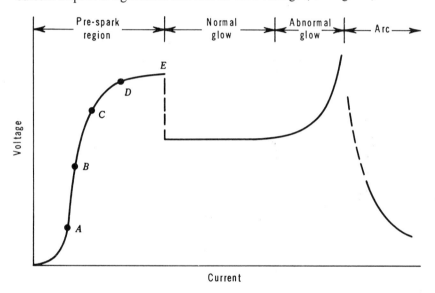

Fig. 8.7. Complete volt-ampere characteristics of a gas discharge tube.

The volt-ampere region where the cathode glow does not entirely cover the cathode is called the *normal glow region*. Once the glow has covered the cathode, the operation is said to be in the *abnormal glow region*. Most gas tubes operate in the normal glow region. Operation in the abnormal glow region can result in a hot spot occurring on the cathode because of intense positive ion bombardment. The elevated temperature at this hot spot causes thermal emission of electrons and sputtering of the metal of the cathode. The additional electrons permit the current to rise, which, in turn, causes the hot spot to intensify and thus supply still more electrons. The result is usually an unstable condition that may quickly lead to the destruction of the tube. This is the *arc region*.

The pattern of visible light emanating from a discharge tube operating in the normal glow region is very interesting and has commanded the attention of many investigators. If the pressure is between 5×10^{-2} and 5 mm Hg, the discharge is characterized by a pattern of light and nearly dark regions. In the following discussion it should be remembered that ultraviolet and very soft x-rays may also be present in the discharge, even in the apparently dark regions.

Figure 8.8 is a sketch of the light and dark regions in a discharge. The dark regions are shaded. Starting with the cathode, the sequence of phenomena is as follows:

1. The *Aston dark space* is a region where newly emitted electrons from the cathode are accelerating toward the electron drift velocity. For the first few electron mean free paths, their energy is probably too low to permit many high-energy exciting collisions with gas molecules. The result is a region of little photon generation. The Aston dark space is only observable in clean samples of the noble gases, although it may be present but unobservable in other gases.

2. The *cathode glow* follows the Aston dark space. In this region there is an intense glow indicating that a large number of atoms are returning to the ground state and releasing their excess energy as photons. Loeb points out that it is unlikely that the relatively small number of electrons available in this region could account for the extent of atomic excitation required to justify the light intensity observed. He favors crediting a large portion of this glow to the deionization occurring at the cathode.

3. The *Crookes dark space*. The anode end of this relatively dark region contains the positive ion head that exists at this end of the plasma. Both the electrons and positive ions receive their maximum acceleration in passing through this region. The energy delivered to the cathode can be shown to be equal to the energy gained by the positive ions in traversing the Crookes dark space.

The electrons are accelerated to high enough velocities in this region to become efficient at ionizing the gas in lieu of excitation collisions. Therefore, there is little visible light generated in the Crookes dark space. The Crookes dark space is also called the *cathode dark space* or the *Hittorf dark space*.

4. The *negative glow*. Electron avalanches occur in the Crookes dark space. This provides a number of new low-energy electrons near the anode end of this region. These slow electrons are efficient at exciting the gas atoms with the result that a region of visible light, known as the *negative glow*, follows the Crookes dark space. Toward the anode end of the negative glow region, both excitation and ionization are intense. The result is a large negative space charge of relatively slow-moving electrons at the anode end of this region.

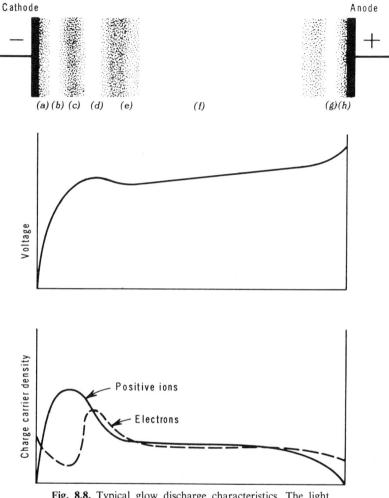

Fig. 8.8. Typical glow discharge characteristics. The light and dark spaces bear the following names and are discussed in the text:

(a) Aston dark space   (e) Faraday dark space
(b) Cathode glow   (f) Positive column
(c) Cathode dark space   (g) Anode glow
(d) Negative glow   (h) Anode dark space

5. The *Faraday dark space*. The electron cloud in the anode end of the negative glow eventually results in such extensive slowing down of the electrons that excitation and ionization drop to low levels with an attendant decrease in visible light. This marks the beginning of the Faraday dark space. In this region the electrons are again accelerated to excitation and ionization energies.

6. The *positive column*. After acceleration in the Faraday dark space, the electrons again become efficient ionizers and a visible glow reappears. This is the region of equal densities of electrons and positive ions. In this plasma a uniform excitation and ionization process exists. The result is a glowing positive column of light.

7. The *anode glow*. The ion density in the positive column decreases as the anode is approached. The result is a space charge of electrons. The electrons entering this space charge from the plasma are able at first to increase their energy. Plasma electrons usually possess energies between 1 and 10 electron-volts. The increased energy permits an increase in the number of electron-molecule collisions, resulting in excitation with the attendant anode glow in the gas.

8. The *anode dark space*. Very near the anode, the increased electron density results in a slowing down of the electrons and an associated decrease in gas excitation. This results in an anode dark space.

In addition to the visible phenomena just described, alternate dark and bright striations may appear in all but the *pure* noble gases under certain distinct conditions of pressure and current density. The striations may be stationary, slowly moving, or traveling so rapidly that the entire plasma may appear to possess a uniform glow. The latter condition of rapidly moving striations is probably associated with plasma oscillations.

The exact origin and mechanism of these striations are incompletely understood. The relatively dark spaces are regions of reduced plasma density and high electric fields. The electrons are accelerated to high energies in these regions. The dark regions are followed by bright regions, indicating that the electrons are now giving up their energy in inelastic collisions that result in ionization and excitation of more gas molecules.

Several investigators have attempted to ascribe various mechanisms to these regions with no conclusive results. The location of the walls of the discharge tube appears to have some effect upon the striations, thus indicating that perhaps lateral charge-carrier diffusion to the walls may play an important role in the mechanism of the striations. An empirical relation for the striation spacing, d, is given by the Thomsons* as

$$\frac{d}{a} = c\left(\frac{1}{aP}\right)^m$$

where the inner radius of the discharge tube is a and c is a coefficient that depends upon the current density. The pressure is P and m is an exponent that depends upon the gas. For hydrogen it has a value of 0.53.

---

* J. J. Thomson and G. P. Thomson, *Conduction of Electricity through Gases*, Cambridge University Press, New York, 1933, Vol. 2, p. 396.

8.8   Probe measurements

The voltage distribution in a gas tube can be measured by the use of electric probes. Basically, the probe is a collector of either electrons or ions, or both under some circumstances. Essentially the probe forms a subminiature electron tube with the plasma under investigation. A knowledge of the applied voltages, the probe current, and a visual measurement of the effective collection area of the probe as well as an assumed knowledge of the velocity distribution function for the ions and electrons permit calculating the potential of the plasma at this point. This procedure will be discussed in detail. Probe measurements are very important in the rocket exploration of the upper atmosphere and outer space.

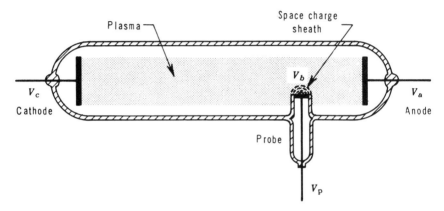

Fig. 8.9. A discharge tube containing a planar probe that is shielded on the sides and back. The potential of the plasma in the immediate vicinity of the probe is V_b. A space-charge sheath separates the probe from the plasma.

The probe may assume any geometrical form; however, the required calculations become quite involved for any but the simplest geometric forms. For this reason, only *planar*, *cylindrical*, and *spherical* probes enjoy widespread use. Because of its usefulness, and for brevity, only the planar probe will be discussed here. An excellent treatise on general probe theory has been presented by Langmuir and Mott-Smith.* They consider the use of planar, cylindrical, and spherical probes in plasmas where the velocity distribution function is (a) velocities equal and parallel in direction, (b) velocities of uniform magnitude but with directions distributed at random in space, (c) Maxwellian distribution of velocities, and (d) Maxwellian distribution with a superimposed drift velocity that is not negligible compared to the random velocity.

* H. M. Mott-Smith and I. Langmuir, *Phys. Rev.*, **28**, 727–763 (Oct. 1926).

In addition to restricting the discussion to the planar probe, we assume a Maxwellian velocity distribution in each case. These assumptions in no way detract from the usefulness of the discussions. In those special cases where it is undesirable to use a planar probe or where a Maxwellian distribution cannot be assumed, the problem may be approached by the methods of Langmuir and Mott-Smith.

In Fig. 8.9 a probe is inserted in a plasma. The sides and back of the probe are shielded and the physical size of the probe is assumed to be sufficiently small to have only a negligible effect upon the plasma. Depending upon the polarity of the probe relative to the potential of the plasma, either positive ions or electrons are attracted to it. These charge carriers form a sheath over the surface of the probe and extend a small distance into the plasma. Let V be the probe-to-plasma potential, then

$$V = V_p - V_b \tag{8.23}$$

where V_p is the probe potential and V_b is the true potential of the plasma. These potentials are all measured relative to any convenient reference point— usually the cathode.

Five distinct cases present themselves and will be considered in sequence, starting with a very negative probe potential. The important voltage in each case is the probe-to-plasma voltage. The volt-ampere characteristics of the probe are sketched in Fig. 8.10. The letters identifying each region correspond to the following cases:

1. Probe quite negative $V_p \ll V_b$. The electric field will be directed from the plasma to the probe; thus, the probe will repel electrons and attract positive ions that form a space charge sheath about the probe. This sheath exists up to a distance d from the probe and it presents an effective surface area A to the plasma (see Fig. 8.11). There is little excitation and subsequent radiation in the sheath. It appears dark and a visual measurement of the sheath thickness, d, may be made.

The pressure is relatively low, which permits the use of Eq. (7.60) to express the density of positive ions crossing the surface between plasma and sheath.

$$J^+ = \frac{4\epsilon_0}{9(M/2e)^{\frac{1}{2}}} \frac{V^{\frac{3}{2}}}{d^2} \tag{8.24}$$

where M is the mass of the positive ion and ϵ_0 is the permittivity of free space.

A Maxwellian velocity distribution has been assumed to hold true for the charge carriers as well as for the neutral gas molecules. In Sec. 2.6 we developed an expression for the average number of molecules per second that cross a unit area (Eq. (2.65)). This calculation was based upon Maxwell-Boltzmann statistics, and therefore it may be directly applied to express the

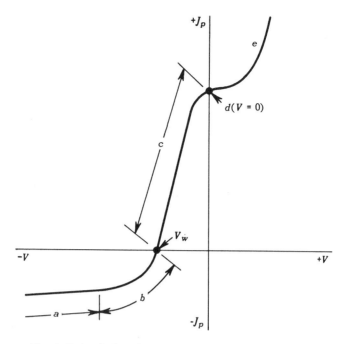

Fig. 8.10. Typical probe volt-ampere characteristics. V is the probe-to-plasma voltage. (The regions indicated by the letters correspond to the identically marked discussions in Sec. 8.8.)

current density arising from positive ions that diffuse across the surface between plasma and sheath.

$$J^+ = \frac{4\epsilon_0}{9(M/2e)^{1/2}} \frac{V^{3/2}}{d^2} = \frac{eN^+ v_a^+}{4} \tag{8.25}$$

where v_a^+ is the average thermal velocity of positive ions. A direct measurement of the probe current density, as well as a visual measurement of the sheath thickness, permits computing the plasma-to-probe voltage. An important point to note is that the effective area of the probe in this case is actually the plasma-to-sheath area, A, which should be used in computing probe current density. The reason for this is that when the probe is highly negative, all positive ions that cross this area into the sheath are collected.

2. If the probe voltage is reduced in magnitude so that $V_p < V_b$, the electric field is still directed from plasma to probe, and positive ions are collected. In addition, electrons that are directed toward the probe and possess a velocity greater than v_0 by virtue of their random thermal movement can overcome this reduced electric field and reach the probe. The probe current in this case is caused by both positive ions and electrons.

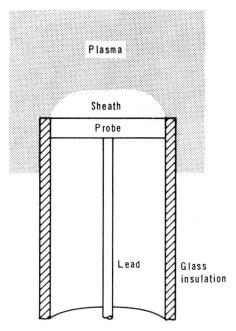

Fig. 8.11. Details of the sheath covering a planar probe located in a plasma. The area defined by the boundary between the plasma and the sheath is the effective area of the probe for those charge carriers that are attracted to the probe. The geometric area of the probe is the effective probe area for charge carriers that diffuse to the probe against a repelling force.

$$I_p = I^+ - I^- \qquad (8.26)$$

Let the $+x$-direction be normal to the probe surface, S, and directed toward the probe. The differential electron current to the probe is

$$dI^- = eN^- Sv_x f(v)\, dv \qquad (8.27)$$

where $f(v)$ is the Maxwell-Boltzmann distribution function. When applying the Maxwell-Boltzmann statistics to the electrons, it is necessary to use the electron temperature, T_e, corresponding to the gas temperature. This relationship is plotted in Fig. 8.1.

Follow the general procedure employed in Sec. 2.6 to integrate Eq. (8.27). The integral in the x-direction should include those velocities directed toward the probe and of magnitude greater than v_0.

$$I^- = \frac{eN^- Sv_p}{\pi\sqrt{\pi}} \int_{-\infty}^{\infty} \int_{-\infty}^{\infty} \int_{v_0}^{\infty} \frac{v_x}{v_p} \epsilon^{-(v_x{}^2 + v_y{}^2 + v_z{}^2)/v_p{}^2}\, d\left(\frac{v_x}{v_p}\right) d\left(\frac{v_y}{v_p}\right) d\left(\frac{v_z}{v_p}\right) \qquad (8.28)$$

Set $x = (v_x/v_p)^2$, etc., and integrate with respect to dy and dz by use of the gamma function, $\Gamma(n)$. This yields

$$I^- = \frac{eN^- S v_p}{2\sqrt{\pi}} \int_{(v_0/v_p)^2}^{\infty} \epsilon^{-x} \, dx$$

$$I^- = \frac{eN^- S v_p}{2\sqrt{\pi}} \epsilon^{-(v_0/v_p)^2} \tag{8.29}$$

The most probable velocity, v_p, may be eliminated by substituting its value

$$v_p = \sqrt{\frac{2kT_e}{m}} \tag{8.30}$$

Also, the least velocity v_0 required to reach the probe can be expressed in terms of the plasma-to-probe potential by the energy equation

$$\tfrac{1}{2}mv_0^2 = eV \tag{8.31}$$

The result, written as a current density, is

$$J^- = \frac{I^-}{S} = eN^- \sqrt{\frac{kT_e}{2\pi m}} \epsilon^{-eV/kT_e} \tag{8.32}$$

The ion current to the probe remains unchanged as long as V_p is negative and not too small in magnitude. The net current density to the probe is, therefore,

$$J_p = J^+ - J^- = \frac{4\epsilon_0}{9(M/2e)^{1/2}} \frac{V^{3/2}}{d^2} - eN^- \sqrt{\frac{kT_e}{2\pi m}} \epsilon^{-eV/kT_e} \tag{8.33}$$

3. Further reductions in the magnitude of the probe potential eventually result in the probe current's passing through zero and then increasing with conventional current flow now directed to the probe from the external circuit. A unique and interesting case occurs when the probe current goes to zero.

$$I_p = 0 = I^+ - I^-$$

and $$V = V_p - V_b = V_w$$

where V_w is called the *wall potential* because this is the potential assumed by the insulated walls of the tube. Electrons and positive ions are continually diffusing in equal numbers to the walls where recombination takes place.

If the probe current is set equal to zero in Eq. (8.33) and $V = V_w$, then

$$\frac{4\epsilon_0}{9(M/2e)^{1/2}} \frac{V_w^{3/2}}{d^2} = \frac{eN^+ v_a^+}{4} = eN^- \sqrt{\frac{kT_e}{2\pi m}} \epsilon^{-eV_w/kT_e} \tag{8.34}$$

The average velocity of the positive ions, v_a^+, may be expressed in terms of the most probable velocity, or

$$v_a^+ = \frac{2}{\sqrt{\pi}} v_p^+ = \sqrt{\frac{8kT_i}{\pi m}}$$

where T_i is the thermal equilibrium temperature of the positive ions. In general, this can be taken as equal to the temperature, T, of the neutral gas. The concentrations of electrons and ions are equal, $N^- = N^+$. Equation (8.34) reduces to

$$\sqrt{\frac{T}{M}} = \sqrt{\frac{T_e}{m}} \epsilon^{-eV_w/kT_e} \tag{8.35}$$

The wall potential is the potential of the wall relative to the plasma. From Eq. (8.35) it is

$$V_w = \frac{kT_e}{2e} \ln \frac{T_e M}{Tm} \tag{8.36}$$

It is a simple matter of substitution to show that the wall potential may also be expressed in terms of the average velocities of the electron and the positive ion.

$$V_w = \frac{kT_e}{2e} \ln \left(\frac{v_a^-}{v_a^+} \right) \tag{8.37}$$

4. For the case $V_p = V_b$, the probe is at the plasma potential. The space charge sheath disappears and both electrons and positive ions arrive at the probe by diffusion. The effective area of the probe is S and the probe current density is

$$J_p = eN^+ \sqrt{\frac{kT}{2\pi M}} - eN^- \sqrt{\frac{kT_e}{2\pi m}} \tag{8.38}$$

The plasma potential can be determined by noting the break in the probe characteristic as indicated in Fig. 8.10, point d.

5. When the probe potential V_p is one or two volts greater than the plasma potential, V_b, all positive ions are repelled. An electron sheath forms and has an effective area A_e. The current is space charge limited so that

$$J_p = J^- = \frac{4\epsilon_0}{9(m/2e)^{1/2}} \frac{V^{3/2}}{d_e^2} = \frac{eN^- v_a^-}{4} \tag{8.39}$$

From the preceding discussion it is apparent that the use of probes is a more intricate undertaking than might be imagined at first. The use of a probe voltage supply possessing a triangular waveform makes it possible to sweep through all five conditions. If suitable recording instruments are used, the volt-ampere characteristic of the probe can be recorded. A similar procedure permits telemetering this information from a probe located on a rocket or satellite to a ground station.

PROBLEMS

1. A tube contains two plane-parallel electrodes spaced 1.5 cm. The tube is filled with argon gas at a pressure of 2 mm Hg. The temperature of the neutral gas is 320°K when the tube is conducting. The voltage drop in the plasma is 15 v and the plasma essentially fills the interelectrode space. What is the approximate electron temperature?

2. What is the collision probability of the free electrons in the plasma of Prob. 1? Use the data of Fig. 7.1. What is their mfp? Compare this with the calculated value of mfp.

3. The device shown in the sketch is known as a *Hittorf tube*. It is a discharge tube that is provided with two independent paths, *A* and *B*. The effective length of path *A* is 20 mm and that of path *B* is 120 mm. The tube is filled with air. Through which path will spark breakdown occur when the

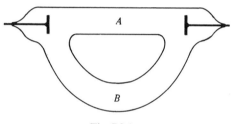

Fig. P8.3

pressure in the tube is 0.2 mm Hg? When the pressure is changed to 0.05 mm Hg? (Use the data of Fig. 8.4.)

4. The probability of n_i electrons per cubic meter having free paths greater than l_i is

$$\frac{n_i}{n} = \epsilon^{-l_i/L}$$

where n is the electron density and L is the electron mean free path. Assume a uniform electric field and *all motion* parallel to the field. Let $l_i E = V_i$, the first ionization potential of the gas. Show that Townsend's expression for α/P is

$$\frac{\alpha}{P} = A\epsilon^{-AV_i/(E/P)}$$

where $PA = 1/L$ and A is a constant. (This equation is based upon many simplifying assumptions and therefore it is of value only in making estimates based upon previous knowledge from similar conditions.)

5. If a probe were inserted into the interelectrode space in Prob. 1, what would be the wall potential?

6. Compute the drift velocities of the electrons and the positive ions in a plasma in N_2 gas at a pressure of 0.1 mm Hg and a temperature of 350°K if the electric field strength is 120 v/m.

7. A plasma probe in mercury gas is highly negative. Assume that the temperature of the gas and of the positive ions is 400°K and the positive ion density is 5×10^{17} ions per cubic meter; also assume that Maxwell-Boltzmann statistics are applicable. Make a sketch of the sheath thickness and probe current density as a function of probe-to-plasma voltage, up to about -150 v.

8. A tube contains two plane-parallel electrodes with an area of 4 cm² each and spaced a distance $d = 0.5$ cm. The tube is filled with argon gas at a pressure of 100 mm Hg and a voltage pulse of 500 v is applied to the electrodes for a short time. The interelectrode space is uniformly irradiated with β rays. The resulting pulse of current is measured with an oscilloscope and found to have a magnitude of 2.5×10^{-8} amp. What is the rate, N_0, of ionization per unit volume in the gas?

9. Compute the sparking potential for a pair of plane-parallel electrodes that are separated 0.5 cm if the gas is (a) argon and (b) nitrogen. The gas pressure is 20 mm Hg. Use the information of Fig. 8.3 and consider the electrodes to be made of either copper, iron, nickel, or platinum. All of these possess a probability of electron emission γ of about 0.06.

10. In Prob. 9 at what pressures will the sparking potentials required be a minimum?

REFERENCES

1. L. B. Loeb, *Fundamental Processes of Electrical Discharge in Gases*, John Wiley & Sons, New York, 1939.

2. L. B. Loeb, *Basic Processes of Gaseous Electronics*, University of California Press, Berkeley, 1955.

3. J. D. Cobine, *Gaseous Conductors*, Dover Publications, Inc., New York, 1941 and 1958.

4. J. S. Townsend, *Electricity in Gases*, Oxford University Press, Fair Lawn, N.J., 1914.

CHAPTER 9

Electric fields

Electron tubes depend upon electric fields to direct and deliver energy to electrons and ions. In addition, magnetic fields are often employed to accomplish more intricate particle trajectories than those possible with electric fields only.

In many design problems the ingenuity of the designer, along with the economics of mechanical fabrication, dictates the geometry of an electron tube. The problem here is one of determining the electric field, including the equipotential lines, for a known geometrical configuration. Often the converse procedure is required. The electric field may be specified and it is necessary to determine a geometric structure for the electrodes that will establish this field. Magnetic fields are seldom shaped. They are usually designed to be homogeneous throughout that portion of the tube where they are employed.

Once the electric and magnetic fields are known, the trajectories of the electrons and ions must be ascertained. This cannot always be accomplished analytically—electronic computers or electrical and mechanical models may be used to determine these trajectories. Again, the converse procedure may be required. The trajectory of a beam of electrons or ions may be specified and it is necessary to establish the electric field required to direct this beam.

The widespread availability of electronic computers has had a pronounced effect upon the solution of all problems in dynamics and electrodynamics. If the analyst can properly set up the equations of motion, perhaps by resorting to powerful methods such as those of Lagrange, then a satisfactory solution can be obtained from either an analogue or digital computer.

However, this has not always been the case. Solutions obtained by hand or by models were often the only methods available, and the required simplifying assumptions limited the results to specialized cases and conditions. The computer has overcome most of these obstacles and a solution can usually be obtained if it is worth the expenditure in time and money. Computers are not always available, nor desirable, and graphical and numerical solutions done by hand as well as the use of mechanical and electrical models still have a place in design and analysis.

9.1 Basic electric field theory

Coulomb's law is the experimental foundation upon which the theories of electromagnetic phenomena and electrodynamics are based. This law expresses the mechanical force between charged bodies in terms of the magnitude of the charges, q_1 and q_2 (coulombs), and their separation, r (meters).

$$\mathbf{F} = \frac{q_1 q_2}{4\pi\epsilon r^2} \mathbf{i}_r \quad \text{newtons} \tag{9.1}$$

where $\mathbf{i}_r$ is a unit vector directed from the center of charge of one body to the center of charge of the other body. The permittivity or dielectric constant of the medium is ϵ (farads/m). Coulomb's law applies only to those cases where the charges can be treated as point charges, usually when the separation between bodies is large compared to the dimensions of the body. There are also many cases when a distributed charge can be replaced by an equivalent point charge even though the separation between bodies is relatively small.

The coefficient ϵ is the permittivity of the medium, and in free space it has the value of 8.854×10^{-12} farads/m provided rationalized mks units are used. Should the reader somewhere encounter the permittivity given as 1.11×10^{-10}, then unrationalized mks units are being used. The difference is a factor of 4π. The permittivity of free space in the cgs system of units is 1. The permittivity of a given medium can be expressed in terms of the permittivity of free space multiplied by a *relative dielectric constant*, ϵ_r or K.

$$\epsilon = \epsilon_r \epsilon_0 \tag{9.2}$$

Some typical relative dielectric constants are given in Table 9.1.

The force on a charged body in an electric field is

$$\mathbf{F} = q_1 \mathbf{E} \quad \text{newtons} \tag{9.3}$$

where q_1 is the charge on the body expressed in coulombs. A combination of Eqs. (9.1) and (9.3) determines the electric field, $\mathbf{E}$, arising from a *point charge, q_2*:

$$\mathbf{E} = \frac{q_2}{4\pi\epsilon r^2} \mathbf{i}_r \quad \text{v/m} \tag{9.4}$$

Table 9.1

Relative dielectric constants

(typical values)

Air. 1.0006
Glass (Pyrex) 4.8
Hydrocarbon oils and waxes 2.2
Mica 6
Polyethylene 2.2
Polystyrene 2.6
Pyranol 5.3
Quartz (fused) 4.5

By definition, the electric field is the negative gradient of the potential distribution in the region, or

$$\mathbf{E} = -\nabla V \tag{9.5}$$

If Eq. (9.4) for the electric field about a point charge is substituted into Eq. (9.5), the potential difference between any two points is given by

$$_aV_b = \int_{r_a}^{r_b} \mathbf{E} \cdot d\mathbf{r}$$

$$= -\frac{q_2}{4\pi\epsilon}\left(\frac{1}{r_b} - \frac{1}{r_a}\right) \tag{9.6}$$

Let the reference point for measuring potential be the point a; further, let point a be a relatively long distance from the charge, q_2. Locate the origin at the charge q_2 and mathematically let $r_a \to \infty$; then the *potential at point b* is

$$V_b = -\frac{q_2}{4\pi\epsilon r_b}$$

and, in general, the potential at any point a distance r from an equivalent point charge is

$$V = -\frac{q_2}{4\pi\epsilon r} \tag{9.7}$$

In the rationalized mks system of units, one *line of force* or *one flux line originates on each unit charge*. A dimensional analysis of Eq. (9.4) yields

$$[\mathbf{E}] = \left[\frac{\text{coulomb}}{\text{meter}^2} \cdot \frac{\text{meter}}{\text{farad}}\right]$$

The ratio of charge to voltage is defined as capacitance measured in farads $(Q/V = C)$. Therefore,

$$[E] = [\text{volts/meter}]$$

In view of this dimensional analysis, if each side of Eq. (9.4) is multiplied by the permittivity, ϵ, then

$$\mathbf{D} = \epsilon\mathbf{E} = \left[\frac{\text{farads}}{\text{meter}} \cdot \frac{\text{volts}}{\text{meter}}\right] \tag{9.8}$$

$$\left[\mathbf{D}\right] = \left[\frac{\text{coulombs}}{\text{meter}^2}\right] = \text{electric flux density}$$

Figure 9.1 is a sketch of a point charge, q, surrounded by a closed surface

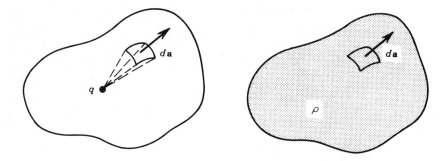

Fig. 9.1. An illustration of the results of Gauss's law of electrostatics. The integral of the flux density passing through a closed surface is equal to the net electric charge contained within the surface. Further, the charge may be either concentrated at one or more points or it may be distributed throughout the enclosed volume.

of any desired shape. The *electric flux* passing through a differential area of this surface is

$$d\psi = \mathbf{D} \cdot d\mathbf{a} \tag{9.9}$$

which may be written as $\qquad d\psi = \dfrac{q}{4\pi r^2}\,\mathbf{i}_r \cdot d\mathbf{a}$

by use of Eqs. (9.8) and (9.4). The unit vector may be written as the vector $\mathbf{r}$ divided by its magnitude or $\mathbf{r}/r$. With this substitution the increment of electric flux is

$$d\psi = \frac{q}{4\pi}\left(\frac{\mathbf{r} \cdot d\mathbf{a}}{r^3}\right)$$

The term in parentheses is the differential solid angle, $d\omega$, subtended at the charge q by the differential area, $d\mathbf{a}$.

$$d\psi = \frac{q}{4\pi}\,d\omega \tag{9.10}$$

The *total electric flux that emanates from the charge q* is found by integrating over the entire closed surface, *a*.

$$\psi = \frac{q}{4\pi} \int_a d\omega = q \tag{9.11}$$

because any solid angle integrated over a closed surface is equal to 4π.

The results of Eq. (9.11) are very important. By combining Eqs (9.9) and (9.11),

$$\psi = \int_a \mathbf{D} \cdot d\mathbf{a} = q = \int_\tau \rho \, d\tau \tag{9.12}$$

where ρ is the charge density distributed in any manner over the volume τ enclosed by the surface *a*. Equation (9.12) is often referred to as *Gauss' law*. From the theorems of vector analysis, the *divergence theorem* states that the integral of any vector $\mathbf{E}$ over a closed surface *a* is equal to the integral of the divergence of $\mathbf{E}$ throughout the volume τ enclosed by the surface *a*. Apply this theorem to Eq. (9.12).

$$\epsilon \int_a \mathbf{E} \cdot d\mathbf{a} = \epsilon \int_\tau \boldsymbol{\nabla} \cdot \mathbf{E} \, d\tau = \int_\tau \rho \, d\tau \tag{9.13}$$

The integrands must be equal; therefore,

$$\boldsymbol{\nabla} \cdot \mathbf{E} = \frac{\rho}{\epsilon} \tag{9.14}$$

By means of the definition of the electric field in terms of the gradient of the potential in the region, Eq. (9.14) can be written as

$$\boldsymbol{\nabla} \cdot (-\boldsymbol{\nabla} V) = \frac{\rho}{\epsilon}$$

$$\nabla^2 V = - \frac{\rho}{\epsilon} \tag{9.15}$$

This is *Poisson's equation*, one of the most important statements in electric field theory. Both the potential, V, and the electric charge density, ρ, may be functions of the coordinates and time. The permittivity ϵ may also be a function of the coordinates, as would be the case in a nonisotopic medium. This condition is not commonly encountered in electron tube design and will not be considered.*

In many cases the region in question is devoid of a distributed volume charge density and $\rho = 0$. For this condition, Poisson's equation reduces to *Laplace's equation*:

$$\nabla^2 V = 0 \tag{9.16}$$

These equations always apply to any region containing an electric field and they must be satisfied by the analytic form assumed by the potential distribution. For this reason, Poisson's or Laplace's equation forms the basis

---

* See J. A. Stratton, *Electromagnetic Theory*, McGraw-Hill Book Co., New York, 1941.

for ascertaining the correct form of the potential distribution for a given geometrical configuration of the electrodes.

In addition to Poisson's equation, it is necessary to obtain some knowledge of the relationship between the electric charge on a conductor and the potential distribution established by this charge in the surrounding medium. This information can be obtained by the use of modified forms of Eq. (9.7).

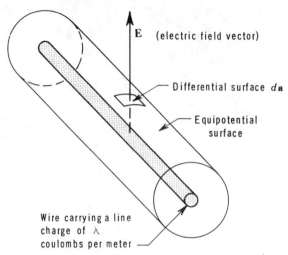

E   (electric field vector)

Differential surface d**a**

Equipotential surface

Wire carrying a line charge of λ coulombs per meter

Fig. 9.2. The application of Gauss's law to the electric field surrounding a charged wire.

The first extension of this equation is made to a charge complex. The net potential at any point caused by this charge complex is

$$V(r) = \sum_n \frac{q_n}{4\pi\epsilon r_n} \qquad (9.17)$$

where r_n is the magnitude of the position vector to the nth charge.

If the charge is distributed continuously over a volume τ, then

$$V(r) = \frac{1}{4\pi\epsilon} \int_\tau \frac{\rho(r)}{r} d\tau \qquad (9.18)$$

If the charge is distributed over a surface a, then

$$V(r) = \frac{1}{4\pi\epsilon} \int_a \frac{\sigma}{r} da \qquad (9.19)$$

In many cases the potential about an electrically charged body can be calculated quite easily by a direct application of Gauss' law. As an example that will be of further interest, consider a wire carrying a *line charge* of λ coulombs/m (see Fig. 9.2). If the wire is sufficiently removed from other charged or conducting bodies, then the *equipotential surfaces* are concentric

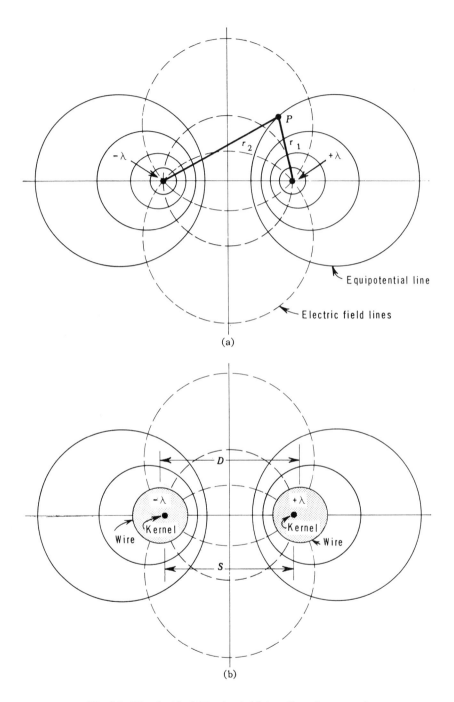

Fig. 9.3. The electric fields about (a) two line charges and (b) two wires.

cylindrical shells. By applying Gauss' law, Eq. (9.12), the electric flux emanating from the charged wire is

$$\psi = \int_a \mathbf{D} \cdot d\mathbf{a} = \lambda L \qquad (9.20)$$

where L is the wire length.

The unit area may be expressed as

$$d\mathbf{a} = Lr \, d\theta \, \mathbf{i}_r$$

where $\mathbf{i}_r$ is a unit vector normal to the surface. From the geometry of the problem, the electric field intensity must be radial; thus,

$$\mathbf{E} = E\mathbf{i}_r \qquad (9.21)$$

With these substitutions, Eq. (9.20) becomes

$$\int_0^{2\pi} (\epsilon E\mathbf{i}_r) \cdot (Lr \, d\theta \, \mathbf{i}_r) = \lambda L$$

$$\epsilon EL2\pi r = \lambda L$$

$$E = \frac{\lambda}{2\pi\epsilon r} \quad \text{v/m} \qquad (9.22)$$

The potential at any point r meters from the axis of the wire is determined by integrating the electric field over a distance r.

$$V = -\int_0^r E \, dr + C$$

$$V = -\frac{\lambda}{2\pi\epsilon} \ln r + C \qquad (9.23)$$

where C is a constant of integration.

As an example of the use of Eq. (9.23), consider two parallel line charges, $+\lambda$ and $-\lambda$ coulombs/m. To determine the potential at any point P in the vicinity of these two line charges, make use of the *theory of superposition.* This permits writing down the contribution to the potential at point P made by each line charge independent of the other and then summing the individual contributions to obtain the net potential at point P.

$$V_P = -\frac{+\lambda}{2\pi\epsilon} \ln r_1 - \frac{-\lambda}{2\pi\epsilon} \ln r_2 + C$$

where r_1 and r_2 are the distances from line charge 1 and line charge 2 to the point in question (see Fig. 9.3). Combine the logarithm terms to obtain

$$V_P = \frac{\lambda}{2\pi\epsilon} \ln \frac{r_2}{r_1} + C \qquad (9.24)$$

If the reference for measuring potential is taken as infinitely remote from the point P as well as from the two wires, then $C = 0$.

A plot of the electric field about these two line charges is shown in Fig. 9.3(a). The separation between the line charges is S meters. To locate two conductors to carry these line charges, it is necessary to fit the surface of the conductors to the equipotential lines. It is easy to show that the equipotential lines are circles of radius

$$R = \frac{r_2 S}{r_1[(r_2/r_1)^2 - 1]} \qquad (9.25a)$$

and with their centers located at the points

$$\pm \frac{S[(r_2/r_1)^2 + 1]}{2[(r_2/r_1)^2 - 1]} \qquad (9.25b)$$

on the axis that passes through the line charges.

Figure 9.3(b) shows the same electric field distribution obtained by replacing the line charges with two conductors of circular cross-section that are positioned so that their surfaces coincide with the equipotential surfaces of Fig. 9.3(a). The electric field is not upset by the presence of the wires. The spacing between wire centers is D, in Fig. 9.3(b). Often, the physical position of the wires is known and it is necessary to determine the proper points or *kernels* at which to place the line charges. The positions of the kernels are specified by Eq. (9.25b). It is necessary to establish a relationship between the spacing S of the kernels and the spacing D of the wires. To do this, set Eq. (9.25b) equal to $D/2$.

$$\frac{S[(r_2/r_1)^2 + 1]}{[(r_2/r_1)^2 - 1]} = D \qquad (9.26)$$

On the surface of a wire of radius R, the ratio r_2/r_1 has a fixed value according to Eq. (9.25a). A simultaneous solution of Eqs. (9.25a) and (9.26) yields

$$\frac{r_2}{r_1} = \frac{D}{2R} \pm \sqrt{\left(\frac{D}{2R}\right)^2 - 1} \qquad (9.27)$$

Equation (9.27) is used to evaluate the ratio r_2/r_1 on the surface of the wire for a given wire radius, R, and spacing, D, between wire centers. This result is substituted in Eq. (9.25b) to determine the positions of the kernels. Once the location of the kernels is known, the electric field may be plotted. The circular electric field lines have their centers lying on the vertical axis and each line passes through the kernels.

9.2 Applications of Laplace's equation

The fundamental importance of Laplace's equation warrants its further examination. The simplest form of the equation occurs in the region between two plane-parallel plates whose lateral dimensions are large compared to the spacing of the plates. In this case, the only variation in potential to be found is in the z-direction normal to the plates (Fig. 9.4). Laplace's equation (Eq. (9.16)) reduces to

$$\frac{\partial^2 V(z)}{\partial z^2} = 0$$

A first integration yields the electric field intensity

$$E(z) = -\frac{\partial V}{\partial z} = E_0$$

where E_0 is the integration constant. A second integration leads to the expression for the potential,

$$V(z) = -E_0 z + V_0 \qquad (9.28)$$

where V_0 is the integration constant. Usually the first electrode ($z = 0$) is taken as the reference potential for measuring voltage, thus making $V_0 = 0$.

Laplace's equation in three-dimensional space and rectangular coordinates is written as

$$\frac{\partial^2 V}{\partial x^2} + \frac{\partial^2 V}{\partial y^2} + \frac{\partial^2 V}{\partial z^2} = 0 \qquad (9.29)$$

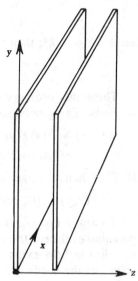

Fig. 9.4. Plane-parallel plates.

and a general solution is obtained by assuming that the potential

$$V(x, y, z) = X(x)\,Y(y)Z(z) \qquad (9.30)$$

where X is a function x alone, Y is a function of y alone, etc. This is known as the *method of separation of variables* and fortunately is applicable to physical problems. (It is the method employed in Sec. 3.7 to solve Schrödinger's equation.) Substitute Eq. (9.30) in Eq. (9.29) and obtain

$$X''YZ + XY''Z + XYZ'' = 0$$

where the double prime superscript indicates the second derivative ($X'' = d^2X/dx^2$, etc.).

Divide Eq. (9.30) by the potential function XYZ,

$$\frac{X''}{X} + \frac{Y''}{Y} + \frac{Z''}{Z} = 0 \qquad (9.31)$$

Now X is a function of x alone, Y is a function of y alone, and Z is a function of z alone. Therefore, X''/X in Eq. (9.31) can only be equal to a constant, k^2, as is also the case with Y''/Y and Z''/Z. Each part of Eq. (9.31) can be written as a separate ordinary differential equation. As an example, consider the very common problem of two degrees of freedom with no variation of potential in the z-direction. Equation (9.31) for this case is written as

$$\frac{X''}{X} + \frac{Y''}{Y} = 0 \qquad (9.32)$$

Set $X''/X = -k^2$; then

$$\frac{Y''}{Y} = k^2$$

These two ordinary differential equations may be solved by the usual methods. The general solution is of the form:

$$V(x, y) = X(x) Y(y)$$
$$= [A_1 \cos kx + A_2 \sin kx] [B_1 \cosh ky + B_2 \sinh ky] \qquad (9.33)$$

If X''/X had been set equal to $+k^2$, then the general solution would be

$$V(x, y) = [C_1 \cosh kx + C_2 \sinh kx][D_1 \sin ky + D_2 \cos ky] \qquad (9.34)$$

To apply Eq. (9.33) or (9.34) to a problem, it is necessary to know the potential or the electric field strength at the boundaries of the region in which the electric field exists. This information is used to determine the proper values of the coefficients, thereby fitting the general solution to the specific problem at hand.

The case of Laplace's equation in two dimensions lends itself to a unique method of solution. The equipotential surfaces are always normal to the electric field lines. This follows from the definition of the electric field as the gradient of the potential at each point in space. Because boundary conditions involve both the potential and the electric field strength, it is usually necessary to deal with the general solution for the potential (Eq. (9.33) or (9.34)) as well as the derivative of this solution. If a method of analysis were available to handle both the electric field and the potential simultaneously, then many problems could be greatly simplified.

Fortunately, such a method is found in the functions of the *complex variable*:

$$z = x + iy \qquad (9.35)$$

(Do not confuse this z with the third Cartesian coordinate.) The complex variable specifies points in a complex plane as shown in Fig. 9.5. This plane will be referred to as the Z-plane. The complex variable can be expressed as the x-axis and the iy-axis components of a radius vector r.

$$z = r(\cos \theta + i \sin \theta) \qquad (9.36)$$

A MacLaurin expansion of Eq. (9.36) yields

$$z = r\epsilon^{i\theta} \qquad (9.37)$$

which is commonly referred to as the *polar form* of the complex variable.

The square of the magnitude of the complex variable is found by multiplying the complex variable by its *conjugate*,

$$r^2 = |z|^2 = zz^* = (x + iy)(x - iy) \tag{9.38}$$

where $z^* = x - iy$ is the conjugate of $(x + iy)$. In a similar manner, $(x + iy)$ is the conjugate of $(x - iy)$.

A real problem in two dimensions is represented by the coordinates x and iy when this method is used. Without the use of the complex variable, the problem would have been represented by a plot in the ordinary x-y plane. Why resort to a complex plane? One of the answers to this question lies in the behavior of the functions of this complex variable that occur in physical problems. Let

$$F(z) = F(x + iy) \tag{9.39}$$

be a function of the complex variable. It is easily shown by substitution that $F(z)$ satisfies Laplace's equation:

$$\frac{\partial F}{\partial x} = \frac{\partial F}{\partial z}\frac{\partial z}{\partial x}$$

but, from Eq. (9.35), $\partial z/\partial x = 1$; hence,

$$\frac{\partial F}{\partial x} = \frac{\partial F}{\partial z}$$

and

$$\frac{\partial^2 F}{\partial x^2} = \frac{\partial^2 F}{\partial z^2} \tag{9.40}$$

In a similar manner,

$$\frac{\partial F}{\partial y} = i\frac{\partial F}{\partial z}$$

and

$$\frac{\partial^2 F}{\partial y^2} = -\frac{\partial^2 F}{\partial z^2} \tag{9.41}$$

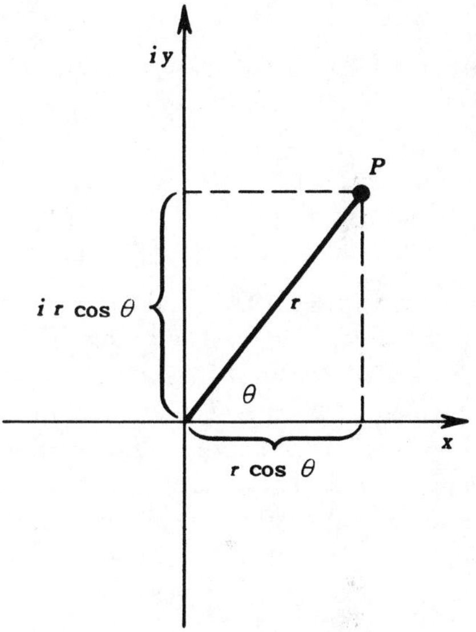

Fig. 9.5. The complex plane.

A combination of Eqs. (9.40) and (9.41) yields Laplace's equation

$$\frac{\partial^2 F}{\partial x^2} + \frac{\partial^2 F}{\partial y^2} = 0$$

This indicates that $F(z)$ is a satisfactory solution of Laplace's equation, and therefore the function may be used to represent the electric potential. If $F(z)$ is separated into its *real* and *imaginary* parts, then

$$F(z) = F(x + iy) = G(x, y) + iH(x, y) \tag{9.42}$$

and each part must in turn satisfy Laplace's equation. Following the preceding development,

$$\frac{\partial G}{\partial y} + \frac{\partial H}{\partial y} = i\left(\frac{\partial G}{\partial x} + i\frac{\partial H}{\partial x}\right) \tag{9.43}$$

Real parts can only be equal to other real parts, and imaginary parts can only equal other imaginary parts. Therefore, from Eq. (9.43),

$$\frac{\partial G}{\partial x} = \frac{\partial H}{\partial y} \tag{9.44}$$

and

$$\frac{\partial G}{\partial y} = -\frac{\partial H}{\partial x} \tag{9.45}$$

Equations (9.44) and (9.45) are known as the *Cauchy-Riemann conditions*. Functions that satisfy these conditions are called *analytic functions*.

If polar coordinates are used, then

$$F(z) = F(r, \theta)$$

and the Cauchy-Riemann conditions become

$$\frac{\partial G}{\partial r} = \frac{\partial H}{r\,\partial \theta} \tag{9.46}$$

and

$$\frac{\partial H}{\partial r} = -\frac{\partial G}{r\,\partial \theta} \tag{9.47}$$

Refer to Eq. (9.42) and examine the two parts of the function $F(z)$ of the complex variable, z. The family of curves obtained by setting $G(x, y)$ equal to a set of constants is intersected at right angles by the family of curves obtained by setting $H(x, y)$ equal to another set of constants. The functions $G(x, y)$ and $H(x, y)$ are said to be *orthogonal*. Notice that $G(x, y)$ and $H(x, y)$ actually represent *surfaces* in ordinary three-dimensional space where there is no variation of potential along the third dimension. The analytic function $G(x, y)$ may be taken to represent either equipotential surfaces or lines of electric field strength; the second analytic function, $H(x, y)$, represents the other quantity.

As an example, consider the following function of a complex variable:

$$F(z) = \ln z \tag{9.48}$$

To represent an electric field problem, this function must be analytic. Express z in polar form:

$$\ln z = \ln r\epsilon^{i\theta} = \ln r + i\theta \tag{9.49}$$

$$= G(r) + iH(\theta)$$

An application of the first Cauchy-Riemann condition in polar form yields:

$$\frac{\partial G}{\partial r} = \frac{\partial}{\partial r} \ln r = \frac{1}{r}$$

$$\frac{\partial H}{r\,\partial \theta} = \frac{1}{r}\frac{\partial}{\partial \theta}\theta = \frac{1}{r}$$

The first condition is satisfied. The second condition yields

$$\frac{\partial H}{\partial r} = \frac{\partial}{\partial r}\, \theta = 0$$

$$-\frac{\partial G}{r\, \partial \theta} = -\frac{1}{r}\frac{\partial}{\partial \theta}\ln r = 0$$

The second condition is also satisfied. The function $\ln z$ is therefore analytic and may properly represent a physical problem in electrostatics.

With reference to Eq. (9.49), the function $G(r)$ represents a cylindrical surface which is an equipotential surface surrounding the charged wire. The function $iH(\theta)$ represents the orthogonal field lines that emanate radially from the wire. The complete function $F(z)$ represents both the equipotential surfaces and the electric field lines.

9.3   Conformal transformations

The method of analysis based upon functions of the complex variable is far more powerful than has been indicated thus far. For example, it is an easy task to write down the potential at a point P arising from line charges on several parallel wires such as those shown in Fig. 9.6(a). If there are many such wires (Fig. 9.6(b)), the expression for the voltage is difficult to obtain and cumbersome to reduce to a simplified form. If the cumbersome geometrical form of the electrodes in the W-plane, which represents the actual physical problem, can be transformed into the relatively simple form shown in the Z-plane, then the analysis can proceed easily. Once the expression for the potential at a point P in the analysis plane (Z-plane) is written down, the same transformation that relates to the Z- and W-planes can be used to transform the expression for the potential into the W-plane.

Transformations of this type can be made by using analytic functions to relate the Z- and W-planes. Such transformations preserve angles between lines and maintain the general shape of incremental areas. The term conformal is used to describe these transformations.

A generalized conformal transformation that is often encountered is

$$w = \frac{az + b}{cz + d} \tag{9.50}$$

Four cases are apparent:

Case 1 $c = 0,$ $a = d = 1,$ $w = z + b$

A surface in the Z-plane undergoes a translation, b, in the W-plane.

Case 2 $b = c = 0,$ $d = 1,$ $w = az$

A surface in the Z-plane undergoes a multiplication, a, in the W-plane.

Case 3 $b = c = 0,$ $d = 1,$ $a = \epsilon^{i\phi},$ $w = z\epsilon^{i\phi}$

A surface in the Z-plane undergoes a rotation, ϕ, in the W-plane.

Cases 1, 2, and 3 are summarized by the transformation:

$$w = az\epsilon^{i\phi} + b \tag{9.51}$$

Case 4 $a = d = 0, \quad b = c = 1, \quad w = 1/z$ (9.52)

This is the unit circle transformation where points inside a circle of unit radius centered at the origin of the axes go outside and points outside the unit circle go inside upon transformation from the Z-plane to the W-plane.

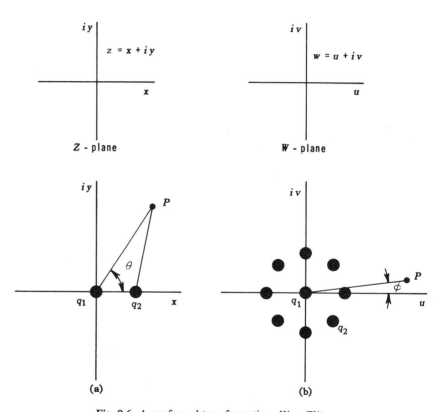

Fig. 9.6. A conformal transformation, $W = Z^{1/n}$.

When the complex variable is raised to a power, it possesses some interesting properties. For instance,

$$z^n = r^n \epsilon^{in\theta} = r^n(\cos n\theta + i \sin n\theta) \tag{9.53}$$

whereas

$$z^{1/n} = \sqrt[n]{r}\, \epsilon^{i\theta/n} = \sqrt[n]{r}\left(\cos \frac{\theta}{n} + i \sin \frac{\theta}{n}\right) \tag{9.54}$$

Equation (9.54) may be written as

$$z^{1/n} = \sqrt[n]{r}\,\epsilon^{i(\theta + 2k\pi)/n} \tag{9.55a}$$

$$= \sqrt[n]{r}\left(\cos\frac{\theta + 2k\pi}{n} + i\sin\frac{\theta + 2k\pi}{n}\right) \tag{9.55b}$$

where $k = 0, 1, 2, 3, \ldots$ Equation (9.55) is obtained by noting that $\cos\theta = \cos(\theta + 2k\pi)$ and $\sin\theta = \sin(\theta + 2k\pi)$ for any integer value of k.

Equation (9.55) may be plotted by setting the complex function

$$w = z^{1/n} = u + iv$$

and plotting in the complex W-plane. It is apparent from Eq. (9.55a) that the position vector w may possess the angles θ/n, $(\theta + 2\pi)/n$, $(\theta + 4\pi)/n$, $(\theta + 6\pi)/n$, etc. As an example, let $z = r\epsilon^{i\pi/3}$, $(\theta = 60°)$. This point is

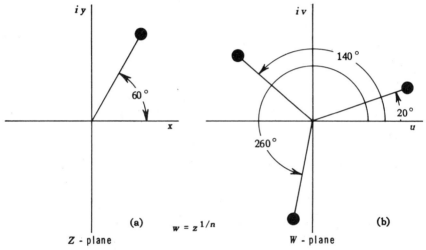

(a) $w = z^{1/n}$ (b)

Z - plane   W - plane

Fig. 9.7. The conformal transformation discussed in the text.

shown plotted in the Z-plane in Fig. 9.7(a). Suppose that $n = 3$; then in the W-plane this point is located by the discrete position vectors $w = r\epsilon^{i\pi/9}$, $r\epsilon^{i7\pi/9}$, and $r\epsilon^{i13\pi/9}$ (see Fig. 9.7(b)). Any additional values of k, such as $k = 3$, $w = r\epsilon^{i19\pi/9} = r\epsilon^{i\pi/9}$, merely repeat the above three points in the W-plane. Therefore, new points are obtained in the W-plane for all values of k through $k = (n - 1)$.

The above example demonstrates the use of conformal transformations in converting a simple two-dimensional geometry into a more complex structure. This is known as *conformal mapping*. Examples of the use of this method for mapping complex electric fields from simple, basic electric fields will be taken up in detail in Chap. 10. For this reason, this subject will be dropped for the present and a numerical method of obtaining the electric field distribution will be considered.

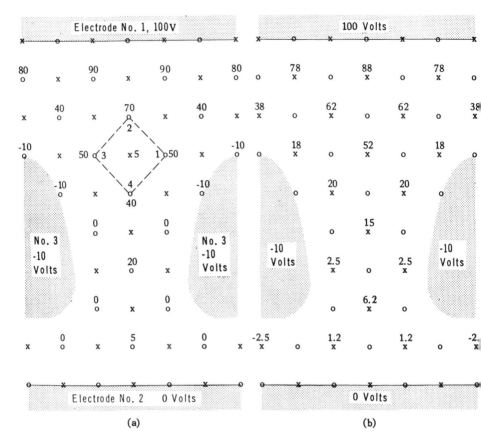

Fig. 9.8. An example of the application and numerical solution of Laplace's equation to determine the potential distribution in an electrostatic device. (a) Double grid of o and x points superimposed on plan view of electrodes. The initial estimate of the potential distribution is marked at each circled point. (b) First recalculation of the potential distribution. (**See facing page for parts (c) and (d).**)

9.4   Numerical determination of electric fields

The electric field that is set up by the electric charges on a group of electrodes that possess a complex geometrical structure can be solved relatively easily by numerical methods. Figure 9.8(a) is the plan view of an electrode arrangement for which the electric field distribution is to be determined. End-effects are to be neglected.

Divide the interelectrode region into a grid. The size of the grid is important—a small grid yields a more accurate plot, but the labor involved in the calculations may become prohibitive. (Note that the grid points are marked

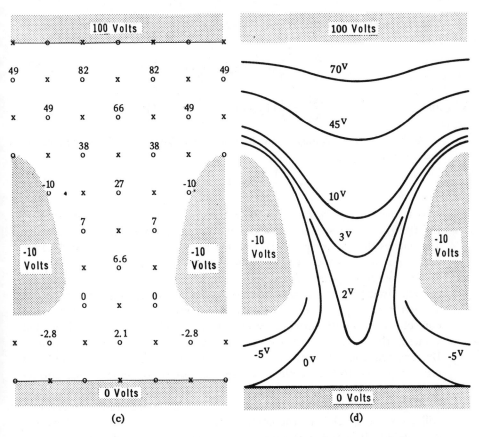

Fig. 9.8, Cont'd. (c) Second recalculation of the potential distribution. (d) Equipotential lines sketched in after several more recalculations of the potential distribution.

alternately with a small circle or a small cross.) For reference purposes, four adjacent points marked by circles have been numbered; also, the enclosed point marked by the cross has been numbered.

Laplace's equation,

$$\frac{\partial^2 V}{\partial x^2} + \frac{\partial^2 V}{\partial y^2} = 0$$

must be satisfied everywhere in the interelectrode space. In incremental form, the equation may be written as

$$\frac{\Delta\left(\dfrac{\Delta V}{\Delta x}\right)}{\Delta x} + \frac{\Delta\left(\dfrac{\Delta V}{\Delta y}\right)}{\Delta y} = 0 \tag{9.56}$$

The incremental derivatives may be evaluated numerically in the following manner:

$$\frac{\Delta V}{\Delta x} = \frac{1}{h}(V_1 - V_5) = \frac{1}{h}(V_5 - V_3) \qquad (9.57)$$

and
$$\frac{\Delta V}{\Delta y} = \frac{1}{h}(V_2 - V_5) = \frac{1}{h}(V_5 - V_4) \qquad (9.58)$$

Substitute these values for the first derivative into Eq. (9.56) and solve for the potential, V_5.

$$V_5 = \frac{1}{4}(V_1 + V_2 + V_3 + V_4) \qquad (9.59)$$

This is the *average potential* in the region in question. The importance of Eq. (9.59) lies in the fact that the mean potential obtained from it usually approaches the correct potential for that region more closely than the four corner potentials, which may be somewhat in error.

To obtain the potential distribution in Fig. 9.8(a), estimate the potential at each circled point. By repeated use of Eq. (9.59), calculate the potential at each crossed point. These calculated potentials should be nearer to the correct values than the original estimated potentials. Now, use the calculated values at the crossed points to recalculate the potentials at the circled points. By repeated and alternate calculation of the potentials at the circled and crossed points, it is possible to make the values converge to the correct potential at each point.

Regions near electrodes that have surfaces with large radii of curvature will converge quickly to the correct potentials. Other regions will require more labor. It is not necessary to do a complete recalculation each time. Those regions that are slow to converge can be recalculated independently several times before another over-all recalculation is made. Figures 9.8(b), (c), and (d) depict the steps in the solution to the example.

9.5 Electric models

In addition to their random thermal velocity, conduction electrons move with a drift velocity that parallels the electric field lines in a conductor. Further, the potential drop throughout the conductor establishes the equipotential surfaces. The use of a conductor that has a reasonably high resistivity makes it possible to maintain a readily measurable voltage gradient throughout the conductor. Thus, the equipotential lines and electric field lines can be measured. Electric fields may be scaled, which permits the use of models.

The simplest form of electric model employs a paper that has been coated with a conducting material. The resistivity of the paper is usually sufficiently high so that a potential difference on the order of several volts per inch can be maintained across the paper (away from the edges) without danger of overheating the conductive coating. The edges of the paper should be avoided—otherwise they will have a pronounced effect upon the experiments.

Conducting electrodes are painted upon the paper with a metallic silver base paint.* (*Note:* ordinary paints, even the so-called metallic paints, are usually nonconductors.) Figure 9.9 is a sketch of a problem "painted on"

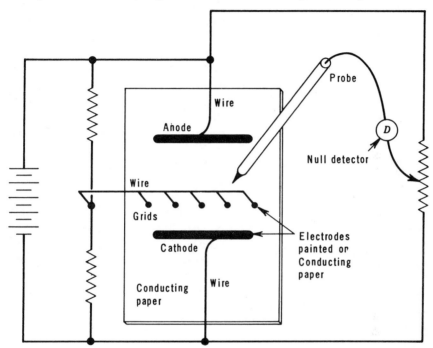

Fig. 9.9. Tracing equipotential lines on conducting paper. The potentiometer is set for the potential to be traced.

conducting paper. The equipotential lines are determined by choosing one electrode as reference and measuring all potentials relative to it. In Fig. 9.9 a bridge arrangement is shown which permits adjusting the bridge so that a detected null corresponds to a desired potential. This method permits a rapid tracing of equipotential lines. Either d-c or a-c voltages may be used, the choice governed by the detector available.

The electric field lines may be sketched in, orthogonal to the equipotential lines. Occasionally this procedure is difficult to follow in regions where the equipotential lines are rapidly altering direction. In such cases it often helps to build a simple double probe for determining the direction of the field lines.

* Available from the General Cement Company through electronic supply houses.

This is done by fixing two needles to an insulated rod. The needles are spaced about $\frac{1}{4}$ in., as sketched in Fig. 9.10. A sensitive millivoltmeter is connected to the needles. By rotating the probe about a selected point (similar to using a drafting compass), two voltage peaks are detected. These voltage peaks indicate when the needles are aligned with the electric field lines in the conducting paper.

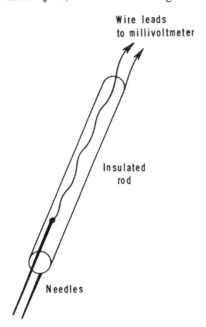

Wire leads to millivoltmeter

Insulated rod

Needles

Fig. 9.10. A double probe for determining the direction of electric field lines.

Instead of conducting paper, a tank of water that contains a mild electrolyte of copper sulfate may be used. In this case the electrodes must be formed and mounted in position in the tank. Thin sheets of copper make practical electrodes because they can be readily formed by hand and altered as necessary. The probe measurements are made in a manner similar to the method described above for the conducting paper.

Electrolytic tanks have been very popular for many years. The inconvenience of the liquid plus the problem of transferring the location of the probe to plotting paper are the major disadvantages. Automatic, servo-controlled plotting machines are popular; they usually employ the electrolytic tank.

9.6 Mechanical models

None of the models discussed thus far will plot the trajectory of the electron in the actual device—they only plot the equipotential lines and the orthogonal electric field lines. Because of its kinetic energy and possible initial velocity, the trajectory of the electron will not necessarily parallel the electric field lines.

A mechanical model that will give a reasonably accurate representation of the electron trajectory is obtained by carefully and uniformly stretching very thin rubber over a frame (Fig. 9.11).* If the frame is tilted, then a potential energy difference exists between the two ends. Small shot or ball bearings roll down the membrane under the influence of the gravitational force caused by the gradient of the potential energy along the surface of the membrane.

* V. K. Zworykin and J. A. Rajchmann, *Proc. I.R.E.*, **27**, 558–566 (Sept. 1939).

The shot may be likened to the electrons moving under the influence of an electric field. Electrode configurations can be formed and placed beneath the rubber membrane at the desired locations. By raising the electrode models the rubber membrane assumes a three-dimensional shape such that the surface

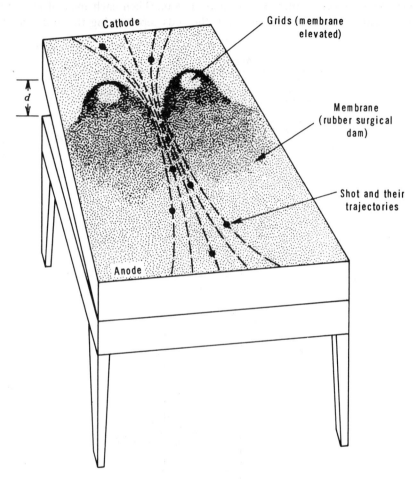

Fig. 9.11. An elastic membrane model of an electron tube. The elevation, d, of the cathode corresponds to the electrical potential difference between anode and cathode.

of the membrane at each point represents a potential energy level in the gravitational field that is analogous to the corresponding potential energy level in the electrical field of the actual device. In this gravitational field model the rolling shot follows trajectories that resemble the trajectories of the electrons in the actual electronic device.

The scaling is quite simple. Suppose that the cathode-to-anode voltage in Fig. 9.11 is 120 v. Let the cathode end of the membrane be elevated a few inches until the shot rolls freely to the anode end. Do not over-elevate or the inertial effect of the shot introduces error. Suppose that the difference in elevation between cathode and anode is 8 in. Then each inch of elevation represents 15 v. With this in mind, the rods representing the grids can be

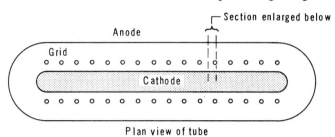

Plan view of tube

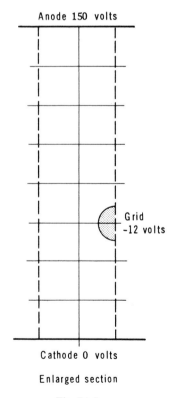

Enlarged section

Fig. P9.5

elevated until they represent a voltage that is negative with respect to the cathode. The elevation in the sketch is 8.8 in., which represents -12 volts bias.

PROBLEMS

1. A spherical shell of outside radius r_b and inside radius r_a contains a uniformly distributed volume charge density, ρ, throughout the shell. By use of Eq. (9.18), show that the potential, a distance L from the center of the spherical shell, is

$$\frac{\rho}{3\epsilon L}(r_b^3 - r_a^3)$$

2. (a) Show that the charged shell in Prob. 1 can be replaced by an equivalent point charge located at the center of the sphere. (b) Show that the charged shell can be replaced by an infinitesimally thin shell containing a surface charge density, σ.

3. Show that the potential at any point r between two concentric cylinders of radii r_1 and r_2 having potentials V_1 and V_2 is

$$V(r) = V_1 + (V_2 - V_1)\frac{\ln (r/r_1)}{\ln (r_2/r_1)}$$

4. An important conformal transformation is the logarithmic function of a complex variable

$$w = \ln z$$

Show that this function is analytic and therefore a proper conformal transformation.

5. Fig. P9.5 represents a section of a planar electron tube. Compute the electric field distribution by the numerical solution of Laplace's equation for the electrode potentials given. For better accuracy, divide the region surrounding the grid wire into small increments.

REFERENCES

1. K. R. Spangenberg, *Vacuum Tubes*, McGraw-Hill Book Co., New York, 1948.

2. W. G. Dow, *Fundamentals of Engineering Electronics*, John Wiley & Sons, New York, 1937.

3. R. V. Churchill, *Complex Variables and Applications*, McGraw-Hill Book Co., New York, 1948.

4. J. A. Stratton, *Electromagnetic Theory*, McGraw-Hill Book Co., New York, 1941.

5. M. Mason and W. Weaver, *The Electromagnetic Field*, Dover Publications, Inc., New York, 1929.

CHAPTER 10

High-vacuum tubes

In this chapter, electron tubes used for voltage amplification will be analyzed mathematically. Included, in addition to a study of their volt-ampere characteristics and basic behavior as circuit elements, will be the basic principles of tube design. (The reader may wish to review Sec. 1.2 and 1.3, which trace the historical design of these tubes.)

Electron tubes may be of either the high-vacuum or gas-filled type and they may depend upon any of the mechanisms of electron emission covered in Chap. 5. The usual amplifier tube employs an indirectly heated, oxide-coated cathode and one or more *grids* for the control of the electron current flow to the *anode*. A typical tube is shown in Fig. 10.1.

10.1 The triode

Since its introduction in 1912 by Lee De Forest, the high-vacuum triode tube has been the mainstay of the electronics field. The introduction of a grid by De Forest permitted control of the cathode-to-anode current in accordance with a potential applied to the grid. Three variables are present: anode-to-cathode voltage e_b, grid-to-cathode voltage e_c, and anode current i_b.

As long as the net grid voltage is maintained negative relative to the cathode, there is no signal current flowing in the grid circuit. There is, however, a very small current (on the order of several micromicroamperes) that is caused by positive ions' arriving at the grid. These positive ions arise from the ionization of some of the residual gas molecules found within the tube. In conventional small-signal-voltage amplifier tubes, this d-c grid

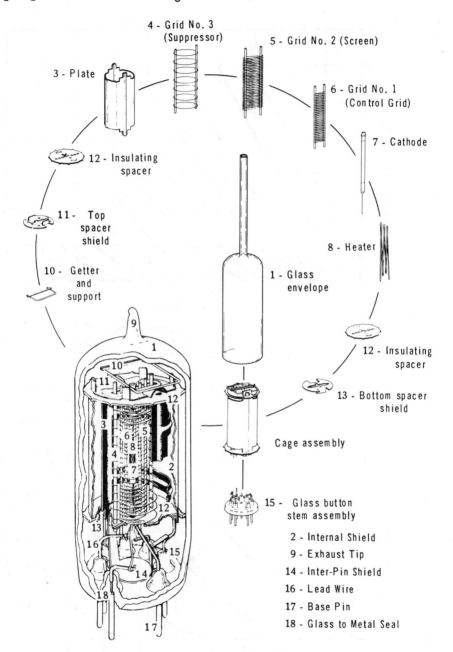

4 - Grid No. 3 (Suppressor)

5 - Grid No. 2 (Screen)

3 - Plate

6 - Grid No. 1 (Control Grid)

7 - Cathode

12 - Insulating spacer

11 - Top spacer shield

8 - Heater

10 - Getter and support

1 - Glass envelope

12 - Insulating spacer

13 - Bottom spacer shield

Cage assembly

15 - Glass button stem assembly

2 - Internal Shield
9 - Exhaust Tip
14 - Inter-Pin Shield
16 - Lead Wire
17 - Base Pin
18 - Glass to Metal Seal

Fig. 10.1. A multigrid electron tube and its component parts. (Courtesy of the Radio Corporation of America.)

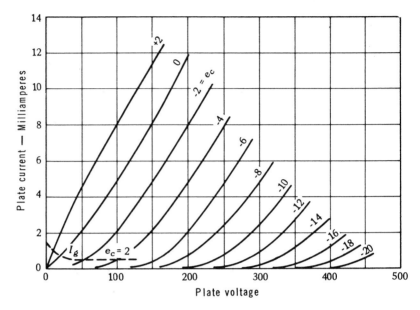

Fig. 10.2. Plate characteristics of a medium-mu triode. The dotted curve expresses grid current as a function of plate voltage for a positive grid voltage for +2 volts.

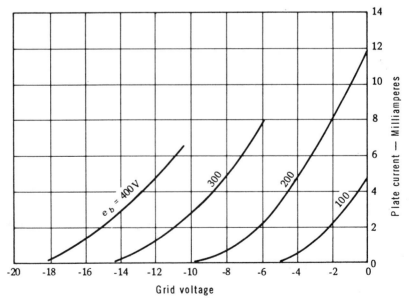

Fig. 10.3. Transfer characteristics. (For the same triode of Figs. 10.4 and 10.5.)

current is usually unnoticed unless a large resistance exists in the external grid-to-cathode circuit, in which case an objectionable noise voltage could appear between grid and cathode.

The relationship among the three variables of the triode tube is usually presented graphically by means of a plot of a family of *plate-circuit characteristics* (see Fig. 10.2). This is a family of curves obtained for various fixed values of grid voltage. The same general information can be presented in the form of the *transfer characteristics* shown in Fig. 10.3 or in the form of the *constant-current characteristics* of Fig. 10.4. Any one set of these characteristic curves supplies all the data necessary to plot the other two graphically.

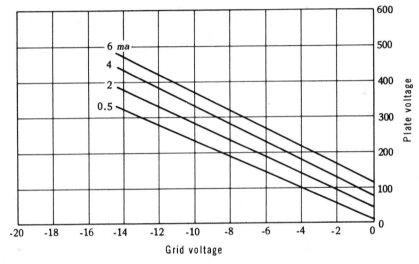

Fig. 10.4. Constant current characteristics.

An electron tube is only part of a complete circuit; to fully understand its operation, its behavior in a circuit must be considered. Figure 10.5 is the schematic diagram of an ordinary grounded-cathode voltage amplifier. This is the most generally used circuit, although grounded-grid and grounded-plate circuits are used for impedance-matching purposes as well as for obtaining other special effects. This circuit is drawn as though it were one stage of a multistage amplifier. The tube is operated so that the net grid-to-cathode voltage always remains less than zero and plate current never cuts off. This is known as Class A_1 operation.

Several features of this circuit should be noted. The grid resistor, R_g, is used to provide a d-c path to ground. As long as the instantaneous grid-to-cathode voltage remains negative, there will be no d-c current flow to or from the grid and, therefore, no d-c voltage drop across R_g. (This is true if the minute current caused by the neutralization of positive ions at the grid is neglected and R_g is normally not more than several megohms.) The fact that there is no d-c voltage drop across R_g places the grid at ground potential as far as d-c is concerned. How small the grid resistor may be made is determined by the internal impedance of the signal source. If R_g is made considerably smaller than the impedance of the signal source, then very little signal voltage appears from grid to ground.

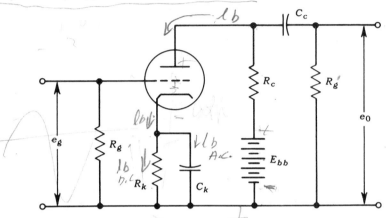

Fig. 10.5. The grounded cathode, R-C-coupled voltage amplifier.

Because the grid is at ground potential for d-c, it is possible to supply *d-c bias* to the grid in a very economical fashion. The *average* or *quiescent* anode current follows the conventional direction from anode to cathode, then through the *cathode-bias resistor*, R_k, and back to the power supply. The d-c drop across R_k places the cathode at a potential that is positive relative to ground. It was shown earlier that the grid is at ground potential for d-c. Therefore, the grid is *biased negative* relative to the cathode by the voltage drop across the cathode resistor.

Normally it is not desirable to produce any signal-voltage drop across the cathode-bias resistor. For this reason it is necessary to bypass R_k with a capacitor, C_k, whose reactance is considerably less than the resistance of R_k at the lowest signal frequency to be passed without attenuation by the amplifier.

The signal voltage, e_g, appears across R_g and is thereby added to the d-c grid-bias voltage, E_{cc}. The net grid-to-cathode voltage is

$$e_c = E_{cc} + e_g \tag{10.1}$$

In the same manner that the grid resistor provides a method of completing the d-c grid circuit and at the same time makes it possible to inject a signal voltage from grid to cathode, the *plate-coupling resistor*, R_c, makes it possible to feed d-c power to the tube and still extract an output signal voltage from the amplifier. The negative terminal of the power supply is grounded for both a-c and d-c currents, whereas the positive terminal is above ground potential for d-c, *but it is at ground potential for a-c.* This occurs because power supplies are designed to have a very low a-c output impedance. For this reason, the power-supply end of the plate coupling resistor is at ground potential for a-c signal current. The anode current, i_b, varies in accordance with the grid signal voltage. It consists of an average or quiescent value, I_b, plus a signal component, i_p.

$$i_b = I_b + i_p \tag{10.2}$$

This results in a varying instantaneous voltage drop across the plate-coupling resistor. This is the amplified a-c signal voltage.

The *coupling capacitor*, C_c, is used to block d-c voltage and current from the succeeding stage. Its size is selected so that its reactance is small over the normal range of signal frequencies to be amplified. The problem of selecting this capacitor will be considered later.

The grid resistor, R_g', of the succeeding stage forms part of the a-c signal load on this stage. The net a-c load resistance, R_L, is given by

$$R_L = \frac{R_c R_g'}{R_c + R_g'} \tag{10.3}$$

The voltage drop across the tube also consists of a quiescent component, E_b, plus a signal voltage, e_o.

$$e_b = E_b + e_o \tag{10.4}$$

The signal-voltage drop across the a-c load is also e_o and is given by

$$e_o = -i_p R_L \tag{10.5}$$

where the minus sign accounts for the 180-degree phase shift between grid and plate circuits. This phase shift arises because the plate signal current increases, thus making the plate end of the coupling resistor *less* positive when the grid signal voltage is becoming *more* positive.

10.2 Graphical solution

A circuit that contains a nonlinear element such as a vacuum tube is usually handled best by graphical analysis. At least the solution to the d-c portion of the problem must be solved graphically. The portion of the problem that concerns the a-c signal must also be handled graphically if the operation of the tube is spread over a large portion of the volt-ampere characteristics, which occurs when the signal is large.

If the signal voltages are small, the operation will be restricted to a limited portion of the tube characteristics and the problem may be treated as one in linear analysis. Small-signal analysis may be carried out analytically; this will be done in Sec. 10.3.

To determine the value of the d-c coupling resistor for a given tube, it is first necessary to specify the bandwidth of signal frequencies over which the amplifier is to operate. From this information an a-c load resistance, R_L, is determined. (The method of obtaining R_L will be treated later in this chapter.) The a-c load consists of the parallel combination of R_c and R'_g. Often R'_g is quite large compared to R_c, and therefore $R_c \approx R_L$. In this manner the d-c coupling resistor R_c is determined.

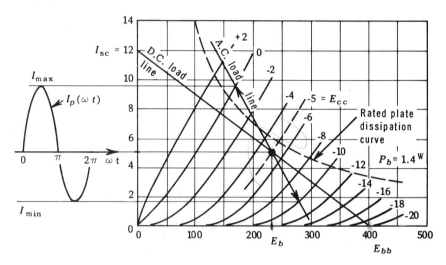

Fig. 10.6. Graphical analysis of a Class A, vacuum-tube amplifier. (Note the large-signal distortion in $i_p(\omega t)$.)

The tube plus the coupling resistor and the cathode-bias resistor, along with the power supply, comprise a series d-c circuit. To solve graphically for the quiescent plate current, first write the equation for the series voltage drops around this loop.

$$E_{bb} = E_b + I_b(R_c + R_K) \tag{10.6}$$

where E_{bb} is the power-supply voltage. This equation may be placed in the form

$$E_{bb} - I_b(R_c + R_K) = E_b \tag{10.7}$$

where the voltages appearing across the linear circuit elements are on the left-hand side, and the voltage drop across the nonlinear tube appears on the right-hand side.

Locate the power-supply voltage on the plate characteristics of the tube (Fig. 10.6). Subtract the voltage drop across $(R_c + R_K)$ by plotting this volt-ampere characteristic. This is called the *d-c load line*. It can be quickly drawn in by imagining the tube to be short-circuited so that the short-circuit current, I_{SC}, is limited by $(R_c + R_K)$ only. Then

$$I_{SC} = \frac{E_{bb}}{R_c + R_K} \qquad (10.8)$$

This short-circuit is located on the plate-current axis. A straight line between this point and the power-supply voltage E_{bb} located on the voltage axis is the d-c load line.

The d-c load line is divided into a grid-voltage scale by the intersections of this line with the family of plate-characteristic curves. The designer may select any grid voltage as the d-c grid bias—the selection is usually based upon a consideration of how much the signal voltage will swing the instantaneous grid voltage. If the operation is to be limited to Class A_1, then the magnitude of the grid bias must always be greater than the peak positive signal voltage. The selection of the *operating point* may also be based upon considerations of amplified signal distortion and upon maintaining the maximum possible amplifier voltage gain or maximum power gain.

The location of the operating point determines the quiescent plate current, I_b, and plate-to-cathode voltage, E_b, This, in turn, determines the $I_b R_c$ voltage drop across the coupling resistor. The product $E_b I_b$ represents the average energy per second delivered to the electrons in accelerating them from cathode to anode. This energy is converted to heat at the anode. The maximum safe plate power dissipation, P_b, for a normal tube life expectancy is determined from extensive testing by the tube manufacturer. A maximum plate dissipation curve for various values of

$$E_b I_b = P_b \qquad (10.9)$$

may be plotted on the plate curves of Fig. 10.6. To avoid excessive heating of the anode, the operating point should be located on or below the maximum plate dissipation curve.

The *a-c load line* is plotted passing through the operating point. Its slope is equal to $(-1/R_L)$ mhos. Notice that the family of plate characteristics calibrates the a-c load line in a grid-voltage scale. Also, note that this scale is not completely linear over a large range of grid voltages. The voltage scale is crowded toward the low plate-current end of the a-c load line. This corresponds to large, negative grid signal voltages. When a large power output is desired, it is necessary to cause the instantaneous plate current to swing as much as possible. This requires that the operating point be carefully selected so that the maximum excursions of grid voltage will neither drive the grid positive nor reduce the plate current to the cut-off point.

The root-mean-square value of the plate signal current is

$$I_p = \frac{I_{max} - I_{min}}{2\sqrt{2}} \qquad (10.10)$$

The associated power output is

$$P_o = I_p^2 R_L \tag{10.11}$$

By the use of graphical constructions, as shown in Fig. 10.6, Eq. (10.10) may be evaluated and the result substituted into Eq. (10.11) to determine the power output.

For the example of Fig. 10.6, the rms signal current is

$$I_p = 2.83 \quad \text{ma}.$$

and the power output delivered to the a-c load of 13,700 ohms is

$$P_o = 0.11 \quad \text{w}$$

10.3 Small-signal analysis

Most voltage-amplifier stages deal with very low-level signal voltages. The maximum signal swing is often too small to permit the use of a graphical solution. In these cases we are perfectly justified in treating the a-c signal operation of the tube as linear in the vicinity of the quiescent operating point.

The mathematical procedure is similar to that used in Chap. 6 for the analysis of the small-signal operation of the transistor and the tunnel diode. First, express the plate current as an implicit function of the grid voltage and the plate voltage.

$$i_b = f(e_c, e_b) \tag{10.12}$$

For the purposes of calculation an explicit equation must be obtained. The differential of this equation is

$$di_b = \frac{\partial i_b}{\partial e_c} de_c + \frac{\partial i_b}{\partial e_b} de_b \tag{10.13}$$

By means of Eqs. (10.1), (10.2), and (10.4), substitute for the differentials in Eq. (10.13). Also note that there is no difference between a differential and a small a-c signal. With these substitutions Eq. (10.13) reduces to the explicit equation:

$$i_p = \frac{\partial i_b}{\partial e_c} e_g + \frac{\partial i_b}{\partial e_b} e_o \tag{10.14}$$

The partial derivatives are to be evaluated at the operating point. The two that appear in Eq. (10.14) are readily evaluated from the plate characteristics of Fig. 10.6. The *dynamic* (a-c) *plate resistance* is

$$r_p = \frac{\partial e_b}{\partial i_b} \tag{10.15}$$

where the partial derivative symbols indicate that all other variables are to be held constant. The *mutual conductance*

$$g_m = \frac{\partial i_b}{\partial e_c} \tag{10.16}$$

expresses the effect of a change in grid voltage upon the plate current. For the example of Fig. 10.6,

$$r_p = 16,900 \quad \text{ohms}$$

$$g_m = 1500 \quad \text{micromhos}$$

If Eqs. (10.15) and (10.16) are written in incremental form and multiplied, then

$$r_p g_m = \frac{\Delta e_b}{\Delta i_b} \cdot \frac{\Delta i_b}{\Delta e_c} = -\frac{\Delta e_b}{\Delta e_c}$$

where the minus sign is necessary to account for the negative slope of the plot of e_b as a function of e_c (see Fig. 10.4). Upon going to the limit, this product may be written as

$$\mu = r_p g_m = -\frac{\partial e_b}{\partial e_c} \qquad (10.17)$$

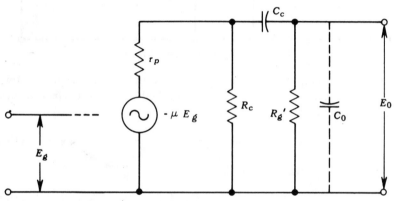

Fig. 10.7. The small-signal equivalent circuit of a vacuum-tube amplifier. The capacitor, C_0, represents the effective-shunt capacitance in the circuit.

This expresses the variation in anode-to-cathode voltage in accord with changes in grid-to-cathode voltage. It is called the *amplification factor* or merely the *mu* of the tube. In the example

$$\mu = 25 \quad \text{v/v}$$

Substitute Eqs. (10.15) and (10.16) into Eq. (10.14):

$$i_p = g_m e_g + \frac{e_o}{r_p}$$

Multiply by the dynamic plate resistance, substitute Eq. (10.17), and re-arrange terms.

$$\mu e_g = i_p(r_p + R_L) \qquad (10.18)$$

where $e_o = -i_p R_L$ according to Eq. (10.5). An equivalent circuit representing Eq. (10.18) may be drawn as shown in Fig. 10.7.

At this point, it is convenient to shift to *phasor* notation. Make this change in notation in Eq. (10.18) and solve for rms signal current, I_p.

$$I_p = \frac{\mu E_g}{r_p + R_L} \tag{10.19}$$

The *voltage gain* of the stage is defined as the ratio of the output voltage, E_o, to the input voltage, E_g. There is a range of frequencies where the voltage

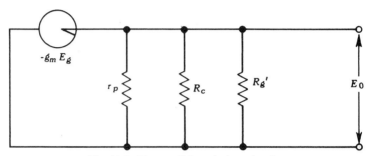

Fig. 10.8. The parallel equivalent circuit.

drop across the coupling capacitor is negligible and where the current flowing through the shunt capacitance, C_o, is also negligible. This is the *mid-frequency range*. In this range the voltage gain is

$$A_{\mathrm{mid}} = \frac{E_o}{E_g} = \frac{-\mu R_L}{r_p + R_L} \tag{10.20}$$

Multiply and divide Eq. (10.20) by r_p

$$A_{\mathrm{mid}} = -\left(\frac{\mu}{r_p}\right)\frac{r_p R_L}{r_p + R_L} \tag{10.21}$$

The term $r_p R_L/(r_p + R_L)$ represents the equivalent resistance, R_{eq}, of the parallel combination of r_p, R_c, and R_g'. In view of this, Eq. (10.21) may be written as

$$A_{\mathrm{mid}} = -g_m R_{eq} \tag{10.22}$$

and a parallel equivalent circuit may be drawn. To do this, place Eq. (10.22) in terms of E_o and E_q.

$$-g_m E_g = \frac{E_o}{R_{eq}} \tag{10.23}$$

The *parallel equivalent circuit* of Fig. 10.8 can be drawn to represent this equation.

From the standpoint of ease of calculation, the series equivalent circuit is usually preferred for triode tubes. The parallel equivalent circuit usually lends itself more readily to calculations involving multigrid tubes.

In the example of Fig. 10.6, the small-signal voltage gain is

$$A_{\mathrm{mid}} = 11.4$$

10.4 Grid circuit impedance

The interelectrode capacities have a pronounced effect upon the high-frequency operation of a vacuum tube. These interelectrode capacities are indicated on the schematic diagram of Fig. 10.9(a). The parallel equivalent

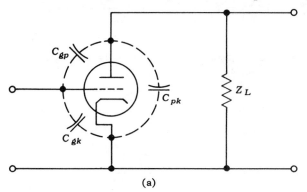

(a)

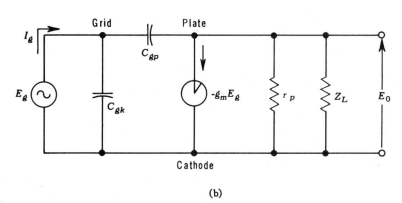

(b)

Fig. 10.9. Interelectrode capacities and the equivalent circuit for computing the grid input admittance.

circuit is shown in Fig. 10.9(b). This equivalent circuit is similar to that of Fig. 10.8 except that the interelectrode capacities and the a-c grid signal source are also included.

The input impedance is given by

$$Y_{in} = \frac{I_g}{E_g} \tag{10.24}$$

and the problem is one of determining I_g. By the theorem of superposition, the current I_g may be expressed as consisting of two components.

$$I_g = I_{g1} + I_{g2} \tag{10.25}$$

The component $\mathbf{I}_{g1}$ is considered to arise from the effect of the constant-voltage generator when the *constant-current generator is open-circuited*. The component $\mathbf{I}_{g2}$ arises from the effect of the constant-current generator when the *constant-voltage generator is replaced by a short-circuit*.

$$I_{g1} = E_g \left[j\omega C_{gk} + \cfrac{1}{\cfrac{r_p Z_L}{r_p + Z_L} + \cfrac{1}{j\omega C_{gp}}} \right] \tag{10.26}$$

The grid-to-plate reactance $1/\omega C_{gp}$ is usually very large compared to the equivalent impedance,

$$\mathbf{Z}_{eq} = \frac{r_p Z_L}{r_p + Z_L} \tag{10.27}$$

With this simplifying assumption, Eq. (10.26) reduces to

$$\mathbf{I}_{g1} = j\omega (C_{gk} + C_{gp}) E_g \tag{10.28}$$

When the generator $\mathbf{E}_g$ is short-circuited, then

$$\mathbf{I}_{g2} = -j\omega C_{gp} \mathbf{E}_o \tag{10.29}$$

where

$$\mathbf{E}_o = -g_m \mathbf{E}_g \mathbf{Z}_L \left(\frac{r_p}{r_p + \mathbf{Z}_L} \right) \tag{10.30}$$

By substituting Eqs. (10.28), (10.29), and (10.30) in Eq. (10.25) and dividing the result by $\mathbf{E}_g$, the input admittance is found to be

$$\mathbf{Y}_{in} = j\omega \left[C_{gk} + C_{gp} \left(1 + g_m \frac{r_p Z_L}{r_p + \mathbf{Z}_L} \right) \right] \tag{10.31}$$

For most purposes, in RC-coupled amplifiers it suffices to treat the load impedance as a pure resistance, R_L. If this assumption is made, then the input admittance is pure capacitance and

$$C_{in} = C_{gk} + C_{gp}(1 + g_m R_{eq}) \tag{10.32}$$

The input capacitance is a direct function of the mutual conductance and the equivalent load resistance. The magnitude of the mid-frequency gain is equal to $g_m R_{eq}$ (Eq. (10.22)). Therefore, the use of higher-mu tubes to achieve increased gain also results in an increase in the input capacitance of the stage.

The input capacitance of one stage acts as a shunt capacitance in the plate circuit of the preceding stage. This is known as the *Miller effect* (see Sec. 1.2).

10.5   Bandwidth and mutual conductance

The bandwidth, B, of an RC-coupled amplifier is usually defined as the frequency range that lies between the *upper half-power frequency*, f_2, and the *lower half-power frequency*, f_1.

$$B = f_2 - f_1 \tag{10.33}$$

The half-power frequencies are the points where the amplifier gain has dropped to $1/\sqrt{2}$ of the mid-frequency value. It is easy to show that at the lower half-power frequency the reactance of the coupling capacitor, C_c, is equal to

$$\frac{1}{2\pi f_1 C_c} = \frac{r_p R_c}{r_p + R_c} + R'_g \tag{10.34}$$

(This result is very similar to that obtained for an RC-coupled transistor. See Prob. 5, Chap. 6.)

The upper half-power frequency is governed by the total shunt capacitance, C_o, that appears in the plate equivalent circuit. This capacitance consists of the sum of the plate-to-cathode capacitance, C_{pk}, of the stage under analysis, plus all stray wiring capacitance, C_s, plus the grid input capacitance of the next stage.

$$C_o = C_{pk} + C_s + C'_{gk} + C'_{gp}(1 + g'_m R'_{eq}) \tag{10.35}$$

The prime values belong to the succeeding stage. It is interesting to note that, because of the dependence of the upper half-power frequency of one stage upon the parameters of the succeeding stage, it is often desirable to design a multistage amplifier by starting at the output and working backward toward the input.

From the equivalent circuit of Fig. 10.7 it is easy to show that at the upper half-power frequency, f_2, the reactance of the shunt capacitance is equal to

$$\frac{1}{2\pi f_2 C_o} = R_{eq} \tag{10.36}$$

The lower and upper half-power frequencies are obtained from Eqs. (10.34) and (10.36). The bandwidth

$$B \approx f_2 \tag{10.37}$$

and the magnitude of the mid-frequency gain is $g_m R_{eq}$, according to Eq. (10.22). A combination of these equations yields the *gain-bandwidth product*

$$A_{\text{mid}} B = \frac{g_m}{2\pi C_o} \tag{10.38}$$

This relationship is very important and forms the starting point for the proper design of a broad-band amplifier. The right-hand side of this equation is essentially a constant for a given vacuum tube. The left-hand side of the equation is the product of the desired bandwidth per stage and the possible associated gain per stage. It should be noted, however, that the voltage gain per stage cannot exceed the value given by $g_m R_{eq}$, regardless of how small the bandwidth may be in Eq. (10.38).

The choice of a tube governs the gain-bandwidth product through g_m. The total shunt capacitance, C_o, is caused in a large part by the stray wiring capacitance. Therefore, when using modern tubes, a change in tubes will not always have a noticeable effect on C_o. This equation is important in the design of high-vacuum tubes because it tells the designer that, to produce a tube suitable for use in a very broad-band (video) amplifier, it is necessary to produce a tube with a high mutual conductance. On the other hand, it warns against permitting the interelectrode capacities to increase. These two requirements are not compatible and a compromise must be made.

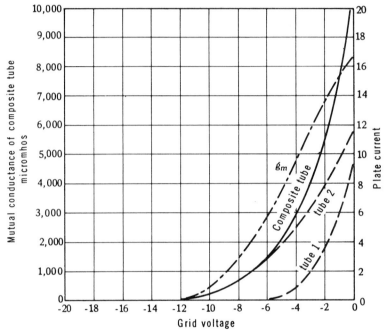

Fig. 10.10. Transfer characteristics for two tubes directly in parallel. The net transfer characteristic and mutual conductance, g_m, of the composite tube are plotted. The result is a variable-mu tube whose mutual conductance can be varied by adjusting the grid bias voltage.

10.6 Modification of tube parameters

From the preceding section it might appear tempting to parallel two vacuum tubes to effectively double g_m and thus obtain a better gain-bandwidth product. This may offer some advantages because the effective dynamic mutual conductance of n tubes in parallel is

$$g_m = g_{m1} + g_{m2} + \cdots + g_{mn} \tag{10.39}$$

The problems encountered in such an endeavor are: (1) The interelectrode and stray capacitances are almost doubled for two similar tubes. Thus, the gain-bandwidth product probably improves only slightly. (2) The effective dynamic plate resistance is halved for two similar tubes and the amplification factor remains the same. In general,

$$r_p = \left(\frac{1}{r_{p1}} + \frac{1}{r_{p2}} + \cdots + \frac{1}{r_{pn}} \right)^{-1} \tag{10.40}$$

Because of the large selection of tube types that are commercially available, there is little reason to actually parallel tubes in amplifier circuits.

This concept of obtaining new tube characteristics by the parallel connection of tubes of known characteristics can be of value to the tube designer. For instance, if two triodes, each with somewhat different transfer characteristics, are connected in parallel, then an interesting composite characteristic is obtained. One transfer characteristic for each tube is plotted in Fig. 10.10. Each are for the same value of plate voltage.

Each of the tubes displays a *sharp plate-current cut-off* for a specific value of grid voltage, e_{co}. The effective transfer characteristic for the two tubes in parallel is also plotted. Notice that this compound tube displays a *remote cut-off* characteristic. This occurs because tube 1 cuts off first, followed later by tube 2.

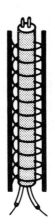

Fig. 10.11. A cathode and a control grid for a sharp cut-off vacuum tube.

Figure 10.11 is the typical cathode and grid structure that is employed in a sharp cut-off vacuum tube. If the pitch of the helix is constantly varied, the effect is the same as paralleling a large number of small tubes, each possessing a slightly different mutual conductance, plate resistance, and amplification factor. The result is a variable-mu tube. This is characterized by the remote cut-off displayed by the transfer characteristics.

10.7   Vacuum-tube design

The design of a vacuum tube is approached analytically by the application of electrostatic field theory and the methods of conformal transformations. In order to do this, it is necessary to neglect the effects of the electron space charge on the potential distribution in the tube. This assumption results in a certain degree of error that is usually not too objectionable. Figure 10.12 is a plot of the plate characteristics of a high-vacuum triode that was designed

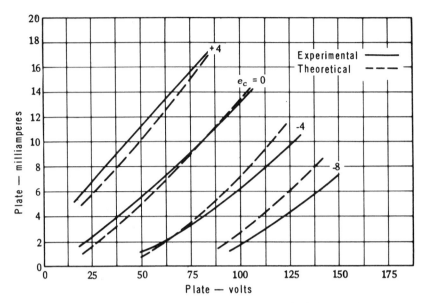

Fig. 10.12. Plate characteristics as determined by experimental measurements and by theoretical analysis for the tube design discussed in the text.

with cylindrical symmetry. The solid curves were obtained by laboratory measurements, whereas the dotted curves were obtained by analytical computations based upon the theoretical equations that are developed in this section.

Two basic tube geometries are in common use. One is based upon electrodes with cylindrical symmetry, the other on planar electrodes. Other tube geometries can usually be treated as combinations or modifications of these two geometries.

The analytical design always starts with a very simple tube geometry in the Z-plane. The potential at any point in the interelectrode space is written by application of the basic laws of electrostatics. This simple geometry is then transformed into the W-plane, where the resultant geometry is that of the actual tube. The conformal transformation employed determines whether the final geometry is cylindrical, planar, or some entirely new form.

These methods may be applied to multigrid tubes as well as to triodes. It is not feasible to go into detailed electron-tube design in this text. Therefore, only the design of the cylindrical electrode triode will be treated in detail. The complete analytical design will be developed, and these principles may be applied to other tube geometries and multigrid tubes.*

---

* The reader interested in further information on vacuum-tube design should consult *Vacuum Tubes* by K. R. Spangenberg, McGraw-Hill Book Co., New York, 1948.

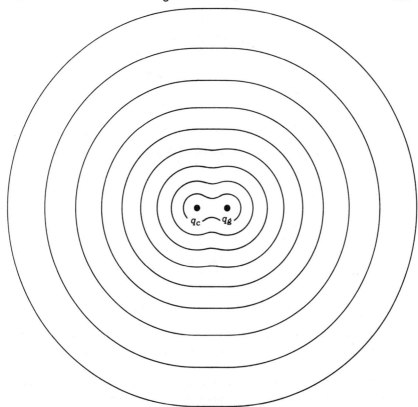

Fig. 10.13. The electrostatic equipotential lines that surround two wires which are at the same potential and both of which are at a large negative potential relative to the surrounding space.

To design a triode tube it is necessary to design first the simplest possible triode tube in the Z-plane. This is a tube that has a line charge, q_c, located at the cathode; a line charge, q_g, located on a single grid wire that is parallel to the cathode wire; and a distributed surface charge, $-[q_c + q_g]$, located on the plate. The cathode wire and the single grid wire can be treated as a two-wire transmission line *where each wire is almost at the same potential and both wires are quite negative relative to the surroundings.*

The equipotential lines about two such wires are very different from those of Fig. 9.3 where a considerable potential difference existed between the wires. In this case the equipotential lines are similar to those shown in Fig. 10.13. Notice that the equipotential lines (or surfaces, because there is Z-axis sym-metry to the problem) become very nearly circles. This permits the designer to locate a conducting metallic plate on one of these equipotential surfaces. This plate represents the electrostatic surroundings for the cathode and grid

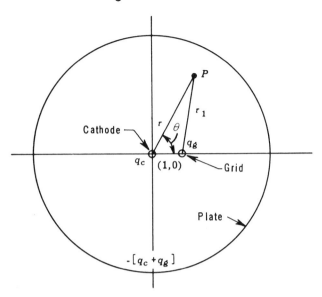

Fig. 10.14. An elementary triode in the Z-plane.

wires; therefore, all lines of electric flux emanating from the cathode and grid wires terminate on the plate. For this reason, the charge on the plate is $-[q_c + q_g]$.

Figure 10.14 is a sketch of the electrode arrangement in the Z-plane. The potential at any point P in the Z-plane is (see Chap. 9)

$$V(r, \theta) = -\frac{q_g}{2\pi\epsilon_0} \ln r_1 - \frac{q_c}{2\pi\epsilon_0} \ln r + C \qquad (10.41)$$

where C is a constant. Square r_1 and r and use the cosine law to eliminate r_1.

$$r_1^2 = r^2 + 1 - 2r \cos \theta \qquad (10.42)$$

where the cathode line charge-to-grid line charge spacing has been taken as a unit distance in the Z-plane. With this substitution the potential is

$$V(r, \theta) = -\frac{q_g}{4\pi\epsilon_0} \ln (r^2 + 1 - 2r \cos \theta) - \frac{q_c}{4\pi\epsilon_0} \ln r^2 + C \qquad (10.43)$$

In Chap. 9 the conformal transformation,

$$w = s_g z^{1/n} \qquad (10.44)$$

was shown to be capable of transforming the geometry of Fig. 10.14 to that of Fig. 10.15 (see Fig. 9.6, Sec. 9.3). The multiplier s_g moves the single grid in the Z-plane from the unit circle to a location on a circle of radius s_g in the W-plane. Therefore, all electrode spacings in the W-plane are given as multiples of s_g.

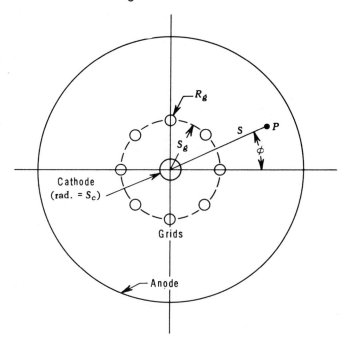

Fig. 10.15. A conventional triode in the W-plane.

The transformation

$$w = s_g z^{1/n}$$

may be expanded in polar coordinate form by setting

$$w = s\varepsilon^{j\phi} \tag{10.45a}$$

and

$$z = r\varepsilon^{j\theta} \tag{10.45b}$$

Then,

$$s\varepsilon^{j\phi} = s_g r^{1/n}\varepsilon^{j\theta/n}$$

The components of the transformation are

$$r = \left(\frac{s}{s_g}\right)^n \tag{10.46a}$$

$$\theta = n\phi \tag{10.46b}$$

Substitute Eqs. (10.46a) and (10.46b) in Eq. (10.43) to transform the expression for the potential into the W-plane.

$$V(s, \phi) = \frac{q_g}{4\pi\epsilon_0} \ln\left[\left(\frac{s}{s_g}\right)^{2n} + 1 - 2\left(\frac{s}{s_g}\right)^n \cos n\phi\right]$$
$$- \frac{2q_c}{4\pi\epsilon_0} \ln\left(\frac{s}{s_g}\right)^n + C \tag{10.47}$$

Thus, by use of a conformal transformation, the simple geometry in the Z-plane has been transformed to a more complicated geometrical structure in the W-plane. The same conformal transformation has been used to transform the general expression for potential in the Z-plane to the proper expression for potential in the W-plane.

The grid structure in the W-plane consists of an array of wires that are parallel to the cathode wire. They are arranged in a "squirrel-cage" type of structure. Some transmitting tubes that are manufactured use the squirrel-cage grid structure. However, it is too expensive for use in ordinary receiving tubes. Helical or modified helical grids are probably the most popular type of construction for ordinary tubes. It will be shown later that most conventional grid structures can be expressed in terms of an *equivalent squirrel-cage grid* for analysis purposes.

The general expression for potential at any point within the interelectrode region is seldom of immediate interest. The designer requires expressions for the specific voltages on the cathode, grid, and anode. Let the radius of the cathode be s_c; then, when $s = s_c$, Eq. (10.47) yields the potential on the cathode. Usually the radius of the cathode is very small compared to the radius s_g of the grid circle $(s_c \ll s_g)$. With these substitutions, Eq. (10.47) yields

$$V_c = 0 - \frac{2q_c n}{4\pi\epsilon_0} \ln\left(\frac{s_c}{s_g}\right) + C \tag{10.48}$$

The cathode is usually taken as the reference point for measuring voltages; therefore, set $V_c = 0$ and solve for the coefficient, C.

$$C(q_c) = \frac{nq_c}{2\pi\epsilon_0} \ln\left(\frac{s_c}{s_g}\right) \tag{10.49}$$

It is apparent that the coefficient C is a function of the charge on the cathode, q_c.

If the radius of the anode or plate is sufficiently large, then the equipotential surfaces are of circular cross-section and an anode can easily be fitted to these surfaces. This requires that the plate radius s_p be much greater than the radius of the grid circle $(s_p \gg s_g)$. With this substitution and setting $s = s_p$, Eq. (10.47) yields the plate potential,

$$V_p = -\frac{2q_g n}{4\pi\epsilon_0} \ln\left(\frac{s_p}{s_g}\right) - \frac{2q_c n}{4\pi\epsilon_0} \ln\left(\frac{s_p}{s_g}\right) + C$$

Substitute Eq. (10.49) for the coefficient C to obtain

$$V_p = -\frac{n[q_c + q_g]}{2\pi\epsilon_0} \ln\left(\frac{s_p}{s_g}\right) + \frac{nq_c}{2\pi\epsilon_0} \ln\left(\frac{s_c}{s_g}\right) \tag{10.50}$$

There remains only the problem of fitting the surface of the grid in the W-plane to the location of the equipotential surfaces in this region. In the

Z-plane the presence of the line charge q_g establishes equipotential surfaces of circular cross-section in the immediate vicinity of this charge. If the radius of the grid wire is quite small compared to the intergrid spacing and to the grid-to-cathode spacing, then the geometric center of the grid wire may be considered to coincide with the line charge. This assumption is valid for low-mu tubes. For medium-mu tubes it is necessary to recognize that the geometric center of the grid wires does not coincide with the kernel where the grid charge is effectively located.

To fit Eq. (10.47) to the grid wires, consider the surface of the grid wire whose center is at $[s_g, 0]$. One point $[s, \phi]$ on the surface of this wire is located at the point $[s_g, R_g/s_g]$. The radius of the grid wire is R_g and

$$\phi = \sin^{-1} \frac{R_g}{s_g} \approx \frac{R_g}{s_g}$$

for values of $\phi < 7.5$ degrees. With these substitutions, Eq. (10.47) yields the grid voltage

$$V_g = -\frac{q_g}{4\pi\epsilon_0} \ln\left[2 - 2\cos\frac{nR_g}{s_g}\right] + C \tag{10.51}$$

By the trigonometric identity,

$$2\sin^2 \alpha = 1 - \cos 2\alpha$$

Equation (10.51) may be written

$$V_g = -\frac{2q_g}{4\pi\epsilon_0} \ln\left(2\sin\frac{nR_g}{2s_g}\right) + C \tag{10.52}$$

where C is given by Eq. (10.49).

The amplification factor by definition is

$$\mu = -\frac{\partial e_b}{\partial e_c}\bigg|_{i_b = \text{constant}}$$

Typical triode plate characteristics are sketched in Fig. 10.16. The amplification factor is obtained graphically by determining the change in plate voltage, Δe_b, for a change in grid voltage, Δe_c, in the vicinity of the operating point. Notice, however, that there would be little error in making this computation for the condition of plate-current cut-off. Plate current ceases when the electric field at the cathode goes to zero (assuming no initial electron emission velocity). When the electric field at the cathode goes to zero, all lines of electric flux emanating from the plate terminate on the grid and thus the charge on the cathode, q_c, must be zero.

If these conditions are inserted in Eqs. (10.49), (10.50), and (10.52), the

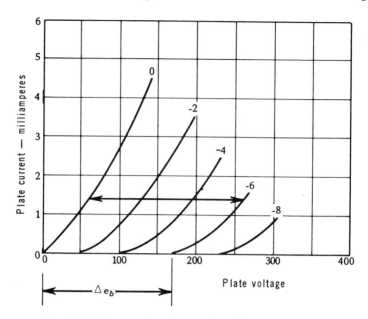

Fig. 10.16. Computation of mu at $I_b = 1.4$ *ma* and at plate-cut-off.

amplification factor can be found by taking 'the ratio of plate potential to grid potential for the condition of plate-current cut-off.

$$\mu = - \frac{n \ln \dfrac{s_p}{s_g}}{\ln\left(2 \sin \dfrac{nR_g}{2s_g}\right)} \qquad (10.53)$$

The numerator displays the manner in which μ varies directly with the number of grid wires, n, and the plate radius, s_p. It also shows that μ increases if the radius, s_g, of the grid wire circle is reduced. The grid thus has more control over plate current.

The denominator of Eq. (10.53) is better handled if the substitution

$$\pi S = \frac{nR_g}{s_g} = \frac{n2R_g l}{2s_g l} \qquad (10.54)$$

is made. The effective length of the tube is l. The coefficient S is called the *screening fraction* and is defined as

$$S = \frac{\text{area geometrically shielded by grids}}{\text{total grid cylinder surface area}}$$

With this substitution,

$$\mu = -\frac{n \ln \dfrac{s_p}{s_g}}{\ln\left(2 \sin \dfrac{\pi S}{2}\right)} \qquad (10.55)$$

Notice that $2 \sin \pi S/2 < 1$; therefore, the denominator is negative and of a magnitude that is less than unity. To maximize μ, it is necessary to reduce the magnitude of the denominator. This requires increasing the screening fraction.

As an example of the computation of μ for an actual tube, consider the tube whose characteristics are given in Fig. 10.2. This tube possesses cylindrical symmetry and a helical grid and has the following dimensions:

$$
\begin{aligned}
\text{cathode radius} &= s_c = 9.77 \times 10^{-4} \text{ meters} \\
\text{grid circle radius} &= s_g = 2.08 \times 10^{-3} \\
\text{plate radius} &= s_p = 3.13 \times 10^{-3} \\
\text{grid radius} &= R_g = 6.09 \times 10^{-5} \\
\text{pitch of grid helix} &= d = 8.05 \times 10^{-4} \\
\text{length of tube} &= l = 1.93 \times 10^{-2} \\
\text{grid support wire radius} &= s_s = 6.85 \times 10^{-4}
\end{aligned}
$$

The first step is to convert the helical grid structure into an equivalent squirrel-cage structure. To do this, express the number of grid wires in the squirrel cage in terms of their total effective length

$$lL_g = nl$$

where l is the axial tube length and L_g is the effective length of grid wire per unit length l of the tube. Thus,

$$L_g = n \qquad (10.56)$$

The linear length of the wire in one turn of a helix is

$$\sqrt{d^2 + (2\pi s_g)^2}$$

where d is the pitch. In an axial length, l, there are l/d turns in the helix; thus, the total length of the helical grid wire is

$$\frac{l}{d}\sqrt{d^2 + (2\pi s_g)^2} = lL_g$$

The effective length of grid wire per unit length of tube is

$$L_g = \sqrt{1 + \left(\frac{2\pi s_g}{d}\right)^2} \qquad (10.57)$$

$$= n_g$$

By use of this equation, the number n_g of effective squirrel-cage grid wires may be determined.

In addition to the helical grid, there is a single grid support wire such as shown in Fig. 10.1. This support acts as a squirrel-cage grid wire in the actual tube. Its effective length, neglecting the difference in radius, is

$$L_g = n_s \tag{10.58}$$

The total effective length of grid wire per unit length of the tube is

$$L'_g = n_g + n_s \tag{10.59}$$

For the example,

$$n' = L'_g = 16.23 + 1 = 17.23$$

The screening fraction (Eq. (10.54)) is

$$\pi S = n' \frac{R_g}{S_g} = 0.507$$

and by the use of Eq. (10.55), the amplification factor is

$$\mu = -\frac{17.23 \ln 1.50}{\ln (2 \sin 0.254)}$$

$$= 10.6$$

This is in excellent agreement with the value of μ for small plate currents that can be obtained graphically from the experimental data of Fig. 10.12.

In accordance with Eq. (10.55), it is necessary to increase the screening fraction a considerable amount if a high-mu tube is to be produced. A major increase in the screening fraction requires that the grid wire radius R_g be increased. The amplification factor is further increased if the grid circle radius is decreased.

Such action usually makes the grid wires large compared to the cathode and brings them close to it. The result is a more complicated problem in fitting the structure to the equipotential lines. The preceding analysis is no longer satisfactory for such high-mu tubes and more elaborate analysis is required.*

10.8 Plate current

In the preceding section the amplification factor was obtained analytically. Before the plate characteristics can be plotted theoretically as in Fig. 10.12, it is necessary to develop an analytical expression for the plate current. Once this has been accomplished, the mutual conductance and dynamic plate resistance can be determined.

---

* There are several methods available which have been collected in *Vacuum Tubes* by K. R. Spangenberg, McGraw-Hill Book Co., New York, 1948.

The plate current is space-charge limited, as discussed in Sec. 7.6. For a cylindrical geometry, the plate current per unit length of the tube is (Eq. (7.71))

$$\frac{I}{l} = 14.66 \times 10^{-6} \frac{V^{3/2}}{s\beta^2} = K \frac{V^{3/2}}{s\beta^2} \tag{10.60}$$

where β^2 is a function of the ratio of the radial position r of any point to the cathode radius, s_c. Solve for the potential $V(s)$ at any point in the tube (Fig. 10.15).

$$V(s) = \left(\frac{Is}{lK}\right)^{2/3} \beta^{4/3} \tag{10.61}$$

It was shown experimentally by Langmuir and Van der Bijl (Sec. 1.2) that the plate current of a triode can be expressed as

$$\frac{I}{l} = A\left(V_g + \frac{V_p}{\mu}\right)^{3/2} \tag{10.62}$$

This equation may also be expressed in equivalent plate voltage as

$$\frac{I}{l} = B(V_p + \mu V_g)^{3/2}$$

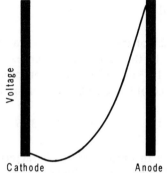

Fig. 10.17. Voltage distribution in a cylindrical diode.

Equation (10.62) treats the triode as though it were an equivalent diode whose current density is given by $AV^{3/2}$. Figure 10.17 is a sketch of the potential distribution in a cylindrical diode. Let a grid be located a distance s_g from the cathode; further, let the grid potential V_g be adjusted so that the presence of the grid does not disturb the potential distribution. Under these particular conditions, Eq. (10.61) is valid and may be used to determine V_g and V_p.

$$V_g = \left(\frac{Is_g}{lK}\right)^{2/3} \beta_g^{4/3} \tag{10.63}$$

and

$$V_p = \left(\frac{Is_p}{lK}\right)^{2/3} \beta_p^{4/3} \tag{10.64}$$

where s_p is the cathode-to-plate radius. Substitute Eqs. (10.63) and (10.64) in Eq. (10.62) and solve for the coefficient A.

$$A = \frac{K}{s_g \beta_g^2 \left[1 + \dfrac{1}{\mu}\left(\dfrac{s_p \beta_p^2}{s_g \beta_g^2}\right)^{2/3}\right]^{3/2}} \tag{10.65}$$

Substitute Eq. (10.65) into Eq. (10.62) to obtain a general expression for the plate current per unit length of the tube that is valid for any grid potential.

$$\frac{I}{l} = \frac{14.66 \times 10^{-6}\left(V_g + \dfrac{V_p}{\mu}\right)^{3/2}}{S_g\beta_g^2\left[1 + \dfrac{1}{\mu}\left(\dfrac{S_p\beta_p^2}{S_g\beta_g^2}\right)^{2/3}\right]^{3/2}} \qquad (10.66)$$

The tube dimensions in meters are substituted into this equation along with the proper values of the β^2-functions. With reference to Fig. 7.11,

$$\beta_g^2 = f\left(\frac{S_g}{S_c}\right)$$

and

$$\beta_p^2 = f\left(\frac{S_p}{S_c}\right)$$

Each of these quantities is read directly from Fig. 7.11.

In the preceding design example, the active length of the tube was 1.93×10^{-2} m. When the appropriate substitution is made, the expression (Eq. (10.66)) for the plate current reduces to

$$I = 3.17 \times 10^{-4}\left(V_g + \frac{V_p}{\mu}\right)^{3/2} \quad \text{amp}$$

The theoretical plate characteristics plotted in Fig. 10.13 are obtained by selecting a grid voltage and then plotting plate current as a function of plate voltage.

The mutual conductance is obtained from Eq. (10.66):

$$g_m = \frac{i_b}{e_c} = \frac{22.0 \times 10^{-6}\left(V_g + \dfrac{V_p}{\mu}\right)^{1/2}}{S_g\beta_g^2\left[1 + \dfrac{1}{\mu}\left(\dfrac{S_p\beta_p^2}{S_g\beta_g^2}\right)^{2/3}\right]^{3/2}} \, l \qquad (10.67)$$

10.9 Planar triode

Tubes with plane electrode geometry are designed with the same basic approach. The analysis begins with the same simple triode shown in Fig. 10.14. In this case, the conformal transformation

$$w = \ln z^{a/2\pi} \qquad (10.68)$$

is used to transform Eq. (10.43) to

$$V(u, v) = -\frac{q_g}{4\pi\epsilon_0}\ln\left(\epsilon^{4\pi u/a} + 1 - 2\epsilon^{2\pi u/a}\cos\frac{2\pi v}{a}\right) - \frac{q_c u}{a\epsilon_0} + C \quad (10.69)$$

This is the expression for the potential at any point within the interelectrode space. It may be used to determine the potentials V_p, V_g, and V_c of the plate, grid, and cathode, respectively. The procedure is identical to that used with the cylindrical electrode tube.*

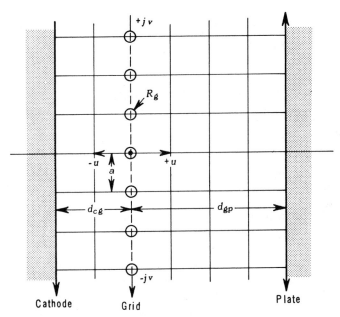

Fig. 10.18. The planar triode in the W-plane.

The geometry in the w-plane is shown in Fig. 10.18. The factor a determines the grid wire spacing. The expressions for the potentials are greatly simplified if the following restrictions are enforced:

$$d_{gp} > a, \qquad d_{cg} > a, \qquad R_g \ll a$$

Under these restrictions the mu of the tube is limited to medium-to-low values if the analysis is to be accurate. The amplification factor is determined at cut-off, as before. The result is

$$\mu = - \frac{2\pi d_{gp}}{a \ln (2 \sin \pi S/2)} \tag{10.70}$$

where $S = 2R_g/a$ is the screening fraction.

The plate-current density is derived in a manner similar to that used for the cylindrical triode. The analysis begins with the general expression for

* See Spangenberg, *Vacuum Tubes op. cit.* 304.

space-charge limited plate current, which was developed in Sec. 7.6 (see Eq. (7.61)). The result is

$$J = \frac{2.335 \times 10^{-6}\left(V_g + \dfrac{V_p}{\mu}\right)^{3/2}}{d_{cg}^2\left[1 + \dfrac{1}{\mu}\left(\dfrac{d_{cp}}{d_{cg}}\right)^{4/3}\right]^{3/2}} \tag{10.71}$$

and the associated mutual conductance is

$$g_m = \frac{3.51 \times 10^{-6}\left(V_g + \dfrac{V_p}{\mu}\right)^{1/2}}{d_{cg}^2\left[1 + \dfrac{1}{\mu}\left(\dfrac{d_{cp}}{d_{cg}}\right)^{4/3}\right]^{3/2}} A \tag{10.72}$$

where A is the total effective area of the anode.

10.10 Multigrid tubes

The *Miller effect* in triode tubes can limit their operation to less than 10 megacycles in straightforward RC-coupled amplifiers (see Sec. 10.4). This limitation was more pronounced in the early triodes where interelectrode capacitances were high by modern standards. For this reason, it was difficult to operate these early triodes in the broadcast band (0.55 to 1.6) megacycles.

Typical values of interelectrode capacitance for a modern tube are on the order of 1.5 $\mu\mu$f (micromicrofarad) grid to plate, 2.2 $\mu\mu$f input (grid to cathode plus all other grounded supporting wires, etc.), and 0.5 $\mu\mu$f output (plate to cathode plus all other grounded wires, etc.). Suppose that the gain of the stage is 10; then the net input capacitance to the grid of this stage is (Eq. (10.32))

$$C_{in} = C_{gk} + C_{gp}(1 + A)$$
$$= 2.2 + 1.5(11)$$
$$= 18.7 \quad \mu\mu\text{f}$$

This input capacitance plus the output or plate-to-cathode capacitance of the preceding stage plus the stray wiring capacitance comprise the net shunt capacitance in the plate circuit of the preceding stage. According to Eq. (10.36), the high-frequency gain of the preceding stage will have fallen off by $1/\sqrt{2}$ when the frequency is

$$f = f_2 = \frac{1}{2\pi R_{eq}C_o}$$

If $R_{eq} = 2500$ ohms and if it is assumed that

$$(C_{pk} + C_{\text{stray}}) = 15 \quad \mu\mu\text{f}$$

then

$$f_2 = 1.89 \quad \text{megacycles}$$

Obviously, one effective way to increase the frequency response without reducing R_{eq} and thereby the gain is to reduce the grid-to-plate interelectrode capacitance. As early as 1919, W. Schottky (Sec. 1.4) proposed that an additional grid might be introduced between the control grid and the plate to reduce this capacitance. A commercial tube employing this *screen grid* was introduced in 1926 by Hull and Williams.

The basic idea underlying the screen grid was to break the grid-to-plate capacitance into, in effect, two capacitances. They are shown in Fig. 10.19. By grounding the screen grid for a-c signals, the grid-to-screen grid capacitance, C_{gsg}, becomes part of the input capacitance. The plate-to-screen grid capacitance becomes part of the output capacitance and, if the screening is perfect, there is no longer any grid-to-plate capacitance. However, perfect screening cannot be

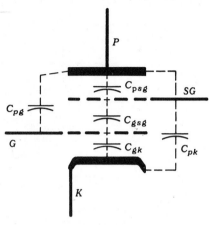

Fig. 10.19. The interelectrode capacities in a tetrode.

achieved but C_{gp} can usually be reduced to a value on the order of 0.005 $\mu\mu$f.

Suppose that an amplifier similar to the one in the preceding example uses a tetrode in place of the triode. Assume that all other interelectrode capacitances are the same except $C_{gp} = 0.005$ $\mu\mu$f. Then C_{in} of this stage is

$$C_{in} = 2.2 + 0.005(11) = 2.26 \quad \mu\mu\text{f}$$

instead of 18.7 $\mu\mu$f. Then C_o of the preceding stage is $(2.26 + 15) = 17.26$ $\mu\mu$f and the upper half-power frequency for the preceding stage is

$$f_2 = \frac{1}{2\pi R_{eq} C_o} = 3.69 \quad \text{megacycles}$$

It is apparent that the tetrode offers a considerable advantage over the triode in high-frequency amplifiers; however, the insertion of the screen grid has had a very pronounced effect upon the plate characteristics of the tube. First of all, it was found necessary to maintain the screen grid at a high positive d-c potential if sufficient plate current were to be obtained. Thus, the screen grid must be held at ground potential for a-c by providing a bypass capacitor, C_{sg}, whose reactance at the lowest frequency to be amplified is much smaller than the impedance of the source that supplies d-c power to the screen grid. The plate characteristics of the tetrode bear little resemblance to those of the triode. The plate characteristics of Fig. 10.20 are typical for a tetrode. They are plotted by holding the screen-grid voltage constant at some selected value, usually less than or equal to the plate-to-cathode voltage.

At high values of plate voltage, the curves have very little slope; thus, the dynamic plate resistance is very high compared to the plate resistance of the usual triode. Values may range from 0.1 to 2 megohms. The tetrode possesses a very interesting, although impractical, "dip" in the plate characteristics (the solid curves of Fig. 10.20). Notice that these dips occur for values

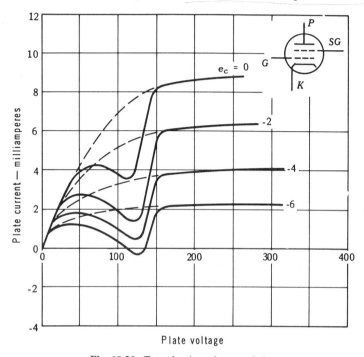

Fig. 10.20. Tetrode plate characteristics.

of plate voltage a little less than the screen-grid voltage. They are caused by the screen grid's collecting secondary electrons that are emitted at the anode. Thus, for a bias of -2 v and a plate voltage of 100, the plate current would be expected to be 5 ma (the dotted curve). Instead, a net electron current of about 3.8 ma reaches the anode, indicating that a secondary emission current of 1.2 ma is collected by the screen grid.

In some tetrodes it is possible that the number of secondary electrons emitted at the anode can exceed the primary electrons arriving at the anode. The result is shown in Fig. 10.20 for the $e_c = -6$ v plate characteristic. The plate characteristic indicates that for a plate voltage of about 125 v the net plate current actually reverses.

The screen grid handles a considerable current in addition to any secondary electrons collected from the anode. This screen-grid current represents a definite fraction of the total tube cathode current that is intercepted by the screen grid. The external circuitry that supplies the screen-grid voltage must be capable of supplying this current. Also, the circuit designer must be careful not to exceed the safe power dissipation limit of the screen grid. If I_{sg} is the screen-grid current and E_{sg} is the voltage, then

$$P_{sg} = I_{sg}E_{sg}$$

is the power dissipated at the screen grid.

The dynamic plate resistance of the tetrode is negative in the low-voltage portion of the plate-current dip. This characteristic of tetrodes is undesirable because it is difficult to design an amplifier that will not tend to break into oscillation because of the presence of this negative a-c plate resistance. Some of the older laboratory signal generators utilized this property of the tetrode, but modern circuits seldom operate on this principle. The tetrode, as a type. has passed into history.

10.11 The pentode

The undesirable negative-dynamic plate-resistance region of the tetrode can be eliminated by suppressing the flow of secondary electrons from the plate to the screen grid. This is accomplished by providing a large electric field immediately adjacent to the anode that accelerates all electrons in this vicinity back to the anode (see Fig. 10.21(a)).

The potential distribution of Fig. 10.21(a) provides an accelerating force on the electrons in the cathode-to-screen grid region. From screen grid to suppressor grid, the electric field is retarding; however, the electrons possess sufficient energy by now to overcome this potential barrier. (Note that the potential in the vicinity of the suppressor grid does not drop completely to zero even though the suppressor grid may be placed at ground potential by connecting it to the cathode. This is because the potential profiles of Fig. 10.21 are sketched for the region between grid wires.) Between the suppressor grid and the plate, the electric field may be either accelerating (A) or retarding (B) as determined by the magnitude of the plate potential in relation to the magnitude of the screen-grid potential. Normally, the plate potential is maintained great enough so that this field is highly accelerating and thus secondary electrons are returned to the plate. This eliminates the undesirable dip found in the tetrode characteristics. Typical pentode plate characteristics are shown in Fig. 10.22.

There is another method of providing the same potential distribution as that found in the pentode without the actual addition of a suppressor grid. The basic tube is a tetrode to which beam-forming electrodes have been added (Fig. 10.21(b)). The purpose of these electrodes is to increase the electron density in the region between the screen grid and the plate. At one point this density will be a maximum and if the beam formation has been properly designed, the space potential at this point will approach the cathode potential. This is the same result that was obtained in the pentode by the addition of the suppressor grid.

Beam tetrodes require large plate currents if a satisfactory *virtual suppressor grid* is to be formed. For this reason, these tubes are designed only as

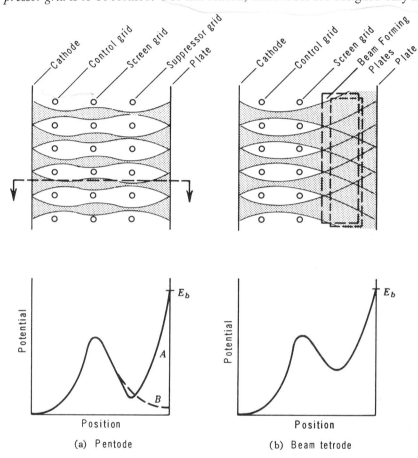

Fig. 10.21. Potential profiles in a pentode and in a beam tetrode. The beam-forming plates in the beam tetrode force the electrons toward the center of the tube structure (normal to the paper).

power amplifiers. *Beam power* tubes are actually pentodes insofar as their plate characteristics are concerned.

The pentode characteristics of Fig. 10.22 include a plot of the quiescent screen-grid current, I_{sg}, for various values of grid bias voltage. The designer locates the quiescent operating point on these characteristics in the same manner as they are located for the triode. The quiescent plate voltage is noted, and for this voltage the corresponding value of the quiescent screen-grid current is read on the plate-current scale in accordance with the dotted curves.

It is not always desirable to operate a pentode with the value of screen-grid voltage specified on the plate characteristics. The designer must either

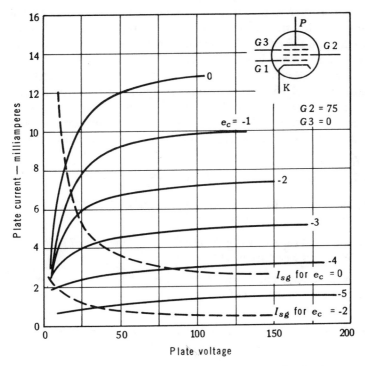

Fig. 10.22. Typical pentode plate characteristics for fixed values of screen grid and suppressor grid voltages.

run a new set of plate characteristics in the laboratory or estimate the new plate characteristics based upon those available. The estimate can be made on the basis that the space current

$$I_s = I_b + I_{sg}$$

can be expressed in terms of the equivalent triode voltage for the tube.

$$I_s = I_b + I_{sg} = K\left(e_c + \frac{e_{sg}}{\mu_s} + \frac{e_b}{\mu}\right)^{3/2} \tag{10.73}$$

where the suppressor grid voltage is assumed to be zero. If this is not the case, a term must be included within the parentheses to account for its effect. The ability of the screen grid to control the plate current is expressed by the amplification factor μ_{sg} of the screen grid.

$$\mu_{sg} = -\frac{\partial e_b}{\partial e_{sg}} \qquad (10.74)$$

The screen-grid amplification factor is approximately equal to the amplification of the tube connected as a triode (screen grid connected to plate). This information is often available in the tube manuals and provides a method for estimating μ_s. If Eq. (10.73) is first fitted to available plate characteristics by evaluating K, then it may be used to estimate the plate characteristics to be expected for a new value of screen-grid voltage.

Multigrid tubes that have more than three grids are available. These tubes are used as signal mixers, converters, and for many other purposes. To fully appreciate the functions these tubes perform, it is necessary to penetrate deeper into the field of radio engineering than is our purpose here. However, the reader will find many sources of information available on these tubes.

PROBLEMS

1. Determine the tube parameters of the pentode of Fig. 10.22 for an operating point in the general vicinity of (100 v, 7 ma).

2. The shunt capacitance in the plate circuit of the tube of Prob. 1 is 27 $\mu\mu$f. What is the gain-bandwidth product?

3. A single-stage amplifier with a bandwidth of 2 megacycles is desired. What gain may be obtained if the above pentode is used? What should be the value of R_{eq}?

4. If the grid resistor of the succeeding stage is very large compared to R_{eq} so that its presence is not noticed when computing R_{eq}, what is the required value of R_c?

5. What value of cathode resistor is necessary to provide -2 v of grid bias?

6. If the quiescent operating point is (100, 7), what d-c voltage must the power supply furnish? Use a series resistor R_{sg} to drop the power-supply voltage to the 75 v required for the screen grid. See the accompanying schematic diagram. What value of resistance is required if the cathode grid bias voltage is -2 v?

7. For a low-frequency half-power point of 20 cps, determine the required value of the coupling capacitor, C_c.

8. What values of C_K and C_{sg} are required to provide complete bypassing at 20 cps?

9. Redesign the grid structure of the cylindrical triode of Sec. 10.7 to obtain an amplification factor of 15.

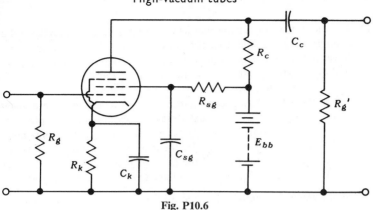

Fig. P10.6

10. The following data are for a high-gain pentode tube operating at the point specified.

$$E_b = 300 \text{ v} \qquad r_p = 1 \text{ megohm}$$
$$E_{G1} = -2.5 \text{ v} \qquad g_m = 9000$$
$$E_{G2} = 150 \text{ v} \qquad I_b = 10 \text{ ma}$$
$$E_{G3} = 0 \text{ v} \qquad I_{G2} = 2.5 \text{ ma}$$
$$C_o = 40 \ \mu\mu\text{f}$$

(a) Determine the gain-bandwidth product.
(b) For $f_2 = 3$ megacycles, determine R_{eq}.
(c) If the grid resistor of the following stage is R_{g2} and $R_{g2} \gg R_{eq}$, determine R_{c1}.
(d) For $f_1 = 3$ cps, determine C_c if $R_{g2} = 25,000$.
(e) Determine R_K and C_K.

11. Compute the actual, transducer, and insertion power gains for a vacuum-tube amplifier. Use the equivalent circuit of the accompanying sketch.

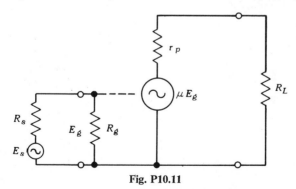

Fig. P10.11

12. Compare A_p, A_{pt}, and A_{pi} for a single-stage triode amplifier driven by a crystal phonograph that has an internal impedance of 270 kilohms. The grid resistor is 100 kilohms and the amplification factor is 18. Let the load resistance be 4K and the plate resistance be 7K.

13. Use the triode whose plate characteristics are given in Fig. 10.16 and design a single-stage amplifier that is to have a bandwidth of 2 megacycles. The lower half-power point is to occur at 30 cps. Use a cathode bias of -3 v and an operating point at $I_b = 1.2$ ma, $E_b = 150$ v.
    (a) Compute the tube parameters at the operating point.
    (b) If the stray wiring capacitance is 15 $\mu\mu$f and the plate-to-cathode capacitance is 2.3 $\mu\mu$f, determine the gain-bandwidth product. Will this tube be satisfactory? What mid-frequency gain is possible?
    (c) If the coupling resistor is also the load resistor, compute the size of the coupling resistor to yield the permissible gain determined in part (b).
    (d) Determine the required d-c voltage from the power supply.

14. What would be the over-all gain and over-all bandwidth of an amplifier consisting of two stages, both identical to those of Prob. 10? (*Hint:* At what frequencies will the upper and lower half-power points occur for the over-all amplifier?)

15. Design your own vacuum tube based upon the theories in Secs. 10.7, 10.8, and 10.9. Plot the theoretical plate characteristics. If high-vacuum (10^{-5} mm Hg or lower) pumping equipment is available, try constructing your tube and testing it under an evacuated bell jar. Use continuous pumping while testing. A tungsten filament will be the simplest to fabricate.

REFERENCES

1. K. R. Spangenberg, *Vacuum Tubes*, McGraw-Hill Book Co., New York, 1948.

2. W. G. Dow, *Fundamentals of Engineering Electronics*, John Wiley & Sons, New York, 1937.

3. F. E. Terman, *Electronic and Radio Engineering*, McGraw-Hill Book Co., New York, 1955.

CHAPTER 11

Ballistics and beams

Throughout this text we have made use of the dual nature of the electron. It has been treated as a particle in many of the calculations, and as a pulse or photon of electromagnetic energy wherever Schrödinger's equation of quantum mechanics was used. This dual approach can be extended to electron ballistics when electron diffraction experiments are studied. Fundamentally, electron ballistics is concerned primarily with the particle aspects of the electron; this will be the subject of this chapter.

The term *ballistics* is employed because of the similarity between the problem of a projectile's moving in the earth's gravitational field and the electron's moving in an electrostatic field. Projectile ballistics includes terms that account for projectile spin and frictional forces that are not present in the usual electron ballistics problem. On the other hand, electron ballistics includes the effects of time- and space-varying electric fields, plus the additional use of magnetic fields which do not have a direct counterpart in the projectile problem. Electron ballistics, therefore, is quite sophisticated. It offers many possibilities to the designer, and complete books are devoted to this subject.*

In this chapter we will consider only those concepts of electron ballistics and electron beams that are necessary to form a satisfactory foundation for electron-device design and for more advanced study. All equations will be written in the form applicable to electrons by setting the electric charge

$$q = -e$$

* For instance, see W. W. Harman, *Fundamentals of Electronic Motion*, McGraw-Hill Book Co., New York, 1953.

If the motion of some positively charged particle is under analysis, then these equations may be used if $-q$ is substituted for e wherever this quantity appears.

11.1 Planar motion in electric fields

All of the problems of electron ballistics and beams exist in three-dimensional space. However, in most cases symmetry exists along one of the coordinate axes. One of the commonest examples is the case of electron motion between two plane-parallel plates, as shown in Fig. 11.1. The z-axis is perpendicular to the paper, and if the initial velocity of the electron has a z-component that is either zero or negligible, then the ballistics problem reduces to motion in a plane.

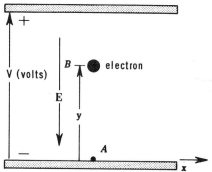

Fig. 11.1. The electron in an electric field.

The *potential energy* of any particle is considered as possessing a positive sign if the particle gives up this energy by falling back to the reference level when released. In this manner, a book that weighs one pound returns three foot-pounds of energy to the system upon falling from a three-foot bench to the floor. The potential energy of the book is positive. On the other hand, an electron released at point B in Fig. 11.1 will not fall back to the reference electrode, and therefore it possesses negative potential energy.

The work done in moving an electron from any point A to another point B in a region that contains an electric field E is found by integrating the force acting at each point along the path ds that is followed in going from A to B.

$$_AW_B = \int_{A(x,y,z)}^{B(x,y,z)} \mathbf{F} \cdot d\mathbf{s} \quad \text{joules} \tag{11.1}$$

where the scalar product for vectors indicates that only the component of $\mathbf{F}$ along the increment of path $d\mathbf{s}$ is to be used in computing the work (see Fig. 11.2).

The force is given by the time rate of change of momentum, or

$$\mathbf{F} = \frac{d}{dt} m\mathbf{v} = m\frac{d\mathbf{v}}{dt} + \mathbf{v}\frac{dm}{dt}$$

where v is the velocity and m is the mass of the electron (9.11×10^{-31} kg).

If relativistic effects are negligible, then dm/dt is zero and

$$\mathbf{F} = m\frac{d\mathbf{v}}{dt} = -e\mathbf{E} \quad \text{newtons} \tag{11.2}$$

where e is the magnitude of the charge on the electron $(1.60 \times 10^{-19}$ coulombs)

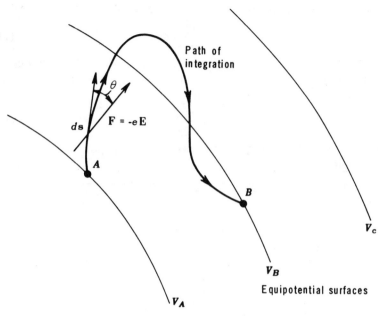

Fig. 11.2. The work done in moving an electron from a point A to a point B in an electric field.

and $\mathbf{E}$ is the electric field strength in v/m and is defined as the gradient of the potential V.

$$\mathbf{E} = -\boldsymbol{\nabla}V \tag{11.3}$$

Substitute Eqs. (11.2) and (11.3) in Eq. (11.1).

$$_A W_B = -e\int_A^B \mathbf{E} \cdot d\mathbf{s} = e(V_B - V_A) \tag{11.4}$$

Thus, the potential energy *given up* by an electron in going from point A to point B in Fig. 11.1 is $e(V_B - V_A)$ joules or $(V_B - V_A)$ *electron-volts*.
By means of Eqs. (11.2) and (11.4),

$$\frac{d}{dt}\int_A^B m\mathbf{v} \cdot d\mathbf{s} = \int_{v_A}^{v_B} m\mathbf{v} \cdot d\mathbf{v} = e(V_B - V_A)$$

$$= \frac{1}{2}m(v_B^2 - v_A^2) \tag{11.5}$$

In many problems, such as the one in Fig. 11.1, the potential of the first electrode (point A) is taken as the reference potential ($V_A = 0$). If the electron starts from rest at point A, then

$$\frac{1}{2} m v_B^2 = e V_B$$

and its velocity at any point B is

$$v_B = \sqrt{\frac{2 e V_B}{m}} \quad \text{m/sec} \tag{11.6}$$

Often the electron will start with initial velocity $v_0 = v_A$. Then, although the potential at point A is zero, it is still possible to speak of the initial energy of the electron in terms of a potential

$$V_0 = \frac{m v_0^2}{2e} \quad \text{ev} \tag{11.7}$$

In this case the total energy of the electron at any point B is ($V_B + V_0$) electron-volts.

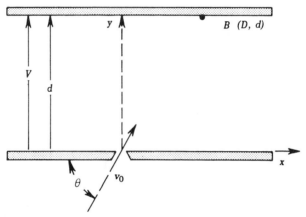

Fig. 11.3. A ballistic problem in two degrees of freedom.

An example of a problem in two degrees of freedom is shown in Fig. 11.3. An electron is injected into a region between the two plates that contains an accelerating electric field, **E**. The injection angle is θ and the magnitude of the initial velocity is v_0. The problem is to determine the required potential on the second plate that is necessary to cause the electron to strike at the point B. A problem of this type is best handled by writing down the *integral equations of motion*.

$$x(t) = \int \int a_x \, dt \, dt + \int v_x \, dt + C_1 \tag{11.8a}$$

and

$$y(t) = \int \int a_y \, dt \, dt + \int v_y \, dt + C_2 \tag{11.8b}$$

where the C's are integration coefficients and may be either constants or functions of time. The acceleration is determined directly from the force equation,

$$\mathbf{F} = m\mathbf{a} = -e\mathbf{E}$$

$$\mathbf{a} = -\frac{e\mathbf{E}}{m} \tag{11.9}$$

where the electric field strength may in general be

$$\mathbf{E} = \mathbf{E}(x, y, z, t)$$

In the example, $\mathbf{E} = -\mathbf{E}_x = $ constant whose magnitude is V/d, where d is the spacing of the plates. Equations (11.8) reduce to

$$x(t) = \int v_0 \cos \theta \, dt + C_1$$

$$y(t) = \int \int \frac{eV}{md} \, dt \, dt + \int v_0 \sin \theta \, dt + C_2$$

The equations integrate to

$$x(t) = v_0 t \cos \theta + C_1$$

$$y(t) = \frac{eV}{2md} t^2 + v_0 t \sin \theta + C_2$$

The first step is the application of the initial and final conditions to these equations. When time $t = 0$, then $x = 0$ and $y = 0$. Therefore, $C_1 = C_2 = 0$. When the x-position of the electron is equal to D, the electron must be at the point (D, d). Thus, the transit time is

$$t = \frac{D}{v_0 \cos \theta}$$

Substitute this result into the expression for $y = d$:

$$d = \frac{eV}{2md} \frac{D^2}{(v_0 \cos \theta)^2} + D \tan \theta$$

The potential is

$$V = (d - D \tan \theta) \frac{2md}{e} \left(\frac{v_0 \cos \theta}{D} \right)^2$$

In other examples it is often more convenient to write down the differential equations of motion from a knowledge of the forces acting on the electron.

$$\frac{d^2x}{dt^2} = -\frac{e}{m} E_x(x, y) \tag{11.10a}$$

$$\frac{d^2y}{dt^2} = -\frac{e}{m} E_y(x, y) \tag{11.10b}$$

11.2   The parametric form

It is interesting to note that in the preceding example the time, t, was eventually eliminated from the integral equations. The same procedure may be followed in the case of the differential equations. Differential equations of motion from which time has been eliminated are said to be in the *parametric form*. The mathematical basis of this method is as follows:

$$\frac{dy/dt}{dx/dt} = \frac{dy}{dt}\frac{dt}{dx} = \frac{dy}{dx}$$

Now let $y' = dy/dx$; then

$$\frac{d^2y}{dx^2} = \frac{dy'}{dx} = \frac{\dfrac{dy'}{dt}}{\dfrac{dx}{dt}} = \frac{\dfrac{d}{dt}\left(\dfrac{dy}{dx}\right)}{\dfrac{dx}{dt}}$$

$$\frac{d^2y}{dx^2} = \frac{\dfrac{dx}{dt}\dfrac{d^2y}{dt^2} - \dfrac{dy}{dt}\dfrac{d^2x}{dt^2}}{\left(\dfrac{dx}{dt}\right)^3} \tag{11.11}$$

Equation (11.11) is the parametric form for d^2y/dx^2.

To place Eqs. (11.10) in the parametric form, first write each equation as

$$\frac{dy}{dt}\frac{d^2x}{dt^2} = -\frac{e}{m}\frac{dy}{dt}E_x$$

$$\frac{dx}{dt}\frac{d^2y}{dt^2} = -\frac{e}{m}\frac{dx}{dt}E_y$$

Subtract the first from the second and divide both sides by $(dx/dt)^3$.

$$\frac{\left[\dfrac{dx}{dt}\dfrac{d^2y}{dt^2} - \dfrac{dy}{dt}\dfrac{d^2x}{dt^2}\right]}{\left(\dfrac{dx}{dt}\right)^3} = \frac{\dfrac{e}{m}\left[E_x\dfrac{dy}{dt} - E_y\dfrac{dx}{dt}\right]}{\left(\dfrac{dx}{dt}\right)^3}$$

By Eq. (11.11),

$$\frac{d^2y}{dx^2} = \frac{e}{m}\left[E_x\frac{dy}{dx} - E_y\right]\left(\frac{dx}{dt}\right)^{-2} \tag{11.12}$$

where dy/dx has been substituted for $(dy/dt)/(dx/dt)$.

The energy of the system is

$$\frac{m}{2}\left[\left(\frac{dx}{dt}\right)^2 + \left(\frac{dy}{dt}\right)^2\right] = eV \tag{11.13}$$

Multiply the left-hand side of Eq. (11.12) by eV and the right-hand side by the equivalent kinetic energy term, according to Eq. (11.13). The result may be placed in the parametric form:

$$2V(x, y)\frac{d^2y}{dx^2} = \left[E_x\frac{dy}{dx} - E_y\right]\left[1 + \left(\frac{dy}{dx}\right)^2\right]$$ (11.14)

This equation does not always lend itself to manual integration. However, it is very useful in the study of electron optics and will be used later in this chapter.

11.3 Motion in a magnetic field

The force exerted upon an electron that is moving with a velocity, $\mathbf{v}$, in a magnetic field of $\mathbf{B}$ webers/m² is

$$\mathbf{F} = -e\mathbf{v} \times \mathbf{B}$$ (11.15)

The vector product may be expanded in the form of a determinant as

$$\mathbf{F} = -e\begin{vmatrix} \mathbf{i}_x & \mathbf{i}_y & \mathbf{i}_z \\ v_x & v_y & v_z \\ B_x & B_y & B_z \end{vmatrix}$$
$$= -e[(v_yB_z - v_zB_y)\mathbf{i}_x + (v_zB_x - v_xB_z)\mathbf{i}_y + (v_xB_y - v_yB_x)\mathbf{i}_z]$$ (11.16)

Two basic motions are possible. The electron may be traveling normal to the magnetic field or it may travel parallel to the magnetic field. An examination of Eq. (11.16) shows that there is no force exerted by the magnetic field that arises from any component of motion parallel to the magnetic field.

If the motion or a component of the motion is normal to the magnetic field, then a force is exerted upon the electron by the magnetic field. Figure 11.4 is a "right-handed" coordinate system. That is, $\mathbf{i}_x \times \mathbf{i}_y = \mathbf{i}_z, \mathbf{i}_y \times \mathbf{i}_z = \mathbf{i}_x$, and $\mathbf{i}_z \times \mathbf{i}_x = \mathbf{i}_y$. Such a coordinate system should always be selected where vector analysis is used. Otherwise the analyst must watch very closely for minus signs that arise continually from the use of a "left-handed" system.

The electron is shot into the region containing the magnetic field in Fig. 11.4. Its entrance velocity is v_0. The force on the electron is

$$\mathbf{F} = m\mathbf{a} = -e\mathbf{v} \times (B_y\mathbf{i}_y)$$

The force is always perpendicular to the instantaneous velocity, which is a constant equal to v_0. This is a central force problem and the trajectory is a circle. The term on the left-hand side of the equation is the centrifugal force

mv_0^2/r; the term on the right-hand side is the centripetal force. The radius of curvature is r.

$$\frac{mv_0^2}{r} = ev_0 B_y$$

$$r = \frac{mv_0}{eB_y} \tag{11.17}$$

The *angular cyclotron velocity* is

$$\omega_0 = \frac{v_0}{r} = \frac{eB_y}{m}$$

Equation (11.17) forms the basis for the design of the mass spectrometer. Positive ions are formed from atoms or molecules which are to be identified by their mass, m. The magnetic field in Fig. 11.4 is reversed because these are

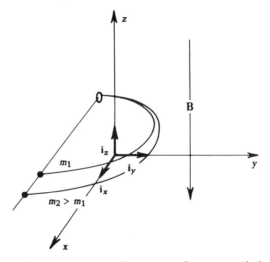

Fig. 11.4. A right-hand coordinate system for vector analysis.

positively charged particles if the trajectory shown is to be obtained. The radius of curvature is directly proportional to the mass of the ion. Therefore, the device can be calibrated to determine the mass of unknown ions and thus serves to identify them.

From the preceding results it is apparent that any electron that moves in a magnetic field with components of velocity parallel to and perpendicular to the magnetic field describes a trajectory that is a spiral about the magnetic field lines.

11.4 Combined electric and magnetic fields

Complex electron trajectories are possible if a magnetic field and an electric field are combined. Equations (11.2) and (11.15) may be combined to form a general expression for the force on an electron that is moving in a region containing both an electric field and a magnetic field.

$$\mathbf{F} = m\mathbf{a} = -e(\mathbf{E} + \mathbf{v} \times \mathbf{B}) \quad (11.18)$$

Many electronic tubes possess a cylindrical geometry. In tubes such as the cathode-ray tube, the electron moves in the radial (r) and the axial (z) directions and there is θ-symmetry. In the magnetron the motion is in the radial and angular (θ) directions and there is z-axis symmetry. Consider a system of cylindrical coordinates (Fig. 11.5). Let a differential segment of path length be

$$d\mathbf{s} = dr\,\mathbf{i}_r + r\,d\theta\,\mathbf{i}_\theta + dz\,\mathbf{i}_z \quad (11.19)$$

The associated velocity is

$$\mathbf{v} = \frac{d\mathbf{s}}{dt} = \frac{dr}{dt}\mathbf{i}_r + r\frac{d\theta}{dt}\mathbf{i}_\theta + \frac{dz}{dt}\mathbf{i}_z$$
$$(11.20)$$

The acceleration is

$$\mathbf{a} = \frac{d\mathbf{v}}{dt} = \frac{d}{dt}\left[\frac{dr}{dt}\mathbf{i}_r + r\frac{d\theta}{dt}\mathbf{i}_\theta + \frac{dz}{dt}\mathbf{i}_z\right]$$
$$(11.21)$$

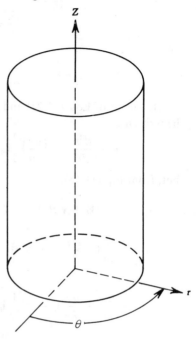

Fig. 11.5. A cylindrical coordinate system.

Before the differentiation indicated on the right-hand side of Eq. (11.21) can be carried out, it is necessary to determine the result of the derivative of a unit vector. Refer to Fig. 11.6. The vector $r\mathbf{i}_r$ has undergone an incremental change in both magnitude and direction to become $r'\mathbf{i}'_r$.

First of all, the unit vector $\mathbf{i}_r$ is a function of angular position alone because certainly no change in r will change the length of the unit vector.

$$\mathbf{i}_r = f(\theta)$$

Then,

$$\frac{d\mathbf{i}_r}{d\theta} = \mathbf{i}_\theta \quad (11.22)$$

In other words, because these are unit vectors, only the direction of the derivative is of interest. From the sketch it is obvious that

$$\frac{d\mathbf{i}_\theta}{d\theta} = -\mathbf{i}_r \quad (11.23)$$

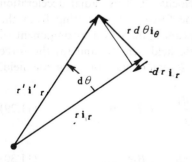

Fig. 11.6. Vector differentiation.

From these equations the time derivatives of the unit vectors may be computed and the results used to evaluate Eq. (11.21).

$$\frac{d\mathbf{i}_r}{dt} = \frac{d\mathbf{i}_r}{d\theta}\frac{d\theta}{dt} = \frac{d\theta}{dt}\mathbf{i}_\theta \tag{11.24}$$

and

$$\frac{d\mathbf{i}_\theta}{dt} = \frac{d\mathbf{i}_\theta}{d\theta}\frac{d\theta}{dt} = -\frac{d\theta}{dt}\mathbf{i}_r \tag{11.25}$$

By means of Eqs. (11.24) and (11.25), the expression for acceleration may be written as

$$\mathbf{a} = \left[\frac{d^2r}{dt^2} - r\left(\frac{d\theta}{dt}\right)^2\right]\mathbf{i}_r + \left[r\frac{d^2\theta}{dt^2} + 2\frac{dr}{dt}\frac{d\theta}{dt}\right]\mathbf{i}_\theta + \left[\frac{d^2z}{dt^2}\right]\mathbf{i}_z \tag{11.26}$$

but, from Eq. (11.18),

$$\mathbf{a} = -\frac{e}{m}(\mathbf{E} + \mathbf{v} \times \mathbf{B})$$

$$= -\frac{e}{m}(-\nabla V + \mathbf{v} \times \mathbf{B})$$

$$= -\frac{e}{m}\left[-\frac{\partial V}{\partial r}\mathbf{i}_r - \frac{1}{r}\frac{\partial V}{\partial \theta}\mathbf{i}_\theta - \frac{\partial V}{\partial z}\mathbf{i}_z\right] - \frac{e}{m}\begin{vmatrix} \mathbf{i}_r & \mathbf{i}_\theta & \mathbf{i}_z \\ \dfrac{dr}{dt} & r\dfrac{d\theta}{dt} & \dfrac{dz}{dt} \\ B_r & B_\theta & B_z \end{vmatrix} \tag{11.27}$$

Equate Eqs. (11.26) and (11.27) and separate the result into the three component equations. (To simplify the writing, the "dot" notation will be used to indicate time derivatives, i.e., $\dot{r} = dr/dt$ and $\ddot{r} = d^2r/dt^2$). For the r-components:

$$a_r = \ddot{r} - r\dot{\theta}^2 = \frac{e}{m}\left[\frac{dV}{dr} + B_\theta\dot{z} - rB_z\dot{\theta}\right] \tag{11.28}$$

Thus, the net radial acceleration consists of simple radial acceleration, $\ddot{r}$, and radial acceleration from angular velocity, $\dot{\theta}$. This radial acceleration arises from three possible forces: (1) the force $e\,dV/dr$ arising from the electric field, (2) the force $eB_\theta\dot{z}$ that appears if there is a z-component of velocity and a B_θ component of magnetic field density, and (3) the force $erB_z\dot{\theta}$ caused by angular rotation in a B_z-component of magnetic field. For the θ-component:

$$a_\theta = r\ddot{\theta} + 2\dot{r}\dot{\theta} = \frac{e}{m}\left[\frac{1}{r}\frac{dV}{d\theta} + B_z\dot{r} - B_r\dot{z}\right] \tag{11.29}$$

and for the z-component:

$$a_z = \ddot{z} = \frac{e}{m}\left[\frac{dV}{dz} + rB_r\dot{\theta} - B_\theta\dot{r}\right] \tag{11.30}$$

where the individual sources of acceleration are easily identified as was done for a_r.

It is very unlikely that symmetry conditions will fail to eliminate one component of the magnetic field and one component of the electric field. In many cases two components of one or both of these fields will disappear. These equations are very useful because they permit the designer to grasp an over-all picture of the various possibilities that present themselves. The undesired acceleration or force terms can be dropped and the remaining components of the electric and the magnetic fields indicate the type of electronic structure to use.

11.5   The cyclotron

A study of Eq. (11.28) reveals that the term $mr\dot{\theta}^2$ is the centrifugal force, whereas the terms $(eB_\theta \dot{z} = erB_z \dot{\theta})$ are the centripetal force on an electron. Eliminate the other terms by requiring that $\ddot{r} = 0$, $V = 0$, and $B = B_z$ only. Equation (11.28) reduces to

$$mr\dot{\theta}^2 = erB_z\dot{\theta} \qquad (11.31)$$

and the centrifugal force is equal to the centripetal force.

The motion is circular with a radius of curvature

$$R = \frac{mr\dot{\theta}}{eB_z} \qquad (11.32)$$

and the *angular cyclotron frequency* is

$$\omega_0 = \dot{\theta} = \frac{eB_z}{m} \qquad (11.33)$$

Equations (11.32) and (11.33) form the basis of the *cyclotron* that was developed by E. O. Lawrence and his associates at the University of California. The cyclotron consists of a source of ions or electrons located at the center of an evacuated region, as shown in Fig. 11.7. The evacuated trajectory region contains two *dees* which act as electrodes for establishing a high-frequency electric field across the small gap between the dees. Within the dees, of course, there is no electric field. The entire assembly of the dees is placed in a uniform magnetic field.

According to Eq. (11.32), the ions or electrons move in a circular orbit with a radius of curvature

$$R = \frac{mr\dot{\theta}}{eB_z} = \frac{mv_T}{eB_z}$$

where v_T is the tangential velocity of the charged particles. The electric field between the dees provides the tangential velocity which causes the radius of curvature of the trajectory to increase. The increase in R results in a further increase in tangential velocity. As a result, the charged particles spiral out, increasing their energy with each pass through the gap between the dees. The highly accelerated particles eventually leave through a thin foil window and are available for experimental use.

The success of this device is based upon the result of Eq. (11.33), which states that the angular cyclotron frequency is independent of everything but the ratio e/m for the particle and the magnetic field density. Thus, the dees

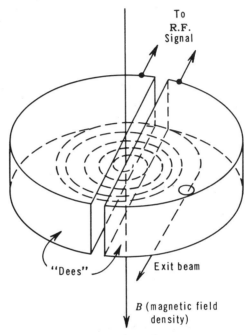

Fig. 11.7. The cyclotron.

may be operated at a constant radiofrequency, although it is common practice to vary the frequency to obtain desired operating characteristics and to compensate for the relativistic change in mass at high electron velocities.

It was found that if radial acceleration of the electrons is ruled out, then only rotation at ω_0 radians/sec can exist. Now suppose that for the same conditions any acceleration in the θ-direction is also ruled out; Eq. (11.29) yields

$$2\dot{r}\dot{\theta} = \frac{e}{m} B_z \dot{r}$$

$$\dot{\theta} = \frac{eB_z}{2m} = \omega_L \tag{11.34}$$

and is called the *Larmor precession* (Fig. 11.8). It follows from Eq. (11.33) that

$$\omega_L = \tfrac{1}{2}\omega_0$$

Atoms act as magnetic dipoles because of the circulating electrons moving around the nucleus. In a magnetic field, atoms precess about the B field at the Larmor frequency, ω_L. In the above calculations only $\dot\theta$ was ruled out; hence, the mean orbit of the electron cannot change. The radial acceleration

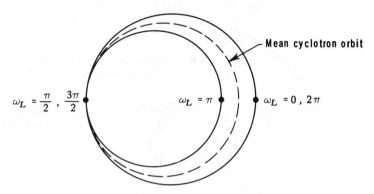

Fig. 11.8. The Larmor precession.

$\ddot r \neq 0$; therefore, the trajectory of the electron can oscillate about the mean orbit and the frequency of this oscillation is ω_L.

11.6   The magnetron principle

Figure 11.9 is the top view of a diode vacuum tube which has a cathode radius r_e and an anode radius r_a. A uniform magnetic field is directed along the z-axis of the tube. If the z-component of velocity of emission of the electrons is neglected, then there is z-axis symmetry. The motion may be considered to be confined to the (r, θ)-plane.

Equations of motion (11.28) and (11.29) apply to this problem. Set $B = B_z$ and $\partial V/\partial \theta = 0$. With these restrictions Eq. (11.28) reduces to

$$m\ddot r - mr\dot\theta^2 = e\frac{\partial V(r)}{\partial r} - erB_z\dot\theta \tag{11.35}$$

for the r-component of motion and Eq. (11.29) reduces to

$$mr\ddot\theta + 2m\dot r\dot\theta = eB_z\dot r \tag{11.36}$$

The force on the left-hand side of Eq. (11.36) can be written in terms of the time rate of change of the angular momentum. This is easily accomplished by applying the definition of the derivative of the product of two variables.

$$\frac{d}{dt}\left(mr^2\frac{d\theta}{dt}\right) = erB_z\frac{dr}{dt} \tag{11.37}$$

Integrate Eq. (11.37) for an electron that starts at the cathode surface $(r = r_c)$ at time $t = 0$ and is at any general position r at time t. The result is

$$mr^2\dot\theta = \tfrac{1}{2}eB_z(r^2 - r_c^2) \tag{11.38}$$

Eliminate $\dot\theta$ from Eqs. (11.38) and (11.35) to obtain a differential equation in r.

$$\ddot r - \frac{e}{m}\frac{\partial V(r)}{\partial r} + r\left(\frac{eB}{2m}\right)^2\left[1 - \left(\frac{r_c}{r}\right)^4\right] = 0 \tag{11.39}$$

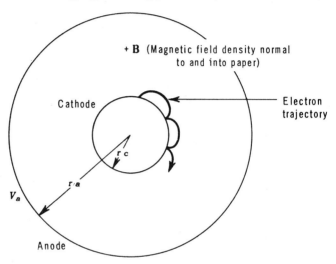

+ **B** (Magnetic field density normal to and into paper)

Cathode

Electron trajectory

$r\,c$

$r\,a$

V_a

Anode

Fig. 11.9. The basic magnetron (cylindrical diode).

The cyclotron frequency, ω_0, can be introduced.

$$\ddot r + \frac{r\omega_0^2}{4}\left[1 - \left(\frac{r_c}{r}\right)^4\right] = \frac{e}{m}\frac{\partial V(r)}{\partial r} \tag{11.40}$$

The electric field $-\partial V/\partial r$ between two concentric cylinders is

$$E_r = -\frac{V_a}{\ln\,(r_a/r_c)}\frac{1}{r}$$

where V_a is the cathode-to-anode potential. This may be substituted into Eq. (11.40). Solutions to Eq. (11.40), however, cannot be obtained in terms of the simple mathematical functions.

The problem may be transformed into plane, rectangular coordinates (Fig. 11.10), where it may be shown that the solution is

$$x = \frac{V_a m}{eB_z D}\left(\frac{eB_z}{m}t - \sin\frac{eB_z}{m}t\right) \tag{11.41}$$

(See Prob. 3 at the end of this chapter.)

If these results are transformed into the cylindrical coordinate system, the trajectories shown on Fig. 11.9 are obtained. The magnitudes of the cathode voltage and the magnetic field determine whether the electrons move around the cathode in approximate cycloidal paths or whether they reach the

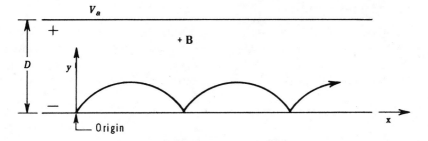

Fig. 11.10. The cycloidal trajectory of an electron in a plane-parallel electrode magnetron.

anode. The condition for electrons merely to cease reaching the cathode may be easily determined from the energy expression,

$$eV = \frac{m}{2}(\dot{r}^2 + r^2\dot{\theta}^2) \quad \text{joules} \tag{11.42}$$

For electrons just to graze the anode, $\dot{r} = 0$, when $r = r_a$, and $\dot{\theta}$ is available from Eq. (11.38).

$$\dot{\theta} = \frac{eB_z}{2m}\left[1 - \left(\frac{r_c}{r_a}\right)^2\right]$$

Substitute into Eq. (11.42) and solve for $V = V_{co}$; the current cut-off condition,

$$V_{co} = \frac{eB_z^2}{8m}r_a^2\left[1 - \left(\frac{r_c}{r_a}\right)^2\right]^2 \tag{11.43}$$

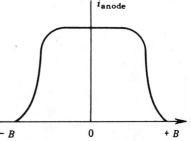

Fig. 11.11. Magnetron anode current as a function of magnetic flux density.

If the anode current is plotted as a function of the magnetic field density, then a plot similar to Fig. 11.11 is obtained. The theoretical cut-off should be sharp. The initial velocities of the electrons and slight constructional deviations from perfect geometry result in the characteristics shown.

The magnetron principle is used in resonant cavity magnetron tubes to generate ultrahigh radiofrequencies. The principle is also employed in magnetron beam-switching tubes that are used as very high-speed switches and counters. In each of these devices the tube is biased near cut-off and a signal voltage is added to the bias voltage. In the magnetron this voltage is derived from the resonant cavities, and in the beam-switching tube it represents the switching signal. Space does not permit a detailed study of these electronic devices; considerable material is to be found in the literature.

11.7   Beams and optics

Figure 11.12 is the cross-sectional sketch of an *electron gun* used to obtain an electron beam. To obtain high-intensity beams, it is necessary to design the cathode-anode portion of the gun very carefully; otherwise, the mutual repulsion of the electrons will spread the beam sufficiently to cause the loss of

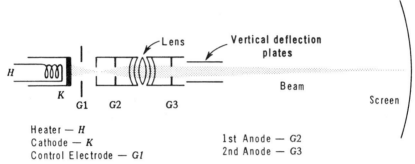

Heater — *H*
Cathode — *K*
Control Electrode — *G1*

1st Anode — G2
2nd Anode — G3

Fig. 11.12. The basic cathode-ray tube.

a large portion of the beam current to the various electrodes of the gun and focusing system. High-efficiency cathodes for guns are designed according to the theories of J. R. Pierce and are called *Pierce cathodes*.*

There is not space here to review the principles of high-efficiency cathode structure, nor can the equations be solved manually. For these reasons, the cathode-to-anode portion of the gun will be omitted. Where high electron beam intensities are not required, it is a simple matter to obtain a satisfactory beam by the use of plane electrodes for the cathode and anode.

Either type of cathode produces a beam cross-over point somewhere in front of the cathode. For the high-efficiency beam, this is a well-defined cross-over. For the simple structure, the cross-over is poorly defined. The next step is to provide an electron lens that focuses those electrons that cross over, at the proper point on the screen of the cathode-ray tube (CRT) or on the proper target, if the tube is other than a CRT. The cathodes are of the indirectly heated, oxide-coated type.

The control electrode functions in a manner similar to a control grid. By varying the potential of this electrode relative to the cathode, it is possible to control the beam intensity and have only a second-order effect upon the

* J. R. Pierce, *Theory and Design of Electron Beams*, D. Van Nostrand Co., Princeton, N.J., New York, 1954.

focusing. Typical cathode-to-control electrode (grid No. 1) voltages run from $+10$ to -50 v. Visual cut-off of the beam occurs for potentials on the order of -75 v.

The first anode is a cylinder fitted with a cap. The cap contains a small aperture which is located at the beam cross-over point of a high-efficiency cathode and serves to establish a cross-over point for the low-efficiency cathode. This anode may be at a potential of 200 to 400 v positive relative to the cathode. The first anode contains a limiting aperture to block wide-angle electrons that will not focus properly and would cause a glow over the entire screen of the CRT.

The second anode is also a cylinder, and in this case it has the same diameter as the first anode. The potential of the second anode might be 800 to 1500 v positive relative to the cathode. The electron lens exists in the region between the two cylinders and extends a short way into each cylinder. The

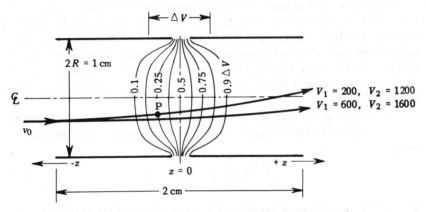

Fig. 11.13. An equal-diameter cylindrical electrostatic electron lens.

remainder of this section is devoted to this electrostatic lens. A magnetic lens could also be used. (Magnetic lenses are commonly used on television CRT tubes. The basic approach to these lenses is quite similar to that which will be used to analyze the electrostatic lens.) Considerable information is available on both types of lenses.*

The equipotential lines (surfaces of revolution) for two cylinders, each 1 cm in diameter and 1 cm in length, are sketched in Fig. 11.13. The potential along the axis of the lens is given by the empirical equation.†

$$V_0(z) = \frac{V_1 + V_2}{2} + \frac{V_2 - V_1}{2} \tanh \frac{1.32z}{R} \qquad (11.44)$$

* K. R. Spangenberg, *Vacuum Tubes*, McGraw-Hill Book Co., New York, 1948.
† *Ibid.*, p. 342.

The path of an electron that enters this electric field is shown. The electron is near the axis and enters with a velocity that is directed nearly parallel to the axis. There is no acceleration tangential to the equipotential surfaces; therefore,

$$v_0 \sin \theta_0 = v_1 \sin \theta_1 = v_2 \sin \theta_2 = \cdots$$

The angle of incidence at the point P is θ_1 and the angle of refraction of the electron is θ_2. The equality

$$v_1 \sin \theta_1 = v_2 \sin \theta_2$$

bears a resemblance to Snell's law for geometrical light optics:

$$n_1 \sin \theta_1 = n_2 \sin \theta_2$$

where n_1 and n_2 are the indices of refraction of two adjacent media. This comparison is the basis for the name *electron optics*.

The electric field is constantly accelerating the electron in the lens. The lower the velocity of the electron, the more pronounced will be the action of the lens. The lens is convergent on the input half and, because of the lower electron velocity, this action is predominant. The lens is divergent on the output half, but, because of the acceleration in the input half of the lens, the electron is less affected by the action. The net effect of the lens is therefore convergent.

The motion of the electron through this lens can be solved by a combination of analytical and numerical methods. Laplace's equation forms a starting point.

$$\frac{1}{r} \frac{\partial}{\partial r} \left(r \frac{\partial V}{\partial r} \right) + \frac{\partial^2 V}{\partial z^2} = 0 \tag{11.45}$$

The voltage $V(r, \theta)$ can be expressed in terms of Bessel functions which will satisfy this equation. Another relationship can be obtained which expresses $V(r, \theta)$ in terms of the potential along the axis, $V_0(z)$, and the radial position r. This second form of a solution is extremely useful because $V_0(z)$ is known from Eq. (11.44).

To obtain a solution to Eq. (11.45), the procedure is very similar to the one that leads to Bessel functions. Assume that the solution can be expressed as a power series

$$V(r, z) = \sum_{n=0}^{\infty} a_n(z) r^n \tag{11.46}$$

Substitute Eq. (11.46) into Eq. (11.45).

$$\sum_{n=0}^{\infty} (n^2 a_n r^{n-2} + a_n'' r^n) = 0$$

where

$$a_n'' = \frac{\partial^2 a_n(z)}{\partial z^2}$$

Evaluate the first two terms of the summation.

$$0 + a_1 r^{-1} + \sum_{n=2}^{\infty} n^2 a_n r^{n-2} + \sum_{n=0}^{\infty} a_r'' r^n = 0 \tag{11.47}$$

The summation limits on the second term may be shifted to 0 to ∞ by substituting $(n + 2)$ for n in this term. The result will be the same.

$$a_1 r^{-1} + \sum_{n=0}^{\infty} (n + 2)^2 a_{n+2} r^n + \sum_{n=0}^{\infty} a_n'' r^n = 0$$

If the assumed series is to be a solution to Laplace's equation, then Eq. (11.47) must be an identity in r. Therefore, the coefficient of each power of r must vanish identically. For the coefficients of r^n,

$$(n + 2)^2 a_{n+2} + a_n'' = 0$$

$$a_{n+2} = -\frac{a_n''(z)}{(n + 2)^2} \tag{11.48}$$

This is a recurrence formula that gives each coefficient of r in terms of one that appears earlier in the series.

Because of θ-symmetry, the potential $V(r, z)$ must be independent of $\pm$ values of r. Thus, the coefficients of all odd powers of r must vanish.

$$a_1 = a_3 = a_5 = \cdots = 0 \tag{11.49}$$

Substitute the results of Eqs. (11.48) and (11.49) into Eq. (11.46).

$$V(r, z) = a_0 - \frac{a_0''}{2^2} r^2 - \frac{a_2''}{4^2} r^4 - \frac{a_4''}{6^2} r^6 - \cdots$$

$$V(r, z) = a_0 - \frac{a_0''}{2^2} r^2 + \frac{a_0^{(IV)}}{2^2 \cdot 4^2} r^4 - \frac{a_0^{(VI)}}{2^2 \cdot 4^2 \cdot 6^2} r^6 + \cdots$$

$$+ \frac{(-1)^k}{(k!)^2} \left(\frac{r}{2}\right)^{2k} a_0^{2k} + \cdots \tag{11.50}$$

where the superscripts indicate the order of the derivative.

Equation (11.50) is the general solution to Laplace's equation in terms of a power series. For $r = 0$, the expression for the axial potential $V_0(z)$ is obtained.

$$V_0(z) = V(0, z) = a_0(z) \tag{11.51}$$

Substitute this into Eq. (11.50) to obtain the general expression for potential.

$$V(r, z) = V_0(z) - \frac{V_0''(z) r^2}{2^2} + \frac{V_0^{(IV)}(z) r^4}{2^2 \cdot 4^2} + \cdots + \frac{(-1)^k V_0^{(2k)}(z)}{(k!)^2} \left(\frac{r}{2}\right)^{2k} + \cdots \tag{11.52}$$

This result is very important. It states that if the axial potential $V_0(z)$ and its derivatives are available, then the potential at any point is known.

The motion of an electron in the lens is a problem in two degrees of freedom because of the θ-symmetry. The motion is in the (r, z)-plane. It was shown previously that motion in two degrees of freedom can be represented by the parametric equation (Eq. (11.14)):

$$2V\frac{d^2r}{dz^2} = \left[\frac{\partial V}{\partial r} - \frac{\partial V}{\partial z}\frac{dr}{dz}\right]\left[1 + \left(\frac{dr}{dz}\right)^2\right]$$ (11.53)

The electrons that will be focused by the lens and passed by the limiting apertures are those whose trajectories make only small angles with the z-axis. These are the *paraxial electrons*. For them $(dr/dt)^2$ is very small and may be dropped in Eq. (11.53). The potential $V(r, z)$ may be evaluated from Eq. (11.52). The derivatives are

$$\frac{\partial V}{\partial r} = -\frac{rV_0''(z)}{2} + \frac{r^3V_0^{(IV)}(z)}{16} + \cdots$$

If the radial displacement is small, then

$$\frac{\partial V}{\partial r} \approx -\frac{rV_0''(z)}{2}$$ (11.54)

In a similar manner, $\quad \dfrac{\partial V}{\partial z} = V_0'(z) - \dfrac{r^2V_0''(z)}{4} + \cdots$

and for the small r, $\qquad \dfrac{\partial V}{\partial z} \simeq V_0'(z)$ (11.55)

Further, $\qquad\qquad\qquad V(r, z) \simeq V_0(z)$ (11.56)

for small r. With these substitutions, the parametric differential equation of motion for the paraxial electrons is

$$\frac{d^2r}{dz^2} + \frac{V_0'}{2V_0}\frac{dr}{dz} + \frac{V_0''}{4V_0}r = 0$$ (11.57)

The potential and its derivatives are known from Eq. (11.44). The solution for the trajectory may be obtained by dividing the potential distribution into a series of straight-line segments (Fig. 11.14). If this is done, then $V_0''(z) = 0$ and Eq. (11.57) reduces to

$$\frac{d^2r}{dz^2} + \frac{V_0'}{2V_0}\frac{dr}{dz} = 0$$ (11.58)

where V_0' is now the slope of a straight-line segment and is, therefore, a constant. Let z_1 and z_2 be two axial positions between which the potential is assumed to be a straight line. An integration of Eq. (11.58) yields the value of the radial position of the electron at point $z = z_2$.

$$r(z_2) = r(z_1) + \frac{2C_1[V_0^{1/2}(z_2) - V_0^{1/2}(z_1)]}{V_0'}$$ (11.59)

The constant of integration is

$$C = \left(\frac{dr}{dz}\right)_{z_{b1}} V_0^{\frac{1}{2}}(z_1) \tag{11.60}$$

where $(dr/dz)_{z_{b1}}$ is the slope to the right of point 1. For the first segment this slope is equal to the initial slope of the trajectory of the electron as it enters the lens.

From these two equations it is possible to compute $r(z_2)$.

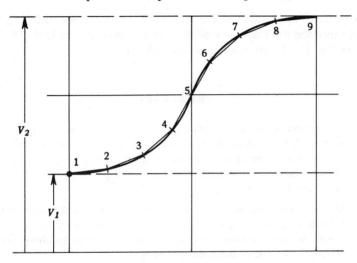

Fig. 11.14. The potential distribution through the lens. All potentials measured relative to the cathode.

The next step is to calculate the position $r(z_3)$ according to Eq. (11.59):

$$r(z_3) = r(z_2) + \frac{2C_2 V_0^{\frac{1}{2}}(z_3) - V_0^{\frac{1}{2}}(z_2)}{V_0'}$$

A problem arises in the evaluation of the constant of integration. It is necessary to know $(dr/dz)_{z_{b2}}$ and this is not immediately available. The slope

$$\left(\frac{dr}{dz}\right)_{z_{a2}} = \left(\frac{dr}{dz}\right)_{z_{b1}} \tag{11.61}$$

is known. To obtain an expression for the derivative on the right-hand side of the discontinuity at point 2, return to Eq. (11.57). At the discontinuity $V_0''(z) \gg V_0'(z)$, the equation may be reduced to

$$\frac{d^2r}{dz^2} + \frac{V_0''}{4V_0} r = 0 \tag{11.62}$$

At the discontinuity both r and V_0 are constants. This permits a straightforward integration of Eq. (11.61) to be made to determine (dr/dz). The result is an expression between the derivative on the right-hand side of the discontinuity in terms of the known slope on the left-hand side and the known slope of the potential segments.

$$\left(\frac{dr}{dz}\right)_{z_b} = \left(\frac{dr}{dz}\right)_{z_a} - \frac{r}{4V_0}\,[V_0'(z_b) - V_0'(z_a)] \tag{11.63}$$

By repeated application of Eqs. (11.59), (11.60), (11.61), and (11.63), it is possible to trace the trajectory of the electron through the lens. The trajectories in Fig. 11.13 were plotted in this manner.

PROBLEMS

1. An electron is injected midway between two plane-parallel plates with a velocity that is parallel to the plates. The energy of the electron is 150 electron-volts. The plates are 4 cm long and the spacing is 1.5 cm. What potential between these deflection plates is required to cause the electron just to graze the positive plate?

2. An alternating voltage, $500 \sin \omega t$, is applied between the deflection plates of Prob. 1. Count time $t = 0$, when the electron just enters the deflection region. What is the minimum frequency that can be used without having the electron strike one of the deflection plates?

3. With reference to Fig. 11.10, the electron is emitted at the origin with zero velocity.
   (a) Show that the differential equations (D.E.) of motion are

$$\ddot{x} = \omega_0 \dot{y} \quad \text{and} \quad \ddot{y} = \frac{eV_a}{md} - \omega_0 \dot{x}$$

   (b) Obtain $\dot{x}$ from the first equation and substitute it into the second to obtain a single D.E. of motion.
   (c) Show that the general solution to the D.E. is

$$y = A_1 \sin \omega_0 t + A_2 \cos \omega_0 t + \frac{mV_a}{eB^2 d}$$

   (d) Apply the initial conditions and show that

$$y = \frac{mV_a}{eB^2 d}(1 - \cos \omega_0 t)$$

and

$$x = \frac{mV_a}{eB^2 d}(\omega_0 t - \sin \omega_0 t)$$

which describes a cycloidal path as sketched in Fig. 11.10.

4. (a) Show that the exit deflection of an electron beam that has passed between the deflecting plates of a cathode-ray tube is

$$y_1 = \frac{eVb^2}{2mv_0^2 d}$$

where y_1 is located at the point of exit between the deflection plates and is measured from the axis which passes midway between the plates. The length of the plates is b and their spacing is d. The deflection potential is V and the entrance velocity of the beam is v_0 and is along the axis of the tube.

   (b) Show that the deflection on the screen of the CRT is

$$\frac{eVbL}{m\, dv_0^2}$$

where L is the radius of curvature of the screen measured from the center of the deflection plates.

5. Develop an expression for deflection sensitivity for the cathode-ray tube.

6. Do a mathematical analysis of Thomson's experiment for determining (e/m). (See Sec. 1.1 and Fig. 1.3.)

7. Select first anode and second anode voltages for the electron gun of Fig. 11.12 and lens of Fig. 11.13 and plot the trajectory of a paraxial electron through the lens. What is the focal length at the image side of the lens? (Electron lenses in general have different object and image focal lengths.)

REFERENCES

1. K. R. Spangenberg, *Vacuum Tubes*, McGraw-Hill Book Co., New York, 1948.

2. W. W. Harman, *Fundamentals of Electronic Motion*, McGraw-Hill Book Co., New York, 1953.

3. J. R. Pierce, *Theory and Design of Electron Beams*, D. Van Nostrand Co., Princeton, N.J., 1954.

Physical constants

$m =$ rest mass of an electron $= 9.11 \times 10^{-31}$ kg
$e =$ charge on an electron $= 1.60 \times 10^{-19}$ coulomb
$h =$ Planck's constant $= 6.624 \times 10^{-34}$ joule-sec
$k =$ Boltzmann's constant $= 1.380 \times 10^{-23}$ joule/°K
$R =$ gas constant $= 8.317 \times 10^{3}$ joule/°K/kilomole
$\quad$ Avogadro's number $= 6.023 \times 10^{26}$ per kilomole
$\quad$ Loschmidt's number $= 2.69 \times 10^{25}$ molecules/m³
$\epsilon_0 =$ dielectric constant of vacuum $= 8.854 \times 10^{-12}$ farad/m
$\mu_0 =$ permeability of vacuum $= 4\pi \times 10^{-7}$ henry/m
$c =$ velocity of light $= 2.998 \times 10^{8}$ m/sec.

APPENDIX II

List and periodic table of the elements

Atomic number Z	Element	Symbol
0	Neutron	n
1	Hydrogen	H
2	Helium	He
3	Lithium	Li
4	Beryllium	Be
5	Boron	B
6	Carbon	C
7	Nitrogen	N
8	Oxygen	O
9	Fluorine	F
10	Neon	Ne
11	Sodium	Na
12	Magnesium	Mg
13	Aluminum	Al
14	Silicon	Si
15	Phosphorus	P
16	Sulfur	S
17	Chlorine	Cl
18	Argon	Ar
19	Potassium	K
20	Calcium	Ca

Atomic number Z	Element	Symbol
21	Scandium	Sc
22	Titanium	Ti
23	Vanadium	V
24	Chromium	Cr
25	Manganese	Mn
26	Iron	Fe
27	Cobalt	Co
28	Nickel	Ni
29	Copper	Cu
30	Zinc	Zn
31	Gallium	Ga
32	Germanium	Ge
33	Arsenic	As
34	Selenium	Se
35	Bromine	Br
36	Krypton	Kr
37	Rubidium	Rb
38	Strontium	Sr
39	Yttrium	Y
40	Zirconium	Zr
41	Niobium	Nb
42	Molybdenum	Mo
43	Technetium	Tc
44	Ruthenium	Ru
45	Rhodium	Rh
46	Palladium	Pd
47	Silver	Ag
48	Cadmium	Cd
49	Indium	In
50	Tin	Sn
51	Antimony	Sb
52	Tellurium	Te
53	Iodine	I
54	Xenon	Xe
55	Cesium	Cs
56	Barium	Ba
57	Lanthanum	La
58	Cerium	Ce
59	Praseodymium	Pr
60	Neodymium	Nd
61	Promethium	Pm
62	Samarium	Sa
63	Europium	Eu
64	Gadolinium	Gd
65	Terbium	Tb
66	Dysprosium	Dy
67	Holmium	Ho
68	Erbium	Er

Atomic number Z	Element	Symbol
69	Thulium	Tm
70	Ytterbium	Yb
71	Lutetium	Lu
72	Hafnium	Hf
73	Tantalum	Ta
74	Wolfram (Tungsten)	W
75	Rhenium	Re
76	Osmium	Os
77	Iridium	Ir
78	Platinum	Pt
79	Gold	Au
80	Mercury	Hg
81	Thallium	Tl
82	Lead	Pb
83	Bismuth	Bi
84	Polonium	Po
85	Astatine	At
86	Radon	Rn
87	Francium	Fr
88	Radium	Ra
89	Actinium	Ac
90	Thorium	Th
91	Protactinium	Pa
92	Uranium	U
93	Neptunium	Np
94	Plutonium	Pu
95	Americium	Am
96	Curium	Cm
97	Berkelium	Bk
98	Californium	Cf
99	Einsteinium	Es
100	Fermium	Fm
101	Mendelevium	Md
102	Nobelium	No

Long form periodic table of the elements

O	Ia	IIa	IIIb	IVb	Vb	VIb	VIIb	VIII			Ib	IIb	IIIa	IVa	Va	VIa	VIIa
0 n 1.0086	1 H 1.0080																
2 He 4.003	3 Li 6.940	4 Be 9.013											5 B 10.82	6 C 12.011	7 N 14.008	8 O 16.000	9 F 19.00
10 Ne 20.183	11 Na 22.991	12 Mg 24.32											13 Al 26.98	14 Si 28.09	15 P 30.975	16 S 32.066	17 Cl 35.457
18 Ar 39.944	19 K 39.100	20 Ca 40.08	21 Sc 44.96	22 Ti 47.90	23 V 50.95	24 Cr 52.01	25 Mn 54.94	26 Fe 55.85	27 Co 58.94	28 Ni 58.71	29 Cu 63.54	30 Zn 65.38	31 Ga 69.72	32 Ge 72.60	33 As 74.92	34 Se 78.96	35 Br 79.916
36 Kr 83.80	37 Rb 85.48	38 Sr 87.63	39 Y 88.91	40 Zr 91.22	41 Nb 92.91	42 Mo 95.95	43 Tc 99.0	44 Ru 101.1	45 Rh 102.91	46 Pd 106.4	47 Ag 107.88	48 Cd 112.41	49 In 114.82	50 Sn 118.70	51 Sb 121.76	52 Te 127.61	53 I 126.91
54 Xe 131.30	55 Cs 132.91	56 Ba 137.36	57 La 138.92	72 Hf 178.50	73 Ta 180.95	74 W 183.86	75 Re 186.22	76 Os 190.2	77 Ir 192.2	78 Pt 195.09	79 Au 197.0	80 Hg 200.61	81 Tl 204.39	82 Pb 207.21	83 Bi 208.99	84 Po 210	85 At 210
86 Rn 222	87 Fr 223	88 Ra 226.05	89 Ac 227.0														

Lanthanides:

58 Ce 140.13	59 Pr 140.91	60 Nd 144.27	61 Pm 147	62 Sm 150.35	63 Eu 152.0	64 Gd 157.26	65 Tb 158.93	66 Dy 162.51	67 Ho 164.94	68 Er 167.27	69 Tm 168.94	70 Yb 173.04	71 Lu 174.99

Actinides:

90 Th 232.05	91 Pa 231	92 U 238.07	93 Np 237	94 Pu 242	95 Am 243	96 Cm 247	97 Bk 249	98 Cf 251	99 Es 254	100 Fm 253	101 Md 256	102 No 253

a—main group.
b—subgroup.

Index